Second Edition **the**
Astronomical Universe

•••

Wasley S. Krogdahl , 1919-

*"The stars bind together all men
and all periods of the world's history."*
A. VON HUMBOLDT

The Macmillan Company
A DIVISION OF THE CROWELL-COLLIER PUBLISHING COMPANY

First Printing

Library of Congress catalog card number: 62-7577

The Macmillan Company, New York
Brett-Macmillan Ltd., Galt, Ontario

Printed in the United States of America

DESIGNED BY RON FARBER

To my Mother and Father

Preface

• • •

"There are some very clever writers who say that it is quite easy not to have an er-h'r'm, but I don't agree with them. I think it is much easier not to have all the rest of the book." [1]

—A. A. MILNE

It has been said that "to be ignorant of science is to be ignorant." It is certainly true that one who is versed only in the arts and letters cannot any longer be considered well educated, though such a standard has long been held as the criterion of the literate man. Such a position has not been universally abandoned, but it is properly in retreat.

I should like to advance the partisan proposition that "to be ignorant of astronomy is to be ignorant of science." At any rate, there is no denying that an acquaintance with astronomy entails a potential acquaintance with an extremely wide array of other scientific fields. Thus, the geometry of conic sections has a classic application to the motion of the planets about the sun and a present application to artificial satellites about the earth. Newton's laws of motion and gravitation are ideally illustrated by rocket ships in their space travels. The perfect gas laws operate perfectly within the sun and stars. Only fundamental optics is required to grasp the functioning of astronomical telescopes. The simplest atomic theory explains how the chemical composition of remote stars can be ascertained. The sun and most stars are kept shining by the most rudimentary nuclear reactions. The theory of the expanding universe stems from an unsophisticated application of the Doppler principle, which has a familiar counterpart in sound. The age of the earth's crust is found from the radioactive decay of heavy elements. Tree rings have helped to carry knowledge of the sunspot cycle back many centuries before the first observations of sunspots. The ice ages were probably caused by some variation in the sun's intrinsic brightness.

It is clear, I think, that the traditional disciplinary categories have become so hybridized that there is a manifest advantage in assaying to learn about science by attacking first that one of them having the maximum

[1] From *Now We Are Six*, by A. A. Milne, published and copyright, 1927, by E. P. Dutton & Co., Inc., New York. Courtesy also of Methuen & Co., London.

number of sibling relationships. It is my considered prejudice that astronomy constitutes such a core and that it thereby deserves to be placed in a central position in the modern intellectual diet. It is my sincere hope that this book will afford a beguiling and accurate presentation of modern astronomy.

In any age, the expositor of astronomy has been abetted by a nearly universal interest in the sun, moon, and stars; never has he had to contrive a stimulus. The expositor of this day has the unprecedented advantage that many of the astronomical problems of the present day are converging upon the large and universally fascinating problems of cosmology: What is the structure of the entire universe? What is the origin of our planetary system, the sun and stars, life on this or other planets, the chemical elements, the universe itself? I doubt that any other field of knowledge can present a lure so seductive.

Unfortunately, the grandeur of the theme is matched by the scientific innocence of the average unspecialized reader. It therefore behooves an author who would assay to treat modern astronomy that he attempt to sophisticate a reader's appreciation of science beyond the "ain't-nature-grand" school of natural philosophy. For example, the general curiosity about whether there is life on Mars should be inverted: Why is there life on earth? In light of the answer, why is there probably no life on Mars or Venus? Again, when the reader finds that hydrogen and helium probably comprise 99 per cent of all matter he should be prompted to ask, "Why is there anything else?"

This book attempts to capture, sharpen, direct, cultivate, and sophisticate an interest in astronomy that will carry the reader well beyond the bounds that idle curiosity envisions. In doing so, the book makes a sincere effort to eliminate or minimize irrelevant obstacles. For example, mathematical symbols and manipulations have been reduced to a minimum number and have been given as simple forms as possible; to cite one instance, use is made of stellar luminosities rather than the logarithmic absolute magnitudes. Similar considerations have prompted me to expound relevant background material from physics at those points where they may receive immediate application to significant astronomical problems. Withal, I have not had the wit to discover where I might have included such corollary topics as constellations and telescopes without their seeming like an intrusion. They have therefore been placed in appendices, to be read or ignored as desired.

The purposes and the techniques of this, the second edition, are substantially the same as those of the previous edition. However, the science of astronomy has enjoyed a greater and more far-reaching advance in the past decade than in any other similar period of history; moreover, the pace of the advance shows no slackening. For the author of a book on the subject, this creates an urgent need for a timely revision and at the same time presents the hazard that even a revision will soon be out of date. It has also meant that a perfunctory substitution of the most recent numerical values will not suffice to make an up-to-date account of one written ten years ago. I am therefore immeasurably indebted to The Macmillan Company for their generosity and understanding in allowing me the opportunity to recast in thoroughgoing fashion the first edition of *The Astronomical Universe*.

The general organization is as before. It has been modified, however, to assimilate the elegant current theory of stellar evolution. The theory of stellar evolution provides both an end and a means, being of interest for its own sake and serving as a perfectly fashioned link to cosmology and cosmogony. These latter departments of natural philosophy I regard as the climax of the subject as well as a continually recurrent theme.

I sincerely hope that the reader will sense in this exposition the acceleration of scientific advance, the breadth and sweep which set modern astronomy apart from that of all other times, and the atmosphere of excitement and exhilaration which permeates all of modern science. No less do I hope that this book will convince the reader that science is a worthwhile end in itself and that it is the fruit of much hard physical and mental labor, a boon not given in such abundance to any age before this, a heritage to be transmitted in increased measure by an enlightened society.

Wasley S. Krogdahl

Lexington, Kentucky

Contents

...

Contents

Contents

Part III   THE UNIVERSE

Contents

Figure 1. COMET BURNHAM (1959 k). This photograph was taken on April 25, 1960, with the 40-inch reflector at the Flagstaff station of the U.S. Naval Observatory. It shows the comet's fuzzy head and stubby tail. As the telescope tracked the comet during the fifteen-minute exposure, the star images were trailed into streaks. (Official U.S. Navy photograph, courtesy Dr. Elizabeth Roemer.)

part I
The Solar System

•••

Introduction

· · ·

"Merely to realize there are more things in heaven and earth than are dreamed of in one's philosophy is hardly an end in itself. The end should be to expand one's philosophy so as to include them."
—LORD RAYLEIGH

Astronomy as a Science

Astronomy is a branch of science. It therefore seems to the point that we should say what *science* is. For a brief but fairly accurate definition one might say that *science is the whole of knowledge that has been acquired by the use of a characteristic method—the scientific method of inductive inference.* As this definition implies, the unique feature of science is the method which scientists use to acquire the knowledge that forms the body of science. This method—the scientific method—is nothing more nor less than a systematic application of the process of learning from experience, a process of making inferences from past experience to predict future experience. This may seem so simple as to be trival, yet as, Bertrand Russell, the brilliant English mathematician and philosopher says so acidly,[1] "Scientific method, simple as it is in essence, has been acquired only with great difficulty, and is employed only by a minority, who themselves confine its employment to a minority of the questions upon which they have opinions."

Since the scientific method appears to be the very heart of science, let us see more specifically what the method is and how it is applied. It consists of three procedures: (1) observations are secured of various phenomena; (2) a hypothesis relating the observations is postulated; and (3) the hypothesis is tested by further, designedly critical observations.

An outstanding example of how the method is applied in practice and, incidentally, of how practically important its application may be, is to be found in the work of the Scotch biologist Alexander Fleming. For the first step, he observed (accidentally) that certain disease-producing bacteria would not continue to grow in bacterial cultures that had become contaminated with a kind of mold called *penicillium notatum.* As a second step, he *postulated* that the mold somehow inhibited the bacterial

[1] *The Scientific Outlook,* pp. 13–14, 1931. By permission of W. W. Norton & Co., New York, and George Allen & Unwin, London.

growth. As a final step, he *tested* his hypothesis by the further observations that either this same kind of mold or a substance which it produces would halt certain kinds of bacterial growth *whenever* it was intentionally introduced into a culture of these bacteria. In short, Dr. Fleming had added to our scientific knowledge the fact that penicillin exists and can be used to control certain disease-producing bacteria.

This particular example comes from that branch of science known as bacteriology. However, examples could be drawn from any other of the departments of science, for they have in common their use of the scientific method; by definition, it is that which makes them sciences. This point was very clearly put by the late Karl Pearson, an outstanding British mathematician and statistician, who said: "The field of science is unlimited, its material endless; every group of natural phenomena, every phase of social life, every stage of past or present development is material for science. *The unity of all science consists alone in its method, not its material.* The man who classifies facts of any kind whatever, who sees their mutual relation and describes their sequences, is applying the scientific method and is a man of science. The facts (themselves) may belong to the past history of mankind, to the social statistics of our great cities, to the atmospheres of the most distant stars, to the digestive organs of a worm, or to the life of a scarcely visible bacillus." [2]

Thus astronomy, as a science, makes use of the scientific method. It is distinguished from the other sciences only by the material it treats of, namely, the content and history of the entire universe. But before we plunge into this subject, the reader may with justice ask what justification his efforts may be given in advance. The justifications are several.

The Value of Astronomy

First of all, astronomy may be displayed as an application of the scientific method. The scientific method, as a powerful tool of logic, has proved the most fruitful single weapon in both the physical and intellectual emancipation of the western world; on this ground alone it warrants our appreciation, and modern astronomy offers some of the most exciting opportunities for achieving this end. We shall therefore pointedly attempt to follow the logic by which every important point is established. [3]

[2] *The Grammar of Science,* p. 16 (Everyman Edition, 1938). By permission of E. P. Dutton & Co., Inc., New York, and J. M. Dent & Sons, London.

[3] At the same time, we shall, by common consent, try to avoid or minimize any mathematical intricacies or any purely technical details, which seem more often than not to bewilder the beginner rather than enlighten him.

Secondly, astronomy offers an esthetic indulgence not duplicated in any other field. This is not an academic or hypothetical attraction and should require no apologies, for the beauty to be found in the skies has been universally appreciated for unrecorded centuries.

Thirdly, astronomy contributes uniquely to intellectual perspective in that it can assist one to estimate both the significance and insignificance of man.

And finally, a study of astronomy is to be recommended as an opportunity both to satisfy and to stimulate intellectual curiosity about the workings of the universe of which we are a part; as with the first justification, the same can be said for any other of the branches of science. These grounds are not to be dismissed lightly, for, in the words of one of the Netherlands' greatest scientists, "It is a significant fact, proved by history, that all the great technical advances have been based on scientific discoveries which at the time appeared to be utterly useless, and were made by men who studied science for its own sake, without giving the slightest thought to the possibility of application. They are the reward accruing to mankind from the disinterestedness of its greatest representatives." [4]

It should not be supposed from this, however, that astronomy is of absolutely no practical value. The world depends upon a few astronomical observatories and their astronomers for the very accurate determination of time. Pilots of plane and ship rely upon the sun, moon, and stars to keep themselves informed of their positions and progress. Astronomy has frequently given stimulus to research in many fields not strictly astronomical, as in optics, atomic physics, photography, and even mathematics. And for a few years past, forecasts of the atmosphere's effects upon radio reception have depended upon special astronomical observations of the sun. But these applications, though they are important, would by themselves not afford a sufficient or cogent reason to the general reader for entering upon the whole of the subject of which the applications comprise a very small part.

It is worth passing mention that astronomy is emphatically of *no* use in foretelling personal fortunes. Such humbuggery is the province of the pseudo-science of astrology, whose practitioners assert that the configurations of the heavenly bodies control the individual destinies of men. Unfortunately such nonsense is still given credence among a great many of the superstitious or ignorant people the world over. The relationship of astronomy and astrology is altogether similar to the relationship between chemistry and medieval alchemy.

[4] Willem de Sitter, *Kosmos,* pp. 136–37 (Harvard University Press, 1932).

And now, having disposed of the preliminaries, we invite the reader on a tour of the universe. Our itinerary will take us across distances more vast than any we have known before; we shall travel at speeds that tax the imagination; we shall survey the universe's most colossal objects, decode the messages from its smallest, witness matter at extraordinary extremes of temperature, density, and pressure. We begin with an examination of the solar system, to which our earth belongs.

chapter 1
How the System Behaves

• • •

"The Pythagoreans . . . were wont to impart their philosophic mysteries only to intimates and friends, . . . fearing lest these so noble and hardly won discoveries should be despised by such as either care not to study aught save for gain, or—if by the encouragement and example of others they are stimulated to philosophic liberal pursuits—yet by reason of the dullness of their wits are, in the company of philosophers, as drones among bees."

—Copernicus

The solar system consists mainly of empty space. What material it does contain belongs almost entirely to a huge dominating incandescent globe —the sun. The remainder, though it is by comparison as a crumb to a loaf, is dispersed in a multitude of lesser bodies, namely, the nine planets (of which the earth is one), their thirty-one known satellites, thousands of planetoids, tens of thousands of comets, and billions of meteorites. By any physical comparison, these lesser members of the solar system are insignificant in contrast to the sun, and it is in fact this very dominance by the sun which gives the system its name, the *solar system.*

Let us imagine a scale model of the system's ten most important members, the sun and the nine major planets. If we let 10,000 miles be represented by 1 inch in the model, the sun will be a globe 7 feet 2½ inches across and the earth is a little marble a shade over ¾ of an inch in diameter placed 775 feet away, i.e., roughly two city blocks distant. Nearest the sun and smallest of all is Mercury, ⅓ of an inch across and at 300 feet. Largest is Jupiter, 9 inches through and ¾ of a mile out. Farthest out is Pluto, about half as large as the earth and some 5½ miles from the sun. A model of this sort serves to demonstrate how very empty the solar system is.

These models, varying in size from marbles to bowling balls, are to be imagined as circling slowly about the sun, each completing one revolution in a period which ranges from 88 days for Mercury to 248 years for Pluto. Let us speed up their motions 100,000 times. Then Mercury will make the trip around in 1 minute, 16 seconds; the earth will revolve in 5¼ minutes while Pluto will require 21 hours, 43 minutes to travel once around its course.

Could we but observe such a model for several days, we would be sure to note as one of its most striking features the regularity of the motion of its members. The essence of this orderliness—which, of course, is not so obvious to us as we view the actual solar system from one of its moving members, the earth—is summed up in the laws of *celestial mechanics;* it

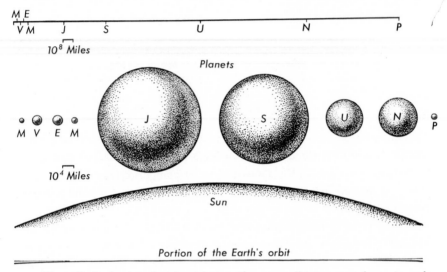

Figure 2. At the top, the planets' respective mean distances are shown to scale. Below them, on an entirely different scale, are the planets themselves, an arc of the sun's surface, and a small arc of the earth's orbit. The markers at right and left show how little the earth's orbit differs from a straight line on this scale.

is the province of celestial mechanics to describe the observed motions of celestial bodies and to predict their future motions. As a science, celestial mechanics has been brought to such perfection as to stand as a model of exactness and precision.

Kepler's Laws of Planetary Motion

Celestial mechanics, as a part of science, can be used to excellent advantage to exhibit the workings of the scientific method. The initial step, then, is to secure observations of the apparent motions of the planets. This was first done adequately by the Danish nobleman and astronomer Tycho Brahe (1546–1601) who, with the patronage of his king, spent his lifetime securing the most extensive and accurate observations ever made of the planets before the invention of the telescope. Heir to Tycho's great accumulation of undigested data was his pupil, Johannes Kepler (1571–1630), who condensed the results of Tycho's observations into three laws, now known as *Kepler's laws of planetary motion*.

THE LAW OF ELLIPSES

Kepler found that the path of each planet (its orbit) about the sun was wholly contained in a plane, the planet's orbital plane. No two planets moved in quite the same orbital plane; the several planes are mutually inclined at small angles. The motion of each planet in its orbital plane is, however, governed by the same laws of planetary motion. The first is known as the *law of ellipses*.

LAW 1. The orbit of any planet is an ellipse with the sun at one focus.

To understand and appreciate this law, we must define an ellipse and specify the position of its foci. An ellipse is a simple closed plane curve having the distinctive property that there is a constant total distance from any point on the ellipse to two fixed points within it; these latter two points are called the *foci*.

This very special characteristic of ellipses serves to differentiate them from all other curves and at the same time suggests how one can be easily drawn. To draw an ellipse, tie each of the ends of a string of convenient length to thumbtacks and place the thumbtacks in a sheet of paper; then press a pencil against the string and draw the curve in which the string constrains the pencil. The two (fixed) thumbtacks mark the positions of the foci, since the pencil point maintains a constant total distance from them (Fig. 3). The foci lie on the *major axis* of the ellipse, and *center* of the ellipse is midway between them. The major axis meets the ellipse at its two *vertices*.

It is evident that ellipses can have a variety of sizes and shapes, for we can make the length of string any amount, and we can separate the tacks by any amount not greater than this. In fact, the length of string is just equal to the distance between the vertices of the ellipse; half this distance, the distance from center to either vertex, is called the *major semi-axis* and it is this quantity which is customarily stated in specifying the size of an ellipse.

The shape of an ellipse is denominated by a pure number called the *eccentricity* of the ellipse. The eccentricity is simply the *ratio* of the distance between the tacks to the length of string between them, or alternatively, the ratio of the distance from center to focus to the distance from center to vertex. Ellipses may in consequence have eccentricities ranging between the values 0 and 1. Ellipses of small eccentricity (foci close

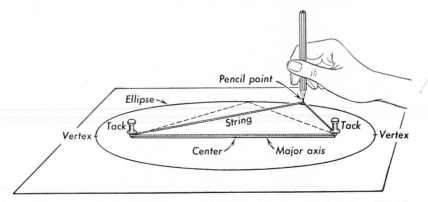

Figure 3. As the figure shows, an ellipse may be constructed easily with string, tacks, and pencil.

together) are almost circular, whereas ellipses of large eccentricity (foci near the vertices) are much elongated. Eccentricity is therefore a measure of the degree of elongation of ellipses. A statement of both the major

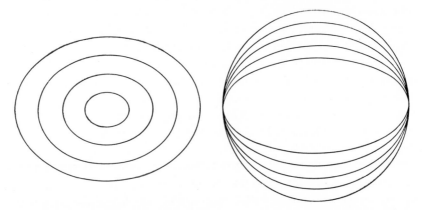

Figure 4. The ellipses on the left all have eccentricity $e = 0.66$; their semi-axes are in the ratios 1:2:3:4. The ellipses on the right all have the same major semi-axis (equal to 4 units on the scale of the ellipses to the left). Their respective eccentricities are $e = 0$, 0.48, 0.66, 0.78, and 0.87, from outer to inner.

semi-axis and the eccentricity of an ellipse suffices to fix uniquely the size and shape of the ellipse.

To this species of curve, the ellipse, the orbits of the planets belong, according to Kepler's first law. The size and shape of each orbit can therefore be given by stating the length of its major semi-axis and the amount of its eccentricity. (The earth's orbit, for instance, has a major semi-axis of 92,913,000 miles and an eccentricity of 0.01673.) Further, one of the foci of each of the planets' orbital ellipses is a point common to all, for it is occupied by the sun; the remaining focus of every one of the

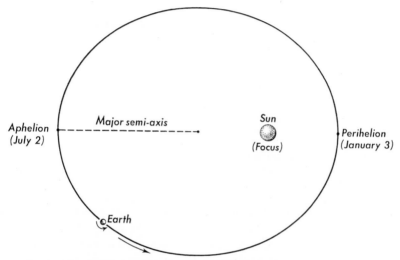

Figure 5. The ellipse of the figure has been made considerably more eccentric than the earth's actual orbit so as to make clearer the sun's eccentric position and its relation to perihelion and aphelion.

orbital ellipses is an unmarked point in space and is of no further interest to us.

Since a planetary orbit is an *ellipse* rather than a circle, and since the sun is at a *focus* rather than at the center of the ellipse, one vertex of the ellipse will mark the planet's point of nearest approach to the sun; the other vertex is the position of the planet when it is farthest from the sun. The former point is called *perihelion,* and the latter is *aphelion.*[1] The earth is at perihelion on about January 3 each year and at aphelion on approximately the Fourth of July.

The average (or mean) of any planet's perihelion and aphelion distances is exactly equal to the length of the major semi-axis of its orbit; consequently this latter quantity is most often called the planet's *mean distance.* Table 1 gives the mean distances of the major planets. It is

[1] The terms *perihelion* and *aphelion* result from a combination of the prefixes *peri-*(near) and *ap-*(away from) with the Greek word *helios* meaning sun.

plain to see that the mean distances of all the planets require awkwardly large figures if they are to be expressed in miles; consequently it is a commoner practice to use a larger and more suitable unit, the astronomical unit.

table 1

Mean Distances of the Major Planets

| | MEAN DISTANCE | | | |
PLANET	(MILES)	(ASTRONOMICAL UNITS)	ORBITAL ECCENTRICITY	PERIOD (YEARS)
Mercury	35,960,000	0.387	0.2056	0.241
Venus	67,200,000	0.723	0.0068	0.615
Earth	92,913,000	1.000	0.0167	1.000
Mars	141,570,000	1.524	0.0934	1.881
Jupiter	483,300,000	5.203	0.0484	11.862
Saturn	886,100,000	9.539	0.0557	29.458
Uranus	1,782,000,000	19.182	0.0472	84.013
Neptune	2,792,000,000	30.058	0.0086	164.793
Pluto	3,664,000,000	39.439	0.2502	248.430

An *astronomical unit* is by definition equal to the mean distance of the earth, which, according to the best and most recent determination, is 92,913,000 miles, or 93 million miles in round numbers. Thus Jupiter's mean distance of 484 million miles is just 5.203 times the earth's mean distance; hence we say that Jupiter has a mean distance of 5.203 astronomical units. The table gives mean distances in astronomical units as well as miles.

Also given in the table are the planets' orbital eccentricities. Notably larger than the rest are the eccentricities of Mercury and Pluto, but the orbit of even Pluto would not seem perceptibly elongated. The most conspicuous reminder of the ellipticity of the planets' orbits would in every case be the sun's plainly eccentric position within the orbit.

THE LAW OF AREAS

And how do the planets move in their elliptical orbits? This question is given a qualitative answer in Kepler's second law, often called the *law of areas.*

LAW 2. The line joining sun and planet will sweep over equal areas in equal intervals of time.

To interpret this law, let us imagine the sun and any one of the planets to be joined by an elastic inked string. Then, during any time intervals of equal duration, no matter when they are begun and even though the

ured by a scale balance); the weight of a body is thus in proportion to its mass. A special and definite meaning is also possessed by "acceleration," namely, the *rate of change of velocity*. Thus a bowling ball which rolls at constant velocity straight down the alley is unaccelerated; its acceleration took place while the bowler changed its velocity from zero to whatever velocity it may have possessed by the time it left his hand. The more rapid the change of velocity, the greater the acceleration, it being understood that a change of velocity may be either an increase or a decrease.

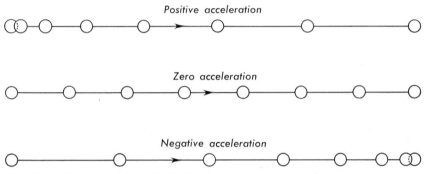

Figure 7. The positions of a ball at intervals of one second indicate respectively accelerated, unaccelerated, and decelerated motion.

It must also be recognized that a change in *direction* of motion is likewise an acceleration. If, for example, a rolling ball changes its direction of motion from north to west, this could have been accomplished only by bringing its northward velocity to zero (negative acceleration) while at the same time increasing its westward velocity from zero (positive acceleration). This may be done without altering the ball's speed in its path at any time, as when the ball moves uniformly about a circle.

The second law merely summarizes such familiar facts as that (1) the acceleration given a bowling ball is in direct proportion to the bowler's effort, and (2) the efforts required to give equal acceleration to balls of different masses (weights) are in proportion to the balls' respective masses (weights).

THE LAW OF REACTION

The third law of motion completes the description of the behavior of moving bodies and their relation to the forces which act upon them. In the form in which it is to be stated, it deals with *momentum;* the momentum of a body is simply the product of its mass and velocity. This definition agrees with the common understanding of the term: A body may possess a great deal of momentum, either by virtue of large mass or high velocity. A falling boulder possesses more momentum than a falling pebble, and a moving car possesses four times as much momentum at 60 miles per hour as at 15 miles per hour.

LAW III. Every change of momentum of a part of a material system is accompanied by an equal and opposite change of momentum by the remainder of the system.

We may illustrate the implications of the third law in the motions of two boats which we suppose to be riding freely but connected by a length of rope. If the rope is reeled in from either or both boats, the boats' momenta will change by equal and opposite amounts; it is impossible, if both are riding freely as supposed, that one boat should remain at rest.

The third law explains actions such as the recoil of a fired cannon, for example. Here the mechanical system is a loaded cannon, and the projectile's change of momentum upon firing is equalled by the cannon's change of momentum in the opposite direction.

The third law of motion is likewise the principle upon which rocket propulsion is based. In this application, the mechanical system is a fueled rocket. As a result of the fuel's combustion and rearward expulsion from the rocket, the rocket itself acquires a forward momentum of the same amount. In interplanetary space, where wheels and propellers have nothing to react upon and jets have nothing to exhaust, the recoil principle of rocket propulsion offers the only possible mode of locomotion.

These selected examples offer reasonably transparent illustrations of the law. To be convinced of its complete generality, however, let us take brief notice of a slightly more subtle application. Let us suppose that a ball is thrown straight up into the air. It has been given an upward momentum; what is not generally appreciated is the fact that the thrower and the whole earth upon which he is standing will simultaneously acquire a downward momentum of equal amount. Because of the vast difference of mass between ball and earth, the earth's downward velocity of "recoil" will be imperceptibly small. But the importance of the distinction *in principle* between a very minutely displaced earth and a stationary one is not to be exaggerated.

Newton's three laws of motion, taken in combination, have repeatedly been found to describe faithfully and fully the interaction of force and matter in terrestrial phenomena; they appear to allow of no exceptions in the realm of ordinary experience. We have in these laws, then, a complete and concise summary of observations of the motions of terrestrial bodies.

As was our plan, we propose to relate these to the observations that have already been made of celestial bodies. This is to be done by predicating some relationship between them (the second step of the scientific method), then devising and applying some decisive test of it (the third step of the scientific method). We therefore postulate that *the laws governing celestial bodies are identically the same as those which apply to terrestrial bodies*. We turn now to means of testing this assumption.

Newton's Law of Gravitation

Our plan of attack is to deduce some of the consequences of our assumption and to check such predictions against further observations. A sufficient number of such comparisons should indicate how close to the truth we have hit.

If our hypothesis is correct, the planets must obey Newton's laws of motion in revolving about the sun. This assumption together with Kepler's laws of planetary motion directly implies a number of results. First of all, since the planets do not move in straight lines, they must (by Newton's first law) be subject to forces. Furthermore, since each planet stays in its own orbital plane, whatever force it may be subject to must act entirely in the planet's orbital plane; if this were not the case, the force would (by Newton's second law) drive the planet from its original orbital plane.

By ingenious geometrical proofs Newton was able to deduce considerably more about these forces which act on the planets. From the law of areas he was able to show that not only was the force entirely contained in a planet's orbital plane but was, in fact, directed along the line joining sun and planet. From the law of ellipses he was able to show that the force is an attraction which diminishes inversely as the square of the distance between sun and planet. And from the harmonic law, Newton deduced that the force of attraction must be proportional to the product of the masses of sun and planet. This last result showed the force to be an attraction of mass for mass. Discovery of that fact led to an immediate generalization, namely, that *every* mass attracts *every other* mass; for it would indeed be peculiar if the mass comprising a planet were to discriminate the mass of the sun from all others, and vice versa. Such attraction of mass for mass is called *gravitation*. The results we have just derived for this force were first announced by Newton in his law of universal gravitation.

NEWTON'S LAW OF UNIVERSAL GRAVITATION. Every particle of matter in the universe attracts every other particle along the line joining them and with a force which is proportional to the product of their masses and inversely proportional to the square of the distance between them.

To give specific illustration to what this statement of the law of gravitation means, let us consider how we would use it. Let us suppose we are interested in the gravitational attraction of a particle of mass M upon a particle of mass m whose center is at a distance d from the center of the first. According to the law, the force of either upon the other will be directly proportional to Mm (the product of their masses) and at the same time also proportional to $1/d^2$ (the inverse square of the distance between them). Stating these relations simultaneously in symbolic form gives us the compact result that $F \propto Mm/d^2$, where the symbol $\propto$ means "is proportional to."

Thus, if by the addition of more material the mass of the first particle is tripled, the attraction between the particles is likewise tripled, since $(3M)m = 3(Mm)$ is three times the original product of masses, Mm; a like result would follow from a change of mass of the second particle. On the other hand, if the original particles of mass M and m are moved apart to twice their initial separation, the force of attraction is quartered, since the new distance is $2d$ and its inverse square is $1/(2d)^2 = \frac{1}{4}(1/d^2)$.

The law of gravitation is thus a prescription of how to compare the gravitational attractions of *any* pairs of particles at any distances apart. This law is to be regarded as a direct implication from observations of celestial and terrestrial phenomena and our postulate that the same laws govern both. In it we have the means of testing our postulate.

The test is straightforward in principle though not simple in application. It consists in using the law of gravitation and Newton's laws of motion to try to predict *in detail* the motions of all the bodies in the solar system. This would include, for example, prediction of the moon's motion about the earth, the calculation of the planets' effects on each other, the determination of the paths of comets, meteorites, planetoids, etc. It is not difficult to imagine, however, that the completely general test is for practical reasons impossible to apply. Without even attempting it, in fact, we select a limited number of bodies for consideration and try to predict their future motions accurately. Time will show how important or unimportant any omissions may have been and, what is more, will indicate quite convincingly whether or not tests of any order are likely to sustain our working hypothesis.

We must therefore consider the idealized (and thus, to some degree, artificial) problems of predicting the future motion of a given number of celestial bodies started from prescribed positions with prescribed speeds in prescribed direction. It is our intention at the present instant, of course, to make these specifications coincide with those of selected bodies in the solar system and see later if our predictions are borne out. Until we are prepared to designate exactly how many bodies are under consideration, we refer to the number of them as *n*; the problem posed for us is therefore called the *n-body problem*.

Celestial Mechanics

The *n*-body problem is not really a single problem but rather a whole set of problems; to every different value given *n* (*n* = 2, 3, 4, . . .), there corresponds a different problem. In general, the larger the value of *n,* the more difficult the problem. Simplest, therefore, is the *two-body problem*.

THE TWO-BODY PROBLEM

Let us consider two bodies revolving alone in space. What do Newton's law of gravitation and laws of motion predict of them? At first sight it might seem that the law of gravitation would be difficult to apply to stars or planets, for the law speaks of "particles" and neither earth nor sun can fairly be called a particle in the usual sense. In a more technical sense, however, any spherical mass constructed of concentric homogeneous layers may be referred to as a "particle," for it behaves gravitationally as though the whole of its mass were concentrated at its center. Since the structures of nearly all stars and planets meet the aforementioned specifications very nearly, we may treat each of them as a particle having no extent. Our problem is therefore to consider the motion of two particles which have been set in motion in an arbitrary way.

The better to keep track of these particles, let us suppose them to be joined by an imaginary straight-line segment whose length can vary to accommodate the particles' motions. Let us select the point upon this line which divides it in the inverse proportion of the masses of the particles: The more massive particle is as many times *nearer* the selected point as it is more massive; if the mass of one particle is five times the mass of the other, for example, we select that point on the line between them which is five times closer the former than the latter. This point is called the *center of gravity* of the system.

The center of gravity may be thought of as the "heart" of any material system; it is the point at which a single applied force could support the whole system, whether it is formed of two particles or is a complicated extended structure. The center of gravity of the pair of revolving particles is of interest to us because it is this point which, by Newton's first law of motion, will move in a straight line with constant speed. It will greatly

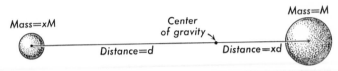

Figure 8. The small body is as many times less massive than the larger body as it is farther from their common center of gravity. Notice that the product of the mass of each by its distance from the center of gravity is the same for both bodies.

simplify matters, therefore, if we adopt the center of gravity of the pair of particles as our point of observation.

From here we could watch the particles revolve about us in a plane, in such fashion that their respective momenta are always equal but oppositely directed, as required by Newton's third law of motion. When the

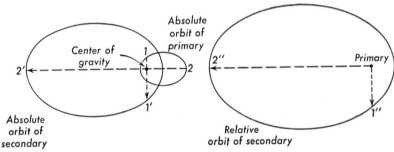

Figure 9. A detached observer would see two mutually revolving bodies describe orbits of the same shape but unequal sizes about their common center of gravity, as at the left. An observer accompanying the primary would see the secondary describe a relative orbit about him as on the right. The figure on the right has been constructed by laying off from the primary a distance to 1″ equal to the distance from 1 to 1′ between corresponding positions of primary and secondary in their absolute orbits on the left. Other points have been found similarly.

more massive particle is at position 1 in Figure 9, the less massive will be at 1′; when the more massive particle has reached 2, the less massive will have reached 2′, etc. Neither particle would ever depart from the original plane of revolution, since by Newton's second law of motion this would require a force which is at least in part at right angles to the plane; the only force on the particles is, however, their mutual gravitational attraction which, by the law of gravitation, is along the line joining them and thus *wholly* in the plane of revolution.

We can summarize our present results by saying that two gravitationally attracting particles set in motion in an arbitrary way will revolve about their center of gravity in a plane of fixed orientation. Each of the particles will have its own orbit about the center of gravity. However, since their respective distances from the center of gravity are always in the same proportion (the inverse ratio of their masses), the orbits of the two particles will be exactly similar in shape, and may differ only in size; these are their *absolute orbits.*

Similar in shape to the absolute orbits is the *relative orbit* of one about the other. It is gotten by selecting either particle, usually the more massive, as the point of reference for describing the motion of the other. The reference particle is called the *primary;* the other, the *secondary.* Complementing the absolute orbits in Figure 9 is the relative orbit. The distance from 1 to 1′ is laid off from the primary, giving the point 1″ in the relative orbit; the distance 2 to 2′ is similarly laid off from the primary, giving the corresponding point 2″ in the relative orbit. A detached observer would see the two mutually revolving bodies describe orbits of the same shape but of unequal sizes about their common center of gravity, as at the left; this is the way binary stars appear to move as seen from the earth (see p. 313). An observer accompanying the primary would see the secondary describe a relative orbit about him, as on the right; this is the way the moon appears to move as seen from the earth. It is clear from the construction that the dimension of the relative orbit equals the sum of the dimensions of the absolute orbits.

Kepler's laws of planetary motion, as previously stated, have applied to the relative motion of any *planet* about the sun. A derivation of them from Newton's laws of motion and law of gravitation shows, however, that they may be generalized to describe the relative motion of *any* two mutually revolving bodies, whether sun and planet, planet and satellite, or two stars. In their more general form, the laws require a slight rephrasing.

LAW I. The relative orbit of any two mutually revolving bodies is a conic section with the primary at one focus.

The principal change contained in this restatement of the first of Kepler's laws is the substitution of the general class of plane curves called *conic sections* in place of ellipses. A conic section is so named because it may be formed as the curve of intersection of a right circular cone by a plane (Fig. 10). If the plane cuts the axis of the cone at right angles, the resulting conic section is a circle; if the plane cuts the axis of the cone at any other angle, the resulting conic section may be an ellipse, a parabola, or hyperbola. The ellipses are closed curves, the parabolas and hyperbolas are not. The whole set of conic sections constitutes a sequence of plane curves of increasing eccentricities: a circle has eccentricity 0; ellipses have eccentricities greater than 0 but less than 1; parabolas have an eccentricity of 1; and hyperbolas have eccentricities greater than 1.

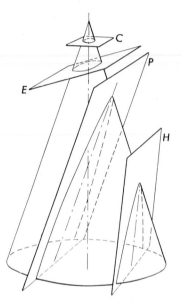

Figure 10. The planes C, E, P, and H intersect the right circular cone in curves which are respectively a circle, ellipse, parabola, and hyperbola.

What is it that determines which of these kinds of curves will represent the relative orbit of any particular pair of mutually revolving bodies? The distinction is made on the basis of the amount of the secondary's orbital velocity at any specified distance from the primary. To any pair of revolving bodies at a specified distance from each other, there is associated an orbital velocity such that (1) an orbital velocity of this amount indicates that the orbit is parabolic, (2) a lesser orbital velocity implies that the orbit is elliptical or circular, and (3) a greater orbital velocity implies that the orbit is hyperbolic. This limiting velocity is appropriately called the *parabolic velocity;* at a distance of one astronomical unit from the sun the parabolic velocity is about 26 miles per second.

The parabolic velocity is also known as the *velocity of escape,* for a secondary whose orbital velocity is as great as or greater than the parabolic velocity will follow an open orbit; it will therefore never return to the vicinity of the primary but will follow a path which carries it ever farther away. Thus, while it can never fail to feel the *influence* of the primary, it is effectively beyond the primary's *control;* in short, it has escaped. We say, for example, that a body whose velocity is 26 miles per second or more at a distance of one astronomical unit from the sun will escape from the solar system and cannot have been a regular member. This is a criterion to be used upon meteors and comets to determine whether or not they are permanently of the sun's family. In similar fashion, we can determine that the velocity of escape from the earth at its surface is 7 miles per second and that therefore any molecule whose outward velocity

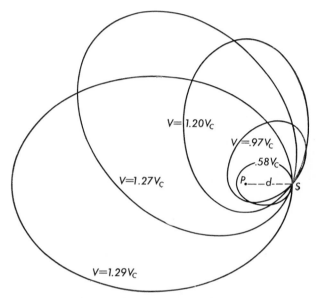

Figure 11. The size of the orbit of the secondary S about the primary P depends upon the secondary's velocity V at standard distance d. The eccentricities of the orbits shown are the same for all ($e = \frac{2}{3}$). The orbital velocity of the secondary at S is given for each of the orbits in terms of V_c, the velocity the secondary would have if it followed a circular orbit of radius d.

is at least this much can be forever lost to our atmosphere; fortunately, such losses are very infrequent.

Kepler's second law requires no essential modification.

LAW II. The line joining two mutually revolving bodies will sweep over equal areas in equal times.

Note that this law now applies not only to elliptical or circular orbits but also to parabolic and hyperbolic orbits.

A derivation of Kepler's third law brings to light a very important incompleteness in the original statement of it. In its general form it involves the masses as well as the mean distance and period of revolution. If we agree to measure masses in units of the combined mass of earth and sun and, as before, take the period in years and the mean distance in astronomical units, the law may then be stated in the following form:

LAW III. The square of the period of two mutually revolving bodies times the sum of their masses is equal to the cube of their mean distance apart.

As before, we can write this symbolically in a simple equation, namely,

$$P^2(M + m) = a^3,$$

where P is the period in years, M and m the masses of the bodies in units of the combined mass of earth and sun, and a their mean distance in astronomical units. It is understood, of course, that this law has a meaning only for two bodies mutually revolving in a closed orbit.

The general statement of the third of Kepler's laws is seen to differ from the approximate statement of it by the inclusion of the factor $M + m$. This might appear to be sufficiently substantial an alteration as to occasion some surprise that the original statement of the harmonic law could have been so highly successful for the planets. This now surprising success must be credited to the fact that all the masses of the planets are so very small in the units of mass we have chosen; even Jupiter, the most massive, has a mass of less than a thousandth the combined mass of earth and sun. On the other hand, the mass of the sun is very nearly 1.0, the earth contributing a trifling three millionths of a unit to the total; in fact, because the resulting inaccuracy is usually so insignificant, we generally ignore the earth's contribution altogether and express astronomical masses in units of the sun's mass.

The extreme disparity between the masses of the sun and the planets has been a piece of good fortune, for it has allowed of a great simplification in the consideration of the motion of any planet about the sun, namely, that in all cases $M + m = 1.0$ to several decimal places. It is doubtful that Kepler could have announced his harmonic law had this not been so. The chain of delays and difficulties that would probably have followed in celestial mechanics for the lack of it might well have retarded the discovery of the law of gravitation and held back advances in widely related fields.

However, it is not only more satisfactory to have the harmonic law in its general form but also more useful, for it can be applied to revolving pairs other than sun and planet. It is valid, for example, in describing the relative motion of a planet and satellite or of a pair of revolving stars. In these circumstances it can be made to give very valuable information that is usually unobtainable otherwise. Thus, by a simple rearrangement of the formula we find that

$$M + m = a^3/P^2.$$

If a and P can be measured (in astronomical units and years, respectively), this formula may be used to find the combined mass of any revolving pair. It is a simple and direct way of determining the masses of those planets

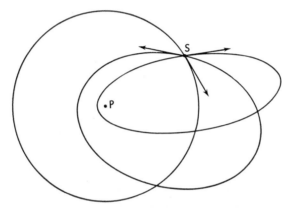

Figure 12. The shape of the orbit of the secondary S about the primary P depends upon the secondary's direction of motion. The distance of S from P and its orbital velocity about P are the same in the three orbits shown. The orbits therefore have the same major semi-axes but differ in eccentricity because of the different directions in which S moves about P.

which have a satellite revolving about them, for instance. Here is a fine illustration of the way in which theory and observation can complement each other.

The harmonic law also calls attention to one other interesting fact, namely, that the period of a planet's revolution is in no way dependent upon the eccentricity of its orbit; both elongated and circular orbits of the same major semi-axis will be traversed in the same length of time. The explanation of this possibly unexpected result is again provided by an exact theoretical analysis. It is shown that while the major semi-axis of a secondary's orbit is determined by the *speed* of its orbital motion at any particular distance (as we have seen), the eccentricity of its orbit is fixed solely by the *direction* of its orbital motion at this point (see Fig. 12). It is thus proved that the relative orbit of a secondary is wholly determined by its speed and direction of motion about the primary at any given point. This result has a very interesting and important application to the motions of meteors (p. 201), for example. It is a principle basic to rocket launchings too. Once a rocket rises beyond the earth's atmosphere, a second rocket motor or some mechanical or explosion mechanism is required to give the rocket the proper velocity in the desired tangential direction. The rocket would otherwise simply fall to earth, retracing the path of its ascent.

THE GENERAL n-BODY PROBLEM

For purposes of prediction, the two-body problem represents at best only a good approximation when applied to pairs of bodies within the solar system. This is so since each large or nearby body produces small but possibly cumulative deviations—known as *perturbations*—in the motions of all the rest. The inadequacy of the two-body approximation therefore cannot be equably overlooked in problems involving long times or requiring great accuracy. A case in point might be the motions of earth, moon, and sun, for example. This is a problem of three bodies. Does the three-body problem have a solution that can be stated in laws that are the analogues of Kepler's laws for the two-body problem?

This is the celebrated three-body problem, as famous among mathematicians and astronomers as the problems of squaring the circle or trisecting an angle with ruler and compass. It engrossed much of the time and effort of the greatest mathematicians and astronomers of the eighteenth and nineteenth centuries. All attacks upon the general three-body problem were so uniformly unsuccessful that in time efforts to solve it gave way to attempts to prove its insolubility. These have proved more fruitful and it has been shown, for instance, that it is not possible to express a general solution of the three-body problem by any finite combination of the symbols and variables of ordinary algebra.

This is a distinctly negative and disappointing result. It indicates, moreover, that there is no hope of solving generally the n-body problem if n is any number greater than two. Does this mean that we can never predict the motions of more than two bodies? Fortunately, it does not. For one thing, the n-body problem is often soluble in special cases, as when all but one or two of the bodies are of very small mass. More important still is the fact that numerical solutions, in contrast to solutions expressed in terms of a formula, can always be had for any number of bodies, provided the circumstances of their motion are known in complete detail at some instant; the price is a considerable amount of tedious numerical calculation. Such a numerical solution is put in the form of a table showing the relative positions of all bodies at each of a series of equally spaced times. Its usefulness is limited to the times between those of the first and last calculations.

The success of numerical predictions in celestial mechanics has been highly gratifying. Predictions can be made with great accuracy for a decade or even a century and oftentimes more; the results appear to be limited only by time, effort, and the accuracy with which the positions and motions of the bodies of the solar system can be specified for any initial instant. We take the success of celestial mechanics as a complete vindication of our postulate that *the laws governing celestial bodies are identically the same as those which apply to terrestrial bodies;* in fact, it shall be a cornerstone of all our future work.

Our faith in this postulate, which is frequently described as the hypothesis of "the uniformity of nature," is so complete that we are often led by it to new and interesting results, for it makes discrepancies highly useful as indicators of the necessity of revising laws or of improving data. An instance of the latter is to be found in the discrepancies in the motion of Uranus which led to the prediction and discovery of Neptune (p. 168). An instance of the former is to be had from the motion of Mercury (p. 141); in this case the discrepancies were removed only by a subtle revision of the laws of motion, a revision known as the theory of relativity (p. 500).

In a literal sense, Newton's laws of motion have now been superseded by the newer relativistic laws of motion. However, it is only under extreme or unusual circumstances that the results of the two sets of laws differ enough to be detected; hence Newton's laws are usually more than good enough for predicting the motion of bodies under all ordinary circumstances. On the other hand we shall make at least three encounters with extraordinary circumstances where the refinements of relativity become imperative (pp. 117, 141, and 500).

In brief retrospect, we call to mind once again that celestial mechanics has illustrated the *modus operandi* of the scientific method. Its beginnings were in observations; these have led to theories; the theories have been tested and refined. It is confidently expected that the refining process will continue indefinitely far into the future. There is no stopping place short of omniscience.

QUESTIONS

". . . we are like the Cockscombs of Paris . . . imagining that the larks will fall in their mouths roasted; . . . we ought (to remember) that vertue is not acquired without labor and taking great pains . . ."
—PIERRE ESPRIT RADISSON

1. How does one specify the size and shape of an ellipse? What is the size and the shape of the earth's orbit? Of Saturn's orbit? What necessary relation have these orbits to each other?

2. If a planet is four astronomical units from the sun at perihelion and if it has a mean distance of six astronomical units, what is its aphelion distance? What is the eccentricity of the planet's orbit?

3. If in twenty weeks the line joining the sun and a certain planet sweeps over 40 per cent of the total area of the orbital ellipse, what is the planet's period?

4. Compare the areal velocities of Mercury, the earth, Saturn, and Pluto. (*Hint:* The area of an ellipse with major semi-axis a and eccentricity e is $\pi a^2 \sqrt{1 - e^2}$.)

5. If a planet had a period of revolution of 8 years, what would be its mean distance from the sun? If its period were 27 years?

6. If a planet has a mean distance of 16 astronomical units, what is its period of revolution? If its mean distance were 169 astronomical units?

7. What forces are acting as a car turns a corner? Why is it so difficult to turn a sled about a corner? Would it be possible to walk if there were no friction?

8. Two men engaged in a game of tug-of-war are at a standstill. Their efforts finally break the rope. If one man weighs 200 pounds and the other 150 pounds, how do their accelerations compare just after the rope is broken?

9. Distinguish between velocity and acceleration. Estimate the acceleration of (*a*) a locomotive starting from rest, (*b*) a pebble thrown into a pool, (*c*) a fly starting from rest, (*d*) a plane at take-off, (*e*) automobiles colliding head-on at 30 miles an hour, (*f*) a sewing-machine needle at the end of a stroke, (*g*) a falling stone. Estimate the velocity of (*a*) a race horse, (*b*) a glacier, (*c*) the tip of an idling airplane propeller, (*d*) a bird in flight, (*e*) the growing tip of a blade of grass, (*f*) the earth in its orbit.

10. Point out the equal and opposite changes of momentum that occur (*a*) as one begins to walk, (*b*) when a gun is fired, (*c*) as a sailboat gets under way, (*d*) as a basketball rebounds from the backboard, (*e*) as steam rises from a lake.

11. A ball *A* attracts a ball *B* gravitationally. If the mass of *A* is doubled, how will this affect the force of attraction between *A* and *B*? If their distance apart is then trebled, what will be the result? What would be the final force if the order of changes were reversed?

12. Particle *A* has 3.8 times the mass of *B* while *B* is 2.3 times farther from *C* than is *A*. Compare numerically the gravitational attractions of *A* and *B* upon *C*.

13. Compare the sun's gravitational attraction upon Mercury at times of Mercury's perihelion and aphelion. Do the same for the earth, Uranus, Pluto. [*Hint:* Perihelion distance is $a(1 - e)$; aphelion distance is $a(1 + e)$.]

14. Compare the sun's gravitational attractions for Jupiter and the earth at their respective mean distances. (Jupiter's mass is 317 times the mass of the earth.)

15. What would a 150-pound man weigh at a height of 1000 miles above the earth's surface?

16. What is the two-body problem? How is the present use of the term *particle* justified?

17. Where is the center of gravity of two particles of respective masses five units and three units if the particles are 20 feet apart? Where is the center

of gravity of two particles of masses M and m, respectively, if their separation is d units of length? Where is the center of gravity of a homogeneous sphere? Of a torus (doughnut)? Of a rod? Of an irregular object?

18. What is meant by the relative orbit of two mutually revolving bodies? In what respect do the relative and absolute orbits of a secondary differ? What is the important distinction between relative and absolute orbits? By what criterion is a body specified as a primary or as a secondary?

19. In what particular must Kepler's law of ellipses be modified? What are conic sections? How are the species of conic sections distinguished among themselves? What factor determines the kind of conic section which will represent the relative orbit of two mutually revolving bodies? What bearing has this upon rockets or upon molecules of the earth's atmosphere?

20. In what way must Kepler's harmonic law be modified? How is it that the necessity for such an essential modification could have been originally overlooked?

21. What factor determines the shape of a secondary's orbit?

22. What is the n-body problem? What solutions are there to the n-body problem? What kind of solutions are known to be impossible?

chapter 2
Earth and Sky

• • •

A. THE EARTH ITSELF

"What is the earth but a lump of clay surrounded by water?"
—BHARTRIHARI

Seen from a convenient distance—as from the planet Venus—the earth and moon would appear as a "double planet," the only one to be seen as such in the whole solar system. Observed from Venus, the earth would outshine any other object in the sky except the sun, being about twice as bright as Venus is to us. Sometimes as much as half a degree (the apparent width of the full moon) away from the bluish earth would be the yellow-white moon, appearing not quite as bright as Sirius, the brightest of the fixed stars in our sky. The brilliance of earth and moon is but reflected glory, however, for they and all the other planets and satellites shine by merely reflecting a fraction of the sunlight which falls upon them. The different brightnesses of earth and moon are the result of both the actual difference in their sizes and the comparatively greater reflecting power of each square foot of the earth's surface.

In the course of a month the moon would be observed by a Venusian to oscillate to either side of the earth. With even modest instruments, a persistent observer would also conclude after a short period of time that (1) the earth is nearly spherical, (2) the earth (but not the moon) possesses an atmosphere, (3) the earth rotates about an axis once every 24 hours, and (4) the earth-moon system revolves [1] about the sun once in approximately 365 terrestrial days. To anyone on Venus these observations might be simple and the conclusions straightforward, but we who do not have his advantage of distance will have to depend upon somewhat less direct but equally conclusive demonstrations of these facts.

[1] In scientific usage, one always observes the distinction that *rotation* is a motion about an axis through a body, whereas *revolution* is motion about a point or an axis outside the body.

■
. . . . 32

Figure 13. THE EARTH FROM HIGH ALTITUDE. Some half million square miles of the southwestern United States and northwestern Mexico can be seen in this composite of photographs taken at a height of 101 miles above the earth's surface by rocket-borne cameras. Easily identifiable as the large dark area in the lower left is the Gulf of California into which the Colorado River can be seen to empty. The Pacific Ocean may be seen beyond the Lower Californian peninsula. The top central portion contains the area about Flagstaff, Arizona. (Official United States Naval Photograph.)

The Size and Shape of the Earth

ITS SHAPE

It is interesting that though the roundness of the earth is a generally accepted fact, few persons can offer a convincing proof that the earth is nearly spherical or can suggest how the value of the earth's diameter might be determined. In fact, any assertion of its roundness plainly contradicts immediate sense experience, and the ancients (with a few exceptions) considered absurd any suggestion that the earth might not be flat.

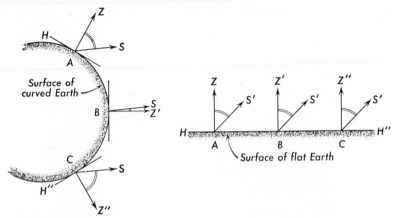

Figure 14. Observers at *A, B,* and *C* can note the direction *S* of any given star in relation to their respective zeniths *Z, Z',* and *Z".* The relation of the directions of *S* and *Z* will vary on the surface of a curved earth, would be invariable on a flat earth.

There is, however, a great weight of evidence to demonstrate that the earth is round. In recent years rocket-borne cameras and manned balloon ascensions have supplied photographs made at very high altitude (Fig. 13). These show such extended stretches of horizon as to reveal unmistakably the curvature of the earth's surface.

Since ancient times it has been recognized that the north- or south-bound traveler will note a progressive shift in the positions of the stars in his sky which is in proportion to the length of his journey. His change in vantage point will have altered the space direction of the enormously distant stars practically not at all; rather does the change of apparent star's position indicate that the traveler has taken a new vertical and with it a new horizon (Fig. 14). The positions of the distant stars in the sky of an observer "down under" (Australia, Argentina) would plainly be as much different from the positions of the same stars for a northern observer as their respective vertical directions. On a round earth the difference would be in proportion to their separation; on a flat earth it would not.

ITS DIMENSIONS

It is evidently no problem to prove that the earth is round. The main effort is to be in determining its *exact* size and shape.

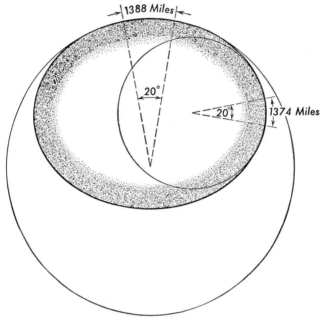

Figure 15. By taking a meridional section through a spheroidal earth, we see that a sphere of smaller radius could be fitted to it at the equator while only one of larger radius fits at the pole. On the spheres of unequal size, as on the actual earth, equal numbers of degrees of latitude would intercept unequal arcs at equator and poles.

The principles involved in this problem are elementary. All that is required is an accurate knowledge of the latitudes and longitudes (p. 46) of a number of places and the distances between them. From the longitudes and latitudes of any two we can compute the number of degrees between them along the earth's surface. If the earth's surface were perfectly spherical, this would be strictly proportional to the linear distance between them and quite independent of the direction from the one to the other.

Accurate measurements of the earth's surface show that this is not quite the case. The distance corresponding to one degree along the earth's surface is the least number of miles when traveling north or south at the equator, greatest when traveling north or south at a pole. These observations can have only one interpretation (Fig. 15), namely, that the earth would be a sphere but for its possession of a slight bulge around the equator.

These measurements give also the earth's dimensions, for by multiplying the number of miles per degree by the 360 degrees of an entire circumference, one obtains the circumference in miles; this is π times its diameter. The best measurements have shown in this way that the earth's diameter at the equator is 7927 miles and that 7900 miles is the distance from pole to pole. The solid figure having these dimensions is known as the *Hayford spheroid*. The difference between its polar and equatorial dimensions is only one part in 297; in a model of convenient size, so small a difference could not be discerned by the most critical eye.

ITS MASS

How much material makes up this great bulk, i.e., what is the mass of the earth? For the answer, we appeal to the law of gravitation for a method to "weigh" the earth. The principle made use of is this: The gravitational attraction of the entire earth is the same as that which would be produced by a particle of the same mass placed at the earth's center, about 3950 miles away. We therefore have only to compare the earth's gravitational attraction with that of a 1-ton particle at an equal distance, to learn the earth's mass in tons. For, by the law of gravitation, their respective attractions upon any third object, such as the experimenter himself or a ball of convenient size, will be in the proportion of their masses; at equal distances, neither has an advantage of proximity and any differences must be due to the effects of unequal masses.

Now, the force of the earth's attraction upon any test body is merely its weight; this can be measured without difficulty by a spring scale, for example. On the other hand, it would be very impractical to try to determine the gravitational attraction of a 1-ton "particle" upon a test body nearly 4000 miles away, for the force of gravity amounts to very little except for enormous masses such as those of the planets or the even larger stars. Consequently, we measure the attraction exerted upon a test body (e.g., a steel ball) by a 1-ton "particle" at very close range. We then determine, using the law of gravitation, what this force would amount to if, in imagination, the 1-ton "particle" were transported to the same distance as the center of the earth. By making use of the law of gravitation, we can in this way eliminate the effect of unequal distances and compare directly the attraction of the earth to that of a 1-ton particle. The earth's attraction will be as many times stronger as there are tons in the earth; in other words, the ratio of the forces of attraction at equal distances will be equal to the earth's mass in tons.

"Weighing" the earth thus consists principally in determining in a laboratory the gravitational attraction between two known masses at a known distance apart. It is accomplished by means of a very delicate experiment requiring extremely sensitive apparatus. Such experiments indicate that the earth has a mass of 6.6×10^{21} tons (66 followed by 20

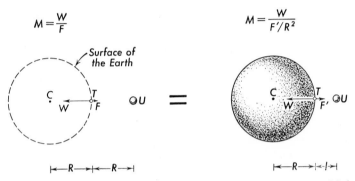

$$M = \frac{W}{F}$$

$$M = \frac{W}{F'/R^2}$$

Figure 16. In principle it is possible to determine the earth's mass, M, by comparing its attraction W upon a test body T with the attraction F of a unit mass U at the same distance R from T. Then $M = W/F$. In practice, the attraction F' of U on T is measured when U is at unit distance from T. Then since $F = F'/R^2$, the earth's mass is WR^2/F'.

zeros). This is slightly more than five and a half times the mass of an equal-sized globe of water. It is a figure of the greatest importance for any absolute determination of the masses of other celestial bodies, since these are otherwise known only in comparison to the earth.

The Earth's Atmosphere

It hardly requires proof that the planet earth possesses an atmosphere; our ability to exist upon it is proof enough. But it is not always realized that the earth's atmosphere is of interest astronomically in that it affects, in a variety of ways, our observations of all astronomical bodies. Contrary to a rather widespread misapprehension, the atmosphere's function as a medium for the meteorological phenomena of clouds, halos, cyclone and anticyclone areas, etc., and for geophysical phenomena such as aurorae and the reflection of radio waves is generally of little professional interest to the astronomer except as it may incidentally affect his observing conditions.

Of more immediate interest to him is the fact that the earth's atmosphere affects the radiation received from the sun, the stars, and all other celestial objects through the processes of (1) absorption, (2) refraction, (3) diffusion, and (4) reflection. Let us consider these effects separately.

ATMOSPHERIC ABSORPTION

The radiation which we receive from any body is really a mixture of radiations. All together they are known as electromagnetic radiations. For convenience, electromagnetic radiations are subdivided into general classes such as radio waves, heat waves, visible light, ultraviolet light, and x-rays (in the order of increasing ability of a single beam to transmit energy). Each subdivision contains a considerable range of varieties of radiation—visible light, for example, including light of each of the pure colors of the rainbow.

Now, the atmosphere does not admit all kinds of radiation indiscriminately; it absorbs certain proportions of the various kinds. Thus, its absorption of x-radiation is practically total; its absorption of visible light is only partial. It is fortunate for us that the atmosphere does absorb part of the sun's radiation (in particular), for the full strength of its ultraviolet rays would be fatal to all forms of life. Astronomically speaking, however, the fact of absorption means that we observe the radiations of celestial bodies only by our atmosphere's leave, which, though provident, is in many respects a severe handicap. For there is every reason to expect that if the whole of the sun's and the stars' radiations could be studied, we could add greatly to our present knowledge of these bodies. Such a well-founded hope, as well as the perennial curiosity as to what is "around the next bend of the river," has led to serious effort to make astronomical observations with automatic rocket-borne instruments that can be carried to heights of several hundred miles, where the atmosphere's absorptive power is greatly reduced.

Atmospheric absorption can also be effective in reverse, preventing the immediate loss from the earth of some of its own radiations, particularly heat radiation. It thus serves to temper both day and night; without absorption by its atmosphere, the earth would suffer great daily extremes of temperature.

In a very different sense the atmosphere also "absorbs" meteorites ("shooting stars"). These small bits of rock or metal collide with the earth by the millions daily, but because of their high relative velocities —8 miles per second at the very least—they are heated to incandescence almost at once by friction with and by the compression of the atmosphere's gases along their paths. By having their outer layers continually and rapidly melted off and swept away, all but a few of the largest ones are consumed before they reach the earth's surface. In this way the atmosphere prevents our being continually peppered by rock and iron fragments.

ATMOSPHERIC REFRACTION

In addition to absorbing, the atmosphere refracts. A beam of light which passes obliquely from a first medium into a second having a differ-

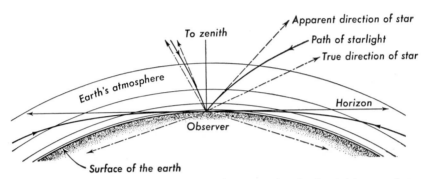

Figure 17. The solid curves represent the true paths of refracted beams of starlight traversing the earth's atmosphere. The observer assigns to the source the direction of the beam as it arrives whereas its true direction is that of the beam as it first enters the atmosphere. The latter is always farther from the zenith than the former (except at the zenith itself).

ent density will suffer a change of direction; the bending of a ray of light in such a way is called *refraction*. It is refraction which creates the illusion that a stick in the water is bent exactly at water level. It is also refraction which makes lenses effective.

Now, the atmosphere is a medium whose density varies continuously —from its greatest value at sea level to a value of zero at its extreme upper limit of a height of 500 miles or so. Hence a ray of sunlight or starlight entering our atmosphere obliquely will be refracted progressively more as it approaches the surface of the earth and in such a way that it will arrive more nearly vertically than it entered (Fig. 17). Therefore, when an observer at the earth's surface seeks to fix the source of a ray he receives, by tracing back along it, he will incorrectly assign to the source a position too near the vertical. In other words, the apparent position of all celestial objects is elevated by atmospheric refraction. The amount of elevation of any source is greatest near the horizon—amounting to slightly over half a degree—and diminishes rapidly to less than one-tenth degree at 10° above the horizon, to zero at the point overhead.

One of the interesting consequences of elevation by refraction is that all celestial objects are made to rise sooner and set later than they otherwise would, for by refraction they are optically brought or kept above the horizon. Hence the sun is up actually more than half the hours of the year.

A second consequence of elevation by refraction is one that is due to the rapid decrease of the amount of refractional elevation with increasing altitude above the horizon. In particular, the bottom edge (called the *lower limb*) of the sun or moon will be more elevated than the upper edge (known as the *upper limb*). Only if both limbs were elevated equally could the rising or setting sun or moon appear to be as high as it is wide; however, since its upper limb is elevated less than its lower limb, the disk of the sun or moon will appear noticeably flattened when near the horizon. Strictly speaking, the lunar or solar disks should appear flattened at any time the sun or moon is not directly overhead, but the amount of the effect is imperceptible at more than a few degrees from the horizon. It is this unequal atmospheric refraction which explains the common observation of flattened solar or lunar disks when sun or moon are near the horizon.[2]

Yet another effect of refraction is one that is of little importance except to astronomers; it is *atmospheric dispersion*. It depends on the fact that no two colors of light are refracted equally, so that the elevation of a star's image is unequal in the different colors forming the image. As a result, a pinpoint of starlight is received at the bottom of the atmosphere as a string of adjacent pinpoints of the different colors. The length of this little "starbow" is as great as 45 seconds of arc near the horizon— an amount far less than the naked eye can appreciate but plain to see in almost any small telescope. Atmospheric dispersion must be reckoned with in making highly accurate measurements of the positions of stars.

But the most common of all effects of refraction is the phenomenon of *twinkling*. If the atmosphere were perfectly steady and motionless from top to bottom, the stars would shine unblinking. A ray of starlight seldom finds tranquillity at all heights in our atmosphere, however;

---

[2] This has no relation to the fact that at moonrise the moon appears to be larger than when it is high in the sky. Actually, its angular dimensions are smaller at moonrise, both because its vertical dimension is reduced by refraction and because it is one earth's radius farther from the observer than when it reaches its highest point in the sky. The explanation seems to be that it is purely an illusion; it is seemingly related to greater experience in the size estimation of objects in a horizontal direction than in a vertical direction, for the magnitude of the illusion diminishes with age.

along its path it usually encounters a great number of local irregularities in the density of the air. These irregularities of density are continually and rapidly adjusting themselves, and as a consequence the amount by which the ray of starlight is refracted is also continually changing. This means that a star is made to appear to be dancing at high speed about its average position, i.e., the star seems to twinkle.[3]

A refractive effect of great practical importance occurs in layers of the upper atmosphere called the *ionosphere*. Strong, unfiltered sunlight breaks down some of the atmospheric molecules into electrically negative fundamental particles called electrons (see p. 229) and the residual positively charged molecules called *ions* (hence the term *ionosphere*). The electrons refract electromagnetic waves of radio wavelength. In fact, some of those which originate from a transmitter on the ground are so bent as they traverse the ionosphere that they are returned to the earth's surface at great distance from the station; the effect is therefore sometimes inaccurately termed "reflection." Were it not for this, all radio reception would be limited to the distance of the horizon, as in television transmission, which takes place in wave lengths very little refracted.

ATMOSPHERIC DIFFUSION AND REFLECTION

A third effect of the atmosphere upon a light beam is that the atmosphere diffuses or scatters light. This effect is brought about by the interaction of individual rays of light with individual molecules of air.[4] A light ray which grazes a molecule may be diverted into any direction as a result of the encounter. This is *diffusion* or *scattering;* it is not to be confused with reflection, which can occur only from a surface of some extent, or with refraction, whereby all rays of a beam are bent in the same way.

Rays of some colors are scattered more than others. For example, the molecules of the atmosphere scatter blue light more effectively than they do red light. Hence, from every point of the sky more blue than red light is being scattered into the direction toward the observer, and

---

[3] It is often pointed out as a distinguishing feature of the planets that they twinkle very little or not at all. The planets' apparently exceptional behavior is due to the fact that they have apparent disks which are measurably large as in contrast to the effectively pinpoint apparent size of the enormously more distant stars. If we think of the light from a star as being a single fragile beam, the light of any planet could be regarded as a bundle of such beams. Each beam of the bundle will twinkle, but the several beams seldom twinkle synchronously. The absence of synchronism results in our seeing no over-all effect. The moon, on a more decisive scale, likewise does not twinkle, and for the same reason.

[4] A *molecule* is the smallest particle of any substance which still exhibits all the properties of that substance. If a molecule were further divided, it would yield either atoms or the fundamental particles of which atoms are made.

therefore mostly blue light will be received by him from all points of the sky; that is to say that the sky will appear blue. Without the atmosphere, the sky would be perfectly black—even in midday—and the untwinkling stars would be always visible. Mountain climbers and balloon ascensionists do, in fact, find this state of affairs approximated at high altitude, where most of the atmosphere is below them.

While diffusion causes light received indirectly to be bluer than it otherwise would be, it will by the same token make light received directly seem redder. Thus the direct rays of sunlight, traveling their longest path through the atmosphere at the time of sunset, will then be more stripped of the blue in them than they will of the red, leaving the red to predominate and to create the beautiful and characteristic red and orange sunset coloring.

Diffusion combines with reflection to bring about twilight. *Reflection* occurs at any surface when an incident beam of light is returned from it. In our atmosphere, large numbers of very small particles of dust and smoke provide reflecting surfaces; although dust particles are very small by ordinary standards, they are immensely larger than molecules, of which they contain billions.

An observer to whom the sun is below the horizon can receive sunlight indirectly from still illuminated regions high in the atmosphere by means of reflection from atmospheric particles and scattering by molecules. This second- and third-hand illumination is *twilight.* If it were not for such a mechanism, daylight would end at sunset as abruptly as though an electric light had been turned off.

The Rotation of the Earth

Since we fail to sense the earth's daily rotation about an axis through its poles, it behooves us to give proof of the assertion that the earth rotates. Of the several proofs that can be given, we shall consider the deflection of freely falling bodies.

Though it may at first seem altogether unreasonable, it is a fact that any body falling freely from rest through still air will not strike directly under its point of release but will land to the east of it. The reason is that a body above the earth's surface is also farther from the earth's axis of rotation and must therefore describe a circle of larger circumference as the earth rotates. At the equator, for instance, a body 1000 feet above the earth's surface will travel more than a mile more per day than the point of the earth's surface directly below it. To do it in the same length of time, one day, this body must travel at a slightly greater speed.

Quite generally, objects above the surface of the earth have greater eastward velocities than the points below them. If they are released, they lose none of this eastward velocity. Consequently the excess of this velocity over what is possessed by the points below will carry a freely falling body east of the point vertically under its starting position. While this effect is present in falls from any height, it is extremely small except for

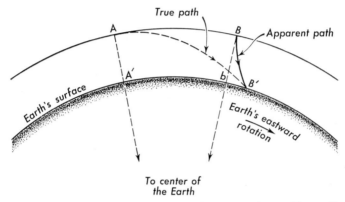

Figure 18. A body at A would be carried to B by the earth's rotation in the time required for the body to fall to earth. Then if A'B' = AB, the body will strike B' when released at A. The point B' is east of b, which is directly below B.

free falls from great altitude. Though they are small, such eastward deflections are observed, as they clearly could not be on a nonrotating earth.

One of the consequences of the earth's daily rotation is the existence of its equatorial bulge. The particles of the spinning earth feel a tendency to fly off tangentially, just as water droplets tend to fly off the rim of a rapidly turning wheel or as the end man tends to lose hold in a game of "crack-the-whip." Such a tendency is ascribed to the action of a *centrifugal force,* which (in accordance with Newton's first law of motion) is really the inertial resistance that must be overcome to divert any mass from straight-line motion into circular motion. It is the action of "centrifugal force" which is utilized in the spin-dryer, the ordinary cream separator, and the blood centrifuge.

The centrifugal force felt by the particles of the earth acts directly outward from the axis of rotation. To be sure, the centrifugal force is more than balanced by the stronger gravitational pull of the earth. Therefore, at the earth's present speed of rotation the material at the earth's equator does not fly off. All the same, the net inward force on the material of the earth, especially that at the equator, is less by the amount of the centrifugal force. Hence the earth has assumed a bulge about its equator, where the rotational velocity and centrifugal force are greatest. The lesser inward force is equivalent to a reduced weight in these regions; this allows of the support of a greater amount of material. The earth's crust has formed like a film over the surface of this slightly distorted sphere. In a sense, therefore, the earth has been "molded" by centrifugal force—all a direct result of its rotation.

The Revolution of the Earth

The assertion that the earth revolves annually about the sun is one so little attested to by sense experience that it, too, must be fortified with convincing proof. We shall consider the apparent semi-annual alternation of approach and recession of stars near the earth's orbital plane.

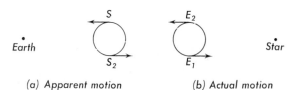

(a) Apparent motion   *(b) Actual motion*

Figure 19. From the earth E it appears that a star near the plane of the earth's orbit is receding at S_2 and six months later approaching at S_1. Actually it is the earth which is approaching the star S at E_1, six months later receding from it at E_2.

From a nonrevolving earth, the line-of-sight velocities of approach or recession of individual stars—called their radial velocities and measured by means of an instrument called the spectroscope (p. 220)—would show no annual variation. On the other hand, from a revolving earth, observers would have the impression of sometimes overtaking a particular fixed star that is near the earth's plane of revolution, sometimes retreating from it (Fig. 19). Since stars are observed to partake of an annual variation of radial velocities, the earth must complete one revolution per year about the sun.

Positions on the Earth

The positions of the earth's geographical poles and equator are fixed by the earth's rotation. The poles are, by definition, the two points on the earth where its surface is intersected by the axis of rotation, that imaginary spindle through the center of the earth, about which it spins. The equator is the uniquely determined imaginary circle midway between the two poles. If the earth had a different axis of rotation, it would have different poles and, as a result, a different equator.

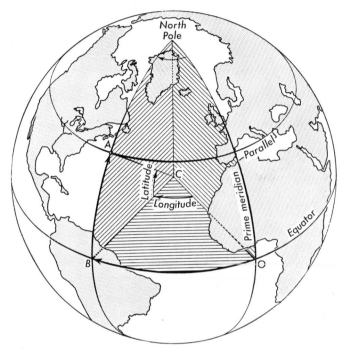

Figure 20. Angle *OCB* is the longitude of *A*. Angle *BCA* is the geocentric latitude.

These two reference points and, more particularly, this derived reference circle form a natural reference system which offers a means of specifying positions in a north-south sense. Supplemented by some measure of east-west position, this reference system may be used to locate unambiguously any point on the earth's surface. Of such *coordinate systems,* the common system of longitude and latitude is almost universally used.

For present simplicity, let us suppose the earth to be perfectly spherical. To measure the longtitude and latitude of any point on the surface of such a sphere, let us first imagine two sets of circles drawn upon it. The first, the *meridians of longitude,* run from pole to pole and are therefore oriented in an exactly north-south direction. The second, the *parallels of latitude,* circle parallel to the equator and consequently run east-west.

One of the meridians has been chosen by common consent to be a standard of east-west reference; it passes through Greenwich, England, and is called the *prime meridian*. The *longitude* of any given point is reckoned as the angle between the prime meridian and the meridian through the given point. It is measured at a pole or along the equator, in degrees east or west up to 180°. The various meridians mark the different longitudes.

The *geocentric latitude* of any given point is defined as the angle, as it would be seen from the center of the earth, between the given point and the equator. It is measured north or south along the meridian of the point in degrees up to 90°. The various parallels mark the different latitudes.

The *astronomical latitude* of any point is defined as the angle between the plumb-line vertical of the locality and the plane of the equator. It is astronomical latitude which is intended in ordinary reference to latitude. Geocentric and astronomical latitudes would be identical were it not for the fact that the earth is spheroidal rather than spherical, as we assumed. In practice, observations yield astronomical latitude to which small calculable adjustments (always less than one-fifth of a degree) may be made to obtain geocentric latitude. Geocentric latitudes are required in a variety of astronomical problems; astronomical latitudes are made use of in navigation and geodesy.

The longitude and latitude of any position on the earth's surface are unique; conversely, there can be only one point corresponding to a given longitude and latitude. Properly speaking, this is true only for one particular time, although for practical purposes it is never far wrong. For, while the axis of the earth maintains itself, the earth's orientation on its axis is continually changing with respect to its own average position. Since the position of the geographical poles is determined by the earth's orientation on its axis, the position of the poles must continually shift as the earth's orientation varies. This shifting is known as the *wandering of the poles*.

Actually the poles never stray very far, staying well within a plot less than 100 feet square. Nevertheless there result small but measurable variations of latitudes; since these are never over one seven-thousandth of a degree, they are usually neglected. It was by accurate latitude determinations, however, that the wandering of the poles was first detected. The cause of the phenomenon is not yet fully known. The weight of seasonal accumulations of ice and snow upon the Asiatic continent is thought to contribute to its existence.

B. THE RELATION OF EARTH TO SKY

What is Heaven? A globe of dew.
—SHELLEY

The Celestial Sphere

As we look at the sky from any point on the earth, we seem to see equally far in all directions, i.e., the sky seems to be a hemisphere and *we are at its center.* This visible hemisphere together with the part of the sky below the horizon form the *celestial sphere.* The celestial sphere is, of course, a fictitious surface, though the ancients believed in the existence of a real material celestial sphere. Let us consider the celestial sphere and its appearance to observers at different points on the earth.

It should be recognized, to begin with, that all celestial objects are seen in projection against the celestial sphere. The celestial sphere thus appears to be a background "behind" even the most remote stars and is therefore said to be at an infinite distance or to have an infinite radius.

It follows that any particular point on the celestial sphere will be in precisely the same direction *in space* from every point on the earth; i.e., the lines directed from any two observers toward the same point on the celestial sphere will be parallel. To see that this is so, we imagine two observers on the earth fixing attention on a relatively nearby object; it is plain that as this object recedes from both of them the difference of the directions of their lines of sight will continually diminish, eventually becoming imperceptibly small. At the ideal limit of infinite recession, the *angle* between their lines of sight would vanish entirely, i.e., the object would appear to be in the same direction in space to both observers and their lines of sight would be parallel.

We obviously cannot measure distances on the infinitely large celestial sphere in miles or feet, as can be done on the surface of the terrestrial sphere. The important distinction between different points of the celestial sphere is instead one of direction and differences of direction are expressed in angles. Consequently, we speak of *angular distance* on the celestial sphere. It is most commonly measured in degrees or their parts; one degree contains 60 minutes of arc, each minute is subdivided into 60 seconds of arc. The full moon, for example, has an apparent diameter of about half a degree (30 minutes of arc) while the separation of the "pointers" of the Big Dipper is about 5 degrees (see Key, Star Map 4).

Figure 21. APPARENT CONVERGENCE OF EXTENDED PARALLELS. This line of poles crosses the Bonneville salt flats in Utah. It shows how parallel lines, such as the line connecting the bases and the line connecting the tops, appear to converge to a common point at a great distance. (By *Life* Photographer Fritz Goro. Copyright *Time, Inc.*)

Positions on the Sky

THE LOCAL REFERENCE SYSTEM

Although the direction in *space* of any object on the celestial sphere (for example, a star) will be the same from every different position on the earth's surface, particular stars will have different *apparent* positions in the sky from different localities. The reason is that the principal reference direction in each locality is the vertical. Since the earth is a spheroid rather than a plane, the vertical at every different point of the earth is a different direction in space and is therefore directed toward a different point on the celestial sphere. The point toward which the vertical is directed is called the *zenith* of the locality and is the point directly overhead. We have demonstrated, in short, that every different point on the earth has a different zenith.

The point directly opposite the zenith on the celestial sphere, i.e., the imaginary point directly under the observer's feet, is called the *nadir*. The imaginary circle midway between zenith and nadir, dividing the sky into two hemispheres, is called the *astronomical horizon*. From the surface of a smooth sea, where there are no irregularities in the local landscape, the astronomical horizon and the visible horizon are the same.

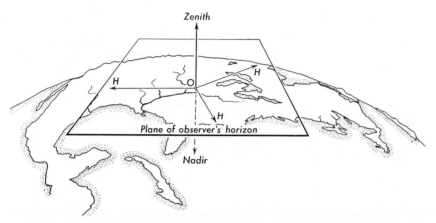

Figure 22. An observer at *O* finds his zenith directly above him, his nadir directly below. In any direction *OH* perpendicular to the zenith-nadir line is the astronomical horizon. (Map after a drawing by Richard Edes Harrison for *Fortune*.)

Since the horizon depends upon the position of the zenith and nadir, it is obviously a local circle of reference and must change with the position of the observer as does the zenith.

THE RELATION OF THE CELESTIAL AND TERRESTRIAL SPHERES

The zenith at the north geographical pole is of special importance; this point on the celestial sphere is called the *north celestial pole*. Opposite it is the *south celestial pole*. Midway between the celestial poles is the *celestial equator;* it divides the celestial sphere into northern and southern hemispheres. (From the definitions, one will see that the nadir at the north terrestrial pole is the south celestial pole, and therefore the astronomical horizon at the north terrestrial pole is also the celestial equator.)

Based on the reference system afforded by the celestial poles and celestial equator is a very useful astronomical coordinate system analogous to the longitude and latitude system on the surface of the earth. To visualize it, let us imagine two sets of circles drawn upon the celestial sphere. The first set, the *hour circles,* run from celestial pole to celestial pole and are therefore oriented in an exactly north-south direction. The second set, the *parallels of declination,* circle parallel to the celestial equator and consequently run east-west.

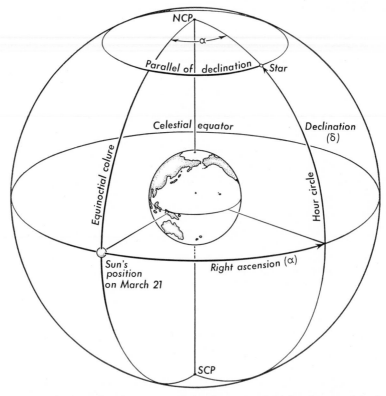

Figure 23. To realize the correct relation between celestial and terrestrial spheres, imagine the rotating globe shrunk to a point at the center of the celestial sphere.

One of the hour circles, called the equinoctial colure, has been chosen by common consent to be a standard of east-west reference; it passes through the position occupied by the sun on the first day of spring. The *right ascension* of any given point on the celestial sphere is reckoned as the angle between the equinoctial colure and the hour circle through the given point. It is measured eastward at a celestial pole or along the celestial equator, in hours and minutes of right ascension, from 0 to 24 hours; since 360° corresponds to 24 hours, there must be 15° to each hour of right ascension, 15 minutes of arc to each minute of right ascension, etc. The origin of this choice of units will become apparent when we consider the determination of time. For the present we note that the various hour circles mark the different right ascensions.

The second celestial coordinate is *declination*. The declination of any given point on the celestial sphere is defined as the angular distance of the

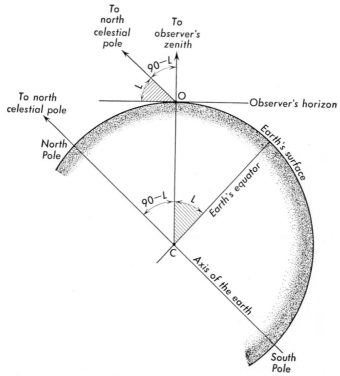

Figure 24. The latitude of the observer is $L°$. It is easy to show from this figure that the elevation of the north celestial pole above the observer's horizon is likewise $L°$.

point from the celestial equator. It is measured north or south along the hour circle through the point, in degrees up to $\pm 90°$. Evidently the various parallels of declination mark the different declinations.

With specific celestial and terrestrial coordinate systems to consider, let us see how the celestial and terrestrial spheres are related. Let us imagine that we are standing at the north pole. The north celestial pole is then at our zenith. If we were to travel along the appropriate geographical meridian to any desired point on the earth's surface, we would evidently have changed the position of our zenith on the celestial sphere by as many degrees as we have changed our latitude, for this is the amount by which the directions of the verticals of the two localities differ. The result will be that the north celestial pole will have been displaced from the zenith by this same amount. In other words, the observer's moving directly away from the north terrestrial pole any number of degrees of latitude will make the north celestial pole appear to move the same number of degrees directly away from the zenith toward the horizon. For example, if one were to travel the 90° of latitude from the north pole to the equator, the position of the north celestial pole would be depressed 90° from the zenith to the astronomical horizon. By retracing one's steps, the north celestial pole can be made to appear to rise again; thus by traveling 10° north from the equator, the celestial pole can be brought to a position 10° above the horizon.

This simple imaginary experiment shows that the number of degrees by which the north celestial pole is elevated above the horizon (a quantity called its *altitude*) is the same as the number of degrees of latitude that the observer is north of the equator. This result is condensed into an easily remembered statement: *The altitude of the north celestial pole equals the latitude of the observer.* This can be taken as true without exception if we agree to count south latitude as negative north latitude and depression below the horizon as negative altitude. Notice that the apparent position of the celestial pole depends *only* on the observer's latitude; all observers in the same latitude will see the celestial pole at the same altitude.

In obtaining the preceding results, we have actually got the cart before the horse. We have supposed that we knew our latitude initially, whereas it is the common practice to determine the latitude of any point on the earth simply by determining the altitude of the celestial pole. (For convenience in locating the north celestial pole, it may be noted that its position is marked approximately by Polaris, the "north star" or "pole star.") Determinations of latitude by this means give astronomical latitude.

Next let us consider the particular hour circle which (momentarily) includes the observer's zenith. Such a circle will divide the sky into east and west halves. It is called the *local celestial meridian*. The observer's celestial meridian is an important local reference circle, for the points where it cuts the horizon are the north and south points of the compass. Moreover, we shall soon find that the celestial meridian is of fundamental importance in determining the time of day and geographical longitude.

It is not difficult to see that the observer's celestial meridian must be directly over the geographical meridian on which he stands, for the celestial pole is directly over the geographical pole whereas the zenith is directly over the observer's position on the earth's surface. The circles connecting these respective points on the celestial and terrestrial spheres are by definition the celestial and terrestrial meridians. We see from this that we may move due north or south while keeping the same celestial or terrestrial meridian but that motion east or west on the earth's surface will change both, and by equal amounts.

The Diurnal Motion of the Celestial Sphere

Just as the earth turns about the terrestrial poles once daily—and because it does—the celestial sphere turns once daily in the opposite direction about the celestial poles. The celestial poles therefore remain stationary to any fixed observer, and every star will appear to circle about the celestial poles from east to west as the earth turns from west to east. The arc thus traced out by any star in its daily motion of rising and setting is called its *diurnal circle*. The diurnal circle of any star coincides with the parallel of declination through the star; it is centered on the celestial pole.

Now let us imagine drawn about the north celestial pole a diurnal circle with radius in degrees equal to our latitude. Since the celestial pole is this same number of degrees above the horizon, the imaginary circle so drawn will at its lowest point just touch the horizon. The diurnal circles of some stars will fall within this imaginary circle and be concentric with it; such stars never set in this latitude, for they are evidently nearer the celestial pole than is the horizon and thus can never go below the horizon. The part of the sky within this imaginary circle with radius equal to the observer's latitude is called the *celestial circumpolar cap*. Stars in the celestial circumpolar cap are *circumpolar stars*.

The size of the circumpolar cap in any locality obviously depends on one's latitude; not all the stars which are circumpolar at any given latitude will be so at any smaller latitude. At the earth's equator, where the latitude is 0°, the circumpolar cap has shrunk to the celestial pole itself. At a terrestrial pole, where the latitude is 90°, it has grown to include the whole visible sky, and whatever stars can be seen can always be seen; here the stars do not rise and set as they seem to elsewhere but forever circle about parallel to the horizon.

Now, it is a common-sense observation that to each visible point on the sky, there is a diametrically opposite point of the celestial sphere which is below the horizon and therefore invisible. It follows, then, that op-

Figure 25. STAR TRAILS. The constellation of Orion and adjacent regions of the winter sky are here shown together with the trails produced by them during a time exposure. (Courtesy John Stofan.)

posite the visible celestial circumpolar cap, which is always visible, there must be a corresponding invisible celestial circumpolar cap which is never visible. Thus, at 40° north latitude, stars within 40° of the north celestial pole never go below the horizon, while those within 40° of the south celestial pole never come above the horizon.

The stars between the celestial circumpolar caps appear for a longer time above or below the horizon according as they are nearer the visible or invisible circumpolar cap. Specifically, stars near the visible circumpolar cap will be up nearly 24 hours a day, those near the invisible cir-

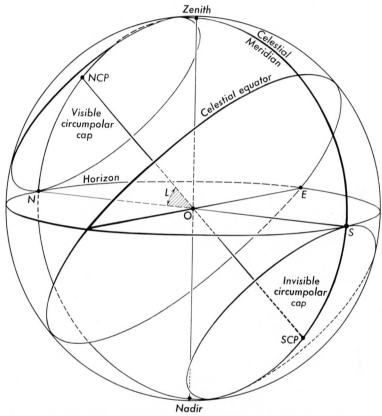

Figure 26. The observer located at O in latitude $L°$ will find the various regions, circles, and points on the celestial sphere as they are shown here.

cumpolar cap will be invisible most of each day, and stars at the celestial equator—being just midway between the circumpolar caps—will be up half a day and set half a day. This relation between the declination of a star and the time it spends above the horizon is illustrated well by the sun: When the sun comes north in spring, we have more daylight than darkness after it has crossed the celestial equator; the opposite is true when it returns south in autumn.

The Apparent Annual Motion of the Sun

THE SUN'S MOTION ON THE ECLIPTIC

We have seen that the plane of the earth's terrestrial and celestial equators is determined by the earth's rotation; if the earth did not rotate upon an axis, there would be no need and no means for defining poles and equator. Also defined by a motion of the earth is a second plane of special importance, the plane of the earth's orbit; it is determined by the earth's motion of revolution.

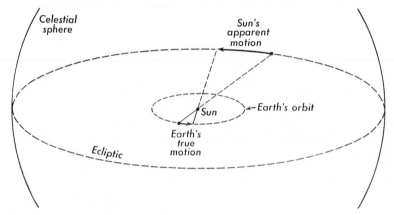

Figure 27. The earth's orbital motion projected through the sun traces out the ecliptic on the celestial sphere.

The simplest way to identify this plane is to trace out on the sky the circle in which it intersects the celestial sphere. This circle is called the *ecliptic* (not to be confused with either "eclipse" or ellipse"). It can be recognized by the fact that the sun seems to move slowly along the ecliptic amongst the stars. This motion is, of course, in addition to its diurnal motion; the two take place simultaneously.

The explanation of the sun's apparent motion on the ecliptic and the ability of the latter to identify the earth's orbital plane is quite simple: As the earth traverses its orbit about the sun, the sun will be viewed by us from continually different positions (Fig. 27). Hence, if we mark the path traced out by the sun on the celestial sphere, we shall have generated the earth's orbital plane, for the line joining the earth to sun is always in this plane, and we can point along this line simply by pointing to the sun. Furthermore, since the earth revolves through 360° about the sun in slightly more than 365 days, the sun will seem to move 360° about the ecliptic in slightly more than 365 days, i.e., not quite a degree a day. We can conclude also that because the sun's apparent motion along the ecliptic is from west to east, the direction of the earth's revolution about the sun must be counterclockwise as seen from the direction of the north celestial pole.

The sun's apparent motion along the ecliptic produces a seasonal progression of the constellations (for constellations, see Appendix 1), making each appear to rise and set earlier from day to day. Thus the stars which today appear to be just east of the sun in the sky and which rise and set just after the sun will shortly be to the west of it and will then rise and set before the sun. The amount of their precedence increases daily until finally, being halfway ahead of the sun, they will begin to overtake it from behind. The stars which are in prominence at any particular hour of the evening will therefore continually change, going through a complete cycle in one year.

Related to the ecliptic but now chiefly of historical interest is the *zodiac*. The zodiac is a belt of sky extending 9° to each side of the ecliptic. Spaced along it are the twelve constellations of the zodiac: Aries (Ram), Taurus (Bull), Gemini (Twins), Cancer (Crab), Leo (Lion), Virgo (Maiden), Libra (Scales), Scorpius (Scorpion), Sagittarius (Archer), Capricornus, (Sea-Goat), Aquarius (Water-Bearer), and Pisces (Fishes). The sun appears to enter a different constellation of the zodiac each month.

THE SEASONS

The ecliptic and the celestial equator are inclined to each other by approximately $23\frac{1}{2}°$ (more exactly, $23°27'$); this angle is known as the *obliquity of the ecliptic*. Since the ecliptic marks the plane of the earth's orbit and the celestial equator indicates the plane of the terrestrial equator, we conclude that these respective planes are inclined to each other by about $23\frac{1}{2}°$. In other words, the earth does not "sit upright" as it goes around the sun but spins about an axis tilted $23\frac{1}{2}°$ from the perpendicular to the plane in which it revolves.

Because of the obliquity of the ecliptic, the sun's right ascension *and* declination will change as it moves eastward along the ecliptic. The variations in declination are seen as an annual north-south motion of the sun on the celestial sphere; half the year it is north of the celestial equator and half the year south. It is on this account that the earth experiences a succession of seasons. For, the apparent north-south motion of the sun will result in a changing amount of sunlight received in any locality because of (1) the changing inclination of the sun's rays and (2) the changing duration of sunlight. The pertinence of the first of these factors is plain when one realizes that the sun's rays are most effective when they beat down perpendicularly; in the northern hemisphere the sunlight falls more squarely on the earth's surface as the sun comes north in the spring. At these same times there are more hours of daylight, for the northward-moving sun is ever approaching the north celestial circumpolar cap and

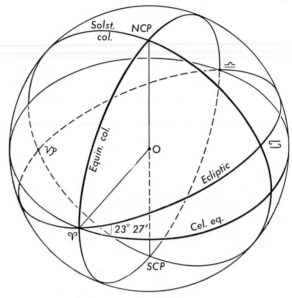

Figure 28. The ecliptic and celestial equator are mutually inclined by 23°27′. Their points of intersection are the vernal equinox (♈) and the autumnal equinox (♎).

therefore will remain risen continually more of the time as its declination increases.

The point and time (March 21) of the sun's crossing the celestial equator northward are both called the *vernal equinox*—called "equinox" (from the Latin meaning equal night) because at such times day and night are of equal length, called "vernal" since in the northern hemisphere it marks the beginning of spring. Three months (and one-quarter of a revolution of the earth) after the vernal equinox, the sun will be at its northernmost point on the ecliptic, a point and time (June 22) known as the *summer solstice*. While continually moving eastward along the eclip-tic, the sun will thereafter move southward, and in another three months (September 23) again crosses the celestial equator; this time and point of crossing are called the *autumnal equinox*. The autumnal equinox marks the official beginning of autumn and the beginning of the seasons when the night is longer than the day. After still another three months (December 22) the sun will be at its farthest south; this is the *winter solstice*.

The seasons are the result of *both* the earth's revolution about the sun *and* the obliquity of the ecliptic (Fig. 30). Since the earth's axis is tilted,

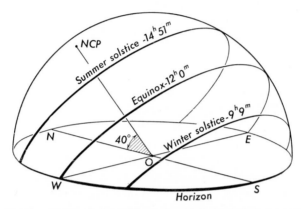

Figure 29. The altitude of the midday sun and the length of the visible arc of its diurnal circle vary with the season.

the northern hemisphere will be tipped sunward in summer; because the tilt is maintained in a fixed direction, half a revolution of the earth will exactly reverse the northern hemisphere's advantage in six months. At the equinoxes, the tilt of the earth's axis is at right angles to the direction of the sun and results in no advantage to either hemisphere.

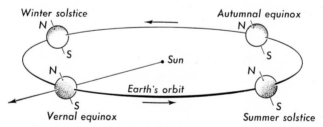

Figure 30. Only at the times of the equinoxes is the earth's axis perpendicular to the line from earth to sun.

Contrary to what is often supposed, the seasons do *not* depend upon the variation of the earth's distance from the sun. If this were so, the effect would be the same in both hemispheres—which it is not—and midsummer should occur when the earth is nearest the sun early in January—which it does not.

The earth's orbital eccentricity is responsible, however, for a slight difference in the lengths of the seasons. The earth is at perihelion early in January and therefore, by Kepler's law of areas, must be moving most rapidly in its orbit; it is at aphelion in July, then moving its slowest. Therefore the time from vernal equinox to autumnal equinox will be longer than the interval from autumnal equinox to vernal equinox. As a result, the northern hemisphere's winter is the shortest season, being 4.5 days shorter than summer, 3.8 days shorter than spring, and 0.9 day shorter than autumn.

Yet in spite of our longer summer, we in the northern hemisphere receive exactly the same amount of sunlight as is received in the southern hemisphere during their shorter summer season (our winter season); the effect of the additional time is offset by the effect of the additional distance. We might expect, therefore, that as a result of distributing the sun's summer heat over more days, our summer would be milder than that of the southern hemisphere—and by a converse argument, our winters also. However, the effect is not great and is largely masked by the effects of a considerably different distribution of land and water areas in the two hemispheres.

At first sight one might expect that the height of the summer season, for example, should coincide with the time of the summer solstice. Then the number of sunlight hours is greatest and the intensity of the sunlight received is a maximum. This is notably not the case, however, for the peak of the season usually comes four to six weeks later; quite generally, midseason seems to occur this much later than the time we might logically expect it. This phenomenon is known as the *lag of the seasons*.

Its explanation is quite simple. The average temperature at a given locality and at a particular time depends upon the temperature at which a *balance* is reached between heat received from the sun and heat lost by reflection and reradiation. So long as more heat is received during daylight hours than is lost the following night, the average temperature will increase, as it does for several weeks after summer solstice. In winter the reverse is true, and for several weeks after December 22 the northern hemisphere loses more heat at night than can be replaced by a less effective sun during the shorter-than-average days.

Time

The earth's two principal motions, revolution and rotation, enforce on its inhabitants the recognition of time intervals, the year and the day. In our habits, our holidays, and our ages we are the unconscious slaves of such impersonal and fortuitous masters as the motions of the earth. Imagine the discomfort and the inconvenience in a society which chose not to be regulated by the apparent diurnal motion of the sun; or picture the ill-success of the farmer who should attempt to cultivate without re·gard for the lengths of the seasons. And yet very few persons know exactly how the time of day is found or what forms the basis of the calendar. Let us consider both problems.

TIME BY THE SUN

As everyone knows, the time of day depends somehow on the position of the sun. As the earth rotates daily, the sun and stars seem to describe diurnal circles from east to west parallel to the celestial equator. In traversing that part of its diurnal circle which is above the astronomical horizon, every celestial object will be half the time rising, thereafter setting. The dividing line between bodies rising and bodies setting is the observer's celestial meridian, for it divides the sky into east (rising) and west (setting) halves. It is natural, then, that we should take midday to be the instant when the sun's center is exactly on the meridian and the sun is, at that instant, neither rising nor setting. So long as the sun has not attained the celestial meridian it is morning, and as soon as the sun has passed the celestial meridian it is afternoon, but at the moment it is on the celestial meridian the time is precisely *local apparent noon*. An *apparent solar day* is the length of time between two successive apparent noons, an hour is one twenty-fourth of a day, etc.

But, as is frequently the case, there are complications. One of them is the fact that the sun appears to move along the ecliptic about 1° a day. To be sure, this would not make the least difference if the sun were to move the same number of degrees eastward through the stars each day. But because the ecliptic has an obliquity of $23\frac{1}{2}$°, the sun's path along the ecliptic is not only eastward but is simultaneously partially northward or southward except at the solstices. Since the proportion of eastward and northward (or southward) motions continually varies, obliquity of the ecliptic is responsible for a daily variation in the amount of the sun's purely eastward motion among the stars. The sun's successive crossings of the celestial meridian, called *upper transits,* will therefore be separated by unequal lengths of time.

In addition to this, the sun does not even move at a uniform rate along the ecliptic; this we know to be a consequence of Kepler's law of areas and the eccentricity of the earth's orbit. The sun's changing rate along the ecliptic introduces its own effects, and the net effect to the sun's apparent eastward motion is the sum of the effects of obliquity and eccentricity.

It is evident that we are too hasty when we say that we tell time by the sun, for our timekeeper runs now slow, now fast. Fortunately, the sun's eastward spurts and laggings alternate in a perfectly regular way, as we should expect, knowing their origin. This gives us assurance that over a

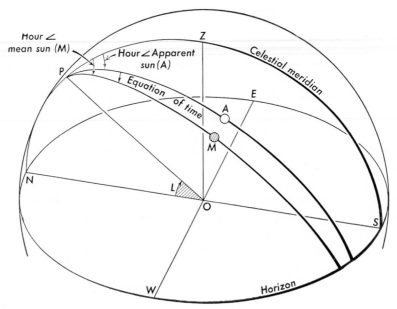

Figure 31. The hour circle through the apparent sun (*A*) has an hour angle of *APZ* west of the observer's (*O*) celestial meridian. The hour angle of the apparent sun is less than the hour angle of the mean sun (*M*) by the equation of time.

whole year the *average* length of all apparent solar days will be the same time interval, year after year; it is called the *mean solar day*.

If we like, we may think of the mean solar day as the interval between transits of a fictitious body moving eastward among the stars at a uniform rate; this body is the *mean sun*. The moment when the mean sun is on the celestial meridian is *local mean noon*. It returns to this position after one *mean solar day*.

Let us consider how we can determine the time of day from the mean sun's position. That we can do so depends upon the fact that the mean sun always requires exactly 24 mean solar hours to trace out its diurnal circle in full. Since that is so, the fractional part of the sun's diurnal circle which it has traced out any instant after transit will be identically the same as the fractional part of 24 hours which has elapsed since transit. In other words, the time elapsed since transit is a measure of the angle at the celestial pole between the observer's celestial meridian and the hour circle passing through the center of the mean sun. This angle measured westward is called the *hour angle* of the mean sun and may be given in degrees or, having regard for its use in time determination, in the equivalent time units ($1^h = 15°$, $1° = 4^m$, etc.).

We may summarize our result by saying that *local mean solar time is equal to the hour angle of the mean sun plus 12 hours;* the extra 12 hours comes from our measuring civil time since midnight instead of noon. But the mean sun is, of course, a fictitious body and our observations have to be made of the apparent sun. We therefore make the analogous definition that *local apparent solar time is equal to the hour angle of the apparent sun plus 12 hours.*

The difference at any instant between local mean solar time and local apparent solar time is called the *equation of time.* It can be calculated from a knowledge of the obliquity of the ecliptic and the eccentricity of the earth's orbit; Table 2 is a table of the equation of time, including the separate contributions of the effects of obliquity and eccentricity. By adding the equation of time to local apparent solar time we obtain local mean solar time. Only in this way can we tell time by the sun.

Even this is not an end to the matter, however, for our definitions and procedure make use of the observer's celestial meridian which, as we have seen, is different for every different terrestrial meridian. There is, then, a different local time for every terrestrial meridian, i.e., every longitude.

Confusion is avoided by compromise. By common consent, meridians for those longitudes which are equal to integral multiples of fifteen degrees (one hour) have been designated as *standard meridians.* Centered on them are time zones having an *average* total width of fifteen degrees in longitude. However, the boundaries of zones are often irregular so as to accommodate states or communities otherwise not wholly within one zone or on which a time difference from nearby regions would work an inconvenience. The time within each time zone is that determined at the zone's standard meridian. It is called standard mean solar time or simply *standard time.* This is the kind of time to which our watches and clocks are set.

Time determined elsewhere than on a standard meridian is called *local time,* such as local apparent solar time or local mean solar time. To local mean solar time we must apply a correction to obtain the correct standard time. This correction is simply the difference of longitude be-

table 2

The Equation of Time *

DATE	OBLIQUITY EFFECT	ECCENTRICITY EFFECT	TOTAL
January 1	$+3^m31^s$	-0^m17^s	$+3^m14^s$
January 15	7 37	$+1$ 35	9 12
February 1	9 49	3 45	13 34
February 15	9 10	5 7	14 17
March 1	6 10	6 28	12 38
March 15	2 1	7 15	9 16
April 1	-3 18	7 30	4 12
April 15	-7 14	7 31	0 17
May 1	-9 39	6 49	-2 50
May 15	-9 33	5 48	-3 45
June 1	-6 34	4 7	-2 27
June 15	-2 22	2 29	$+0$ 7
July 1	$+3$ 2	0 29	3 31
July 15	7 3	-1 19	5 44
August 1	9 41	-3 24	6 17
August 15	9 31	-4 55	4 36
September 1	6 39	-6 24	0 15
September 15	2 44	-7 12	-4 28
October 1	-2 22	-7 39	-10 1
October 15	-6 25	-7 23	-13 58
November 1	-9 29	-6 52	-16 21
November 15	-9 40	-5 50	-15 30
December 1	-7 1	-4 15	-11 16
December 15	-2 41	-2 34	-5 34

* The equation of time as here tabulated is mean solar time minus apparent solar time. It is therefore the negative of the equation of time as given in the *American Ephemeris and Nautical Almanac.*

tween observer and standard meridian, measured, of course, in time units, for the celestial meridian at the longitude of the standard meridian is as many degrees east or west of the observer's celestial meridian as their respective terrestrial meridians are apart. If this is measured in units of time, it represents exactly the length of time until (or since) the apparent position of the celestial sphere will be (or was) the same for an observer who is located that amount west (or east) of the standard meridian. In other words, *difference in time equals difference of longitude.*

We really should have put this result the other way about. Longitude differences are in practice determined by local time differences. A locality whose local time is 6 hours slower than that of Greenwich, England, must have a longitude of $6 \times 15° = 90°$ west; one whose local time is

$3\frac{1}{2}$ hours faster than that of Greenwich must have a longitude of $3\frac{1}{2} \times 15° = 52\frac{1}{2}°$ east, etc.

Now let us take an imaginary trip around the world. If we travel west, we must set our watches back 1 hour as we enter each new time zone.

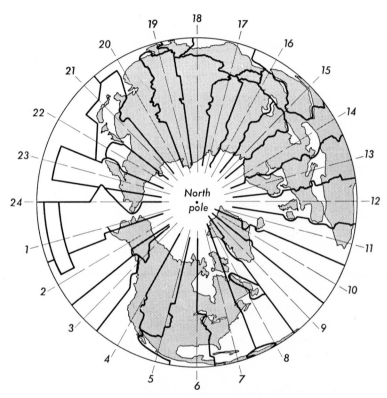

Figure 32. The broken lines represent the standard time meridians and are designated by the appropriate standard times when it is noon in Greenwich (the prime meridian). The solid lines show the irregularity of the legal time zone boundaries. (Map outline after a drawing by Richard Edes Harrison for *Fortune.*)

As our trip approaches its end and we near our starting point, it may occur to us, in addition to memories of a pleasant journey and many interesting sights, that having passed through 24 time zones, we have set our watches back 24 hours or one whole day!

At first it might seem an attractive possibility to exploit such trips by gaining or losing days as desired. A moment's reflection assures us, however, that what has taken place is that we have made the sun overtake us by more than one revolution each day, in effect subtracting one complete apparent diurnal revolution of the sun by our journey. Therefore, at some time, we are going to have to advance our time by one whole day.

By international agreement this is always done at the International Date Line, which for the most part runs along the terrestrial meridian of 180° longitude. On crossing the date line westward, the calendar date advances one day; on crossing the date line eastward, the calendar date regresses one day. It is seldom realized that over the whole earth there are always two calendar days simultaneously in progress in the different longitudes.

The final complication—and one which might seem to ensure confusion—is the fact that, contrary to our tacit assumption, the length of the mean solar day and the period of the earth's rotation are subject to slight variations. Even a very small change, however, will in time accumulate (as it sometimes has) to as much as a thirty-second difference between the observed time and the "correct" time. Why such changes take place no one yet knows, although it has been suggested that they may be due to variations as slight as a few feet in the earth's equatorial diameter. A slightly smaller earth would have to spin faster on its axis to keep a constant angular momentum, as it must, while a slightly larger earth would spin a little more slowly.

In addition to unpredictable changes of this sort, there is also the much smaller effect of a minute braking action of tides upon the spinning planet. This is so small, however, that its magnitude can be stated only as approximately a rate of increase of the length of the day by one-thousandth second per century.

TIME BY THE STARS

It has been natural enough that we should choose to tell time by the sun, but in a sense we have also been quite arbitrary. We could equally well use *any* star as a time reckoner. In fact, this would be simpler, for there would then be no necessity to correct observations of the time reckoner by the addition of an equation of time. Actually, all astronomical observatories do have clocks which show time according to the stars— *sidereal time*. Sidereal time is determined by using the vernal equinox as time reckoner. Similar to the rule for determining local solar time is the rule that *the hour angle of the vernal equinox is equal to the local sidereal time*. Unlike the solar day, the sidereal day *begins* at the upper transit of the time reckoner.

Since the vernal equinox is a well-determined point among the stars on the celestial sphere and since the stars daily rise earlier by the sun than they did the preceding day, the sidereal day must be slightly shorter than the mean solar day; it is, in fact, 3 minutes and 56 seconds of mean solar time

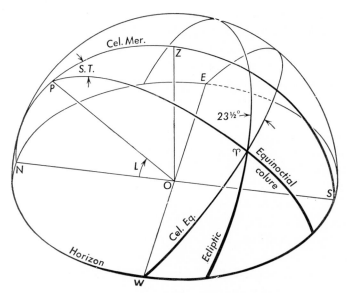

Figure 33. The hour angle of the vernal equinox ($ZP\Upsilon$) is the local sidereal time at O.

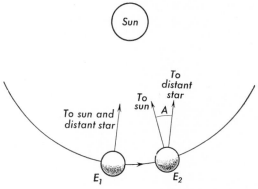

Figure 34. Angle A is the amount by which the sun has fallen behind the star during the time the earth has revolved from E_1 to E_2. It is this lag by the sun which causes the solar day to be longer than the sidereal day.

shorter. It is easy to see (Fig. 34) that if the earth did not revolve about the sun, the sun would appear to remain stationary among the stars, and sidereal and mean solar days would be of equal length. If the earth were to travel its orbit in the reverse direction, the mean solar day would be shorter than the sidereal.

In practice, one does not actually observe the vernal equinox to determine sidereal time, for the vernal equinox is an unmarked point on the celestial sphere. Rather does one observe any of a large number of the brighter stars. The angle between the hour circle through each of these and the equinoctial colure through the vernal equinox is the star's right ascension and is known with great accuracy. The hour angle of the vernal equinox can therefore be gotten at once from that of the star simply by adding to the latter the star's right ascension. In particular, since a star on the meridian has an hour angle of zero hours, we can say simply that *the local sidereal time at any instant is equal to the right ascension of any point on the meridian at that instant.*

Observations of the times of upper transit of stars are made by means of a *transit instrument,* a small telescope so mounted that it can sweep only along the local celestial meridian. A set of cross-hairs in its focal plane permits one to gauge the precise instant when any star is on the celestial meridian.

Determining sidereal time by transit observations of stars can serve also to determine the mean solar time indirectly, for sidereal and apparent solar time differ only by 12 hours at the time of the vernal equinox when the reckoners for both, the vernal equinox and the apparent sun, coincide. The rate of increase of sidereal over mean solar time is accurately known, so that the difference between them at any later time can be easily calcu-

table 3

DATE	AMOUNT BY WHICH LOCAL SIDEREAL TIME EXCEEDS LOCAL MEAN SOLAR TIME	DATE	AMOUNT BY WHICH LOCAL SIDEREAL TIME EXCEEDS LOCAL MEAN SOLAR TIME
January 1	6^h39^m	July 1	18^h33^m
January 15	7 35	July 15	19 28
February 1	8 38	August 1	20 35
February 15	9 37	August 15	21 30
March 1	10 32	September 1	22 37
March 15	11 27	September 15	23 33
April 1	12 34	October 1	0 36
April 15	13 29	October 15	1 31
May 1	14 32	November 1	2 38
May 15	15 28	November 15	3 33
June 1	16 35	December 1	4 36
June 15	17 30	December 15	5 31

lated. Hence, by observing transits of the stars and making proper allowances only for the day of the year and the longitude, the standard mean solar time is gotten from the local sidereal time. To avoid a false impression of simplicity, however, it should be noted that it is nonetheless necessary to observe the sun carefully in order to determine very accurately the time and position of the vernal equinox.

The refinements in the details of making time observations have been many, but the fundamental principles remain unchanged. In the United States, time determination is one of the principal services undertaken at the U.S. Naval Observatory in Washington, D. C. Here, clocks of fabulous accuracy are continually checked by new transit observations, and from here time correct to a thousandth of a second is distributed by radio and telegraph signal. All other major nations of the world maintain similar institutions.

THE CALENDAR

Whereas the day is one natural time unit, the year is another. It is the time interval required for one orbital revolution of the earth. Strange as it may seem, a revolution may be defined in several ways. The *sidereal year* has perhaps the best claim to being the true period of the earth's revolution, for it is the length of time required for the sun to go once around the ecliptic and resume its original position among the stars; it is because the sun's position is taken in reference to the stars that this time interval is called the "sidereal" year. Its length is 365.2564 mean solar days, or 365 days, 6 hours, 9 minutes, and 9.50 seconds.

The *tropical year* is the year upon which the calendar is based—and with good reason, for it is the year of the seasons. Its length is determined as the time from one vernal equinox to the next—namely, 365.2422 mean solar days, or 365 days, 5 hours, 48 minutes, and 45.99 seconds.

The tropical year would have the same length as the sidereal year were it not for a phenomenon called precession of the equinoxes (p. 89), which results in a very gradual westward regression of the equinoxes, an effect due primarily to an action of the moon, secondarily to the sun. Precession takes place so slowly, at a rate of 50 seconds of arc per year, that an equinox will regress once around the celestial equator to its original position only after 26,000 years. On account of the smallness of precession we have felt justified, heretofore, in considering the vernal equinox as a point which is fixed among the stars; we see that this is not strictly true, though true enough for short periods of time. The amount of precession is sufficient, however, to create a difference between sidereal and tropical years of 20 minutes and 23.51 seconds of mean solar time. The difference arises from the fact that since the equinox moves a trifle westward while the sun is moving eastward once entirely around the ecliptic, the sun will meet the equinox a bit ahead of schedule—another way of saying that the tropical year will be shorter than the sidereal.

In order to keep track of the seasons and the years, all but the most primitive societies have devised calendars. Calendar history forms an interesting parenthesis to the subject of time reckoning. Our own calendar, which has achieved general adoption among all nations of the western world, is descended from the Egyptians after being subjected to modifications, contributions, and reforms from numerous other cultures, notably the Roman, Hebrew, and Teutonic.

The difficulty of calendar construction lies in the incommensurability of the length of the day and year; the year is of such length that there is not an integral number of days in one year or even in any whole number of years. Consequently, if one uses a calendar having an invariable number of days, it will be either too long or too short, and a given calendar date will not maintain a fixed relation to the seasons. Thus, if a particular calendar has too few days, it will end before a full tropical year is up and be started on the next before its time; as a result, any given calendar date will fall continually earlier with reference to the seasons. If a calendar has too many days in its year, the opposite will take place.

Besides this inherent difficulty of calendar construction, there was for the ancients also the problem of actually determining the length of the tropical year. They were long in even realizing that this was necessary, and when they had, their results were of low accuracy because of crude instruments and methods. To the Egyptians belongs the credit of first determining the year's length even approximately—first as 360 days and then, after centuries, as 365 days. With this latter value they devised a 12-month calendar in 4236 B.C. Each month had 30 days, and the 12 months were supplemented by five consecutive year-end holidays. Much later, they recognized that the year was more nearly 365¼ days long, but the decree of Ptolemy Euergetes I (238 B.C.) which provided for leap year every fourth year did not receive popular acceptance even in Egypt. It remained for Julius Caesar, with his authority over all the Roman Empire, to institute the necessary changes in the calendars then in use.

His reforms were, of course, enacted upon the Roman calendar, whose history was quite different from the Egyptian. The Roman calendar consisted of a set of 29- and 30-day lunar months, a lunar month being the period between successive new moons. Though historians are not agreed, it is probable that the Roman calendar first contained only 10 lunar months,[5] was early revised to include 12. But 12 lunar months amount to only 354 days and it was found necessary, therefore, to insert or "intercalate" a month about every other year so as to be able to observe festivals and religious rites at their proper seasons. Intercalation was the prerogative of the priests, who so abused their authority—lengthening terms of friends' offices, shortening those of enemies, assessing tithes for their services—that reform became imperative.

In 46 B.C., Julius Caesar undertook the needed reform. By extensive intercalation, making that year 445 days long (it was known as the "year of confusion"), he restored the time of the vernal equinox to its ancient date of March 25. On the advice of the Alexandrian astronomer Sosigenes, who knew of the Egyptians' determination of the approximate length of the year, he settled the length of the year as $365\frac{1}{4}$ days, prescribing the insertion of an additional day in February every fourth year. The "lucky" uneven-numbered months were made 31 days long; the "unlucky" even-numbered months were 30 days each except February (the month of the dead), which was gladly given only 29.

The advances effected by the Julian reform were (1) the use of a $365\frac{1}{4}$-day year, long known to the Egyptians, and (2) the calendar's independence of the phases of the moon, a merit of even the oldest Egyptian calendar. But even the much simpler new Julian calendar was at first mismanaged by the Roman priests, and by 8 B.C., Augustus Caesar, nephew and successor of Julius Caesar, found it necessary to decree a lesser reform in the omission of the three succeeding leap-year days. A further change within the Julian calendar was enacted by the Roman Senate, which named the month following July "August," giving it a thirty-first day at the expense of the unpopular February.[6] Then, to avoid three consecutive 31-day months (July, August, September), a day was taken from both September and November and added to October and December, respectively.

The form of the calendar was now fixed but for one important internal modification of structure. In the early fourth century A.D., the

---

[5] It is supposedly for this reason that September, October, November, and December are literally the seventh, eighth, ninth, and tenth months; the two additional months were placed after these.

[6] Legend would have it that the Senate acted at the bidding of Augustus, who was jealous of his uncle's having a 31-day month, July, named after him and who may also have wished to avoid being commemorated by an "unlucky" 30-day month. In recent years, historical researches have cast doubt upon the authenticity of this legend.

emperor Constantine, newly converted to Christianity, introduced the use of the Christian seven-day week. Whatever else this may have done, it complicated the calendar by dividing it into intervals of which there is not an integral number per year.

No further changes were made in the calendar until 1582, when Pope Gregory XIII proceeded to correct an accumulated error of the Julian calendar. The Julian calendar allows three too many leap years in every four centuries so that by the sixteenth century the vernal equinox occurred on March 11. Since the date of Easter depends upon the date of the vernal equinox in a way prescribed by the Council of Nicaea (A.D. 325), Pope Gregory ordered the omission of ten days, to restore the vernal equinox to March 21 as it was in A.D. 325. He also ruled that century years would not be counted as leap years unless divisible by four hundred, thereby preventing the accumulation of three days' error every four centuries; thus, although 1900 would have been a leap year by the Julian calendar, it was not so by the Gregorian, whereas A.D. 2000 will be by both. The adoption of the Gregorian calendar has been piecemeal over the world, local political and social considerations frequently having taken precedence over all others.

The Gregorian reform is the latest thus far. As it stands, the Gregorian calendar would serve without error for another 3300 years. It is plainly accurate enough for all purposes far into the future. There are, however, movements to institute further reforms for a more conveniently constructed calendar. One of them, called the "World Calendar," proposes that each year should contain four equal quarters (91 days apiece), each beginning on a Sunday, ending on a Saturday, and consisting of two 30-day and one 31-day months. The last day of December (a Saturday) would be followed by another Saturday, the 365th day. In leap years, the last day of June (a Saturday) would be followed by another Saturday, the leap year day. With such a calendar a given calendar date would fall on the same weekday every year and the quarters would be of equal length.

Another proposed reform is the 13-month calendar. It would create 13 months, each just an even four weeks long. The thirteenth month (for which the name "Sol" is suggested) would be inserted between June and July. The 13 identical 28-day months comprise 364 days; year-end and leap-year days would be made extra Saturdays, as in the world calendar. The factors working most strongly against this very simple calendar are superstition and the fact that 13 is a prime number.

The Motions of the Planets as Seen from the Earth

We have seen how the earth's motion of rotation on its axis gives to the distant stars an apparent diurnal motion of rising and setting, how the earth's motions of rotation and revolution together give the sun both an apparent diurnal motion across the sky and an apparent annual motion along the ecliptic. The final degree of complication is to be found in the apparent motions of the planets. Though we can regard the sun and stars as stationary, we know that the planets are in motion about the sun. We on the earth are therefore viewing moving objects, the planets, from a moving observing station, the earth. What may we expect to see?

THE ELEMENTS OF PLANETARY ORBITS

To be able to answer the foregoing question, we must know the positions of the planets (the earth included) relative to the sun. For many purposes this is most conveniently done by specifying unambiguously (1) the orbit of each planet and (2) its position in that orbit. The size and shape of a planetary orbit can be given, as we know, by a statement of the orbit's major semi-axis, a, and eccentricity, e. It remains to characterize the orientation of the orbit.

We know, to begin with, that the orbit of each planet is in a plane, but we must at the same time note that no two are always in the *same* plane. The one to which the rest are referred is, naturally, the plane of the earth's orbit—the plane of the ecliptic. The angle by which each planet's orbital plane is inclined to the plane of the ecliptic is called the *inclination, i,* of the orbit (Fig. 35). The inclinations of the planets' orbits are given in Table 4.

The inclination alone is not enough to specify the orientation of a planet's orbit completely, however; there are indefinitely many different planes with the same inclination i. To be of interest to us, however, a plane must pass through the center of the sun, for the orbital plane of every planet contains the sun. Consequently every planet's orbital plane will intersect the plane of the ecliptic in a straight line that passes through the sun's center; this line of intersection is called the *line of nodes.* The line of nodes, being in the earth's orbital plane, is directed toward two diametrically opposite points on the ecliptic called the *nodes.* Viewed from the sun, any planet will be seen to cross northward from "below" the earth's orbit to "above" the earth's orbit at one of these, the *ascending node;* at the other, the *descending node,* the planet will cross southward from "above" the earth's orbit to "below." The position of the ascending node is given by its angular distance from the vernal equinox, measured in degrees eastward along the ecliptic. This angle is called the *heliocentric longitude of the ascending node* and is given the symbol ☊. The inclination

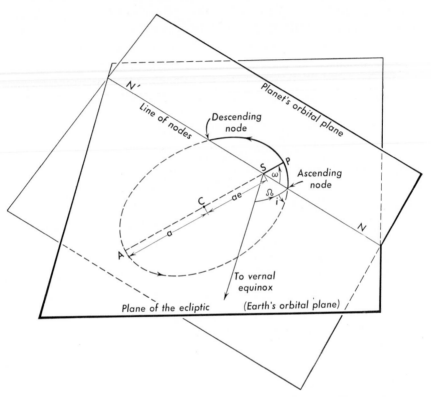

Figure 35. The five orbital elements shown here completely determine the orbit of any planet.

and the longitude of the ascending node together uniquely determine the position of an orbital plane.

The orientation of an orbit in a given orbital plane is fixed by the *longitude of the perihelion point, ω.* It is the angle in the orbital plane between the line of nodes and the direction of perihelion, measured in the direction of the planet's orbital motion. The five quantities *a, e, i,* ☊, and ω serve to describe any planet's orbit completely and are called the *orbital elements.* They are given in full in Table 4.

A planet's actual position in an orbit can be had from a knowledge

table 4

Orbital Elements of the Planets (1960.0)

PLANET	*a*	*e*	*i*	☊	ω	*T*
Mercury	0.387	0.2056	7° 0′14″	47°45′	28°57′	1950.993
Venus	0.723	0.0068	3 23 39	76 14	54 39	1950.700
Earth	1.000	0.0167	. . . .	. . . . . .	102 6	1951.008
Mars	1.524	0.0934	1 51 0	49 11	285 59	1950.998
Jupiter	5.203	0.0484	1 18 21	99 57	273 35	1951.891
Saturn	9.539	0.0557	2 29 25	113 14	338 52	1944.684
Uranus	19.182	0.0472	0 46 23	73 45	96 7	1966.697
Neptune	30.058	0.0086	1 46 28	131 14	272 57	1880.984
Pluto	39.439	0.2502	17 10 12	109 53	114 16	1989.

of a sixth orbital element; this is the *time of perihelion passage, T*. If it is known when a planet was once at perihelion, its exact position in the orbit can be found at any later time with the aid of Kepler's laws.

The six orbital elements may be given not only for the major planets but also for any other bodies in the solar system which have elliptical orbits. The orbits of all bodies change with time, however, because of their mutual perturbative interactions. These changes are usually discussed in terms of the rates at which any or all of the elements vary. For example: the earth's orbital eccentricity will decrease for the next 24,000 years, and its present rate is -0.00004 per century; Mercury's longitude of the perihelion point is increasing at a rate of 574″ per century, etc. Only in the cases of lesser bodies which experience substantial perturbations during relatively near approaches to a major planet are the changes in orbital elements very great or very rapid.

The orbital elements of any body in the solar system are, of course, known only after a tedious analysis of three or more observations of the body's apparent position. As long as the elements so obtained do not change appreciably on account of perturbations, they are of the greatest use in predicting the body's position in the solar system. For the planets, these predictions are tabulated in publications such as the *American Ephemeris and Nautical Almanac,* prepared at the U.S. Naval Observatory.

THE RELATIVE SPACE MOTIONS OF THE PLANETS

Let us try to visualize the positions and motions of the planets, the earth included, as they would be observed from somewhere "above" the sun. The planets will be seen to revolve in a counterclockwise sense about the sun, very nearly in the same plane, and in ellipses of small

eccentricity. As Kepler's harmonic law specifies, their periods increase
with their mean distances.

Suppose we fix our attention upon the earth and one other, Jupiter,
for example. Jupiter has a period of nearly 12 years, while the earth's
is exactly 1 year. Therefore, as the earth goes one revolution about the
sun, Jupiter goes but a twelfth of a revolution. To keep track of Jupiter
and the earth with their different paces, let us draw a diagram of their

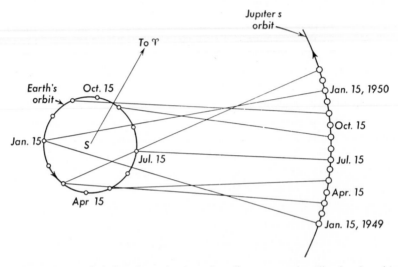

Figure 36. By their lengths and orientations lines connecting like-dated positions
of the earth and Jupiter indicate Jupiter's respective distances and directions from
the earth at the times given. The observer has assumed a position high above the
earth's orbital plane and refers the positions of the earth and Jupiter to the sun.

respective paths for a period of 15 months or so, marking the respective
positions occupied by each at several different dates. Then lines drawn
between like-dated positions will indicate the planets' relative directions
and distances.

Because we are in fact viewing Jupiter from the earth rather than
from the sun, we shall appreciate only Jupiter's *relative* motion. Therefore a diagram of Jupiter's motion relative to the earth is what is wanted,
and this we get by laying off from our seemingly fixed earth the appropriate distance (as measured from the first diagram) in the direction which
Jupiter appears to have at that time. The result, which can be verified
by performing the process for one's self, is the second diagram. It is
seen that Jupiter's motion is generally eastward through the background
of stars but that at times it will appear to reverse itself. Its eastward mo-

tion in our sky is called *direct motion;* its westward motion is called *retrograde motion.* At the same time, because the orbits of Jupiter and the earth are slightly inclined to each other, Jupiter will appear to have a

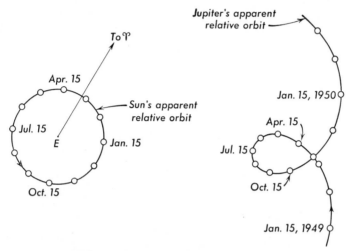

Figure 37. An observer who refers the positions of the sun and Jupiter to the earth will find that they follow the paths indicated.

northward or southward motion. The combined effect of this motion and the simultaneous direct or retrograde motion causes Jupiter to appear to follow a path in the sky that contains a loop, a "Z," or an "S." It is this

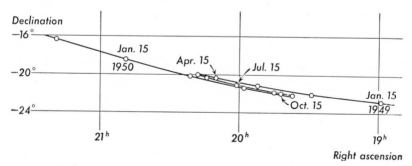

Figure 38. Jupiter's relative motion projected onto the celestial sphere is shown for the same period of time as the two preceding figures.

apparently more complicated motion of Jupiter and the other planets which led the ancients to call the planets "wanderers," the literal translation of "planets."

THE CONFIGURATIONS OF THE PLANETS

All the relative motion curves of all the planets are alike in character and differ only in their scales of time and distance. The planets' motions are not alike, however, in their apparent relation to the sun in our sky. Let us consider the apparent relative dispositions or arrangements of the sun and planets on the celestial sphere; such arrangements are called *configurations*.

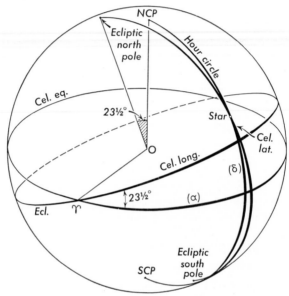

Figure 39. Celestial latitude and longitude form an ecliptic coordinate system analogous to the equatorial coordinate system of declination and right ascension.

The sun's apparent position on the celestial sphere is generally taken as the point of reference with respect to which the positions of all the other bodies are compared. The comparison is expressed in the planets' *elongations* from the sun. A planet's elongation in right ascension is the difference between the right ascension of the planet and that of the sun, expressed in degrees (rather than hours and minutes) east or west of the sun.

It is also often the practice to give elongations in celestial longitude rather than right ascension. *Celestial longitude* and *celestial latitude* form a system of *ecliptic coordinates* based upon the ecliptic as reference plane and the vernal equinox as reference point. This system is entirely analogous to geographical longitude and latitude: The celestial latitude of any object measures its angular distance north or south of the neares point on the ecliptic; its celestial longitude measures the angular distance of this latter point east along the ecliptic from the vernal equinox.[7] A planet's elongation in celestial longitude is the difference between the celestial longitude of the planet and that of the sun, expressed in degrees east or west of the sun.

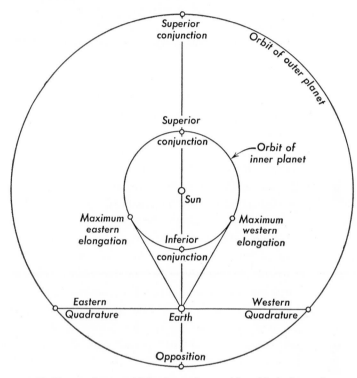

Figure 40. To an observer high above the earth's orbital plane, the earth, sun, and planets would have the indicated positions in space at times of the various planetary configurations.

The elongations which the inner planets Venus and Mercury can attain are definitely limited (Fig. 40). Since Mercury, for example, can never actually be more than four-tenths of an astronomical unit from the sun in space, it can never *appear* very far from the sun in the sky when seen from the earth. A configuration of note for each of the inner planets is therefore that of *maximum elongation,* the instant when the planet's elongation is greatest. The value of Mercury's maximum elonga-

---

[7] From the definition of celestial latitude, it is plain that the sun always has a celestial latitude of 0°. Its celestial longitude at the vernal equinox is evidently 0°, at summer solstice, 90°.

tion ranges between 18° and 28° because of the considerable eccentricity of Mercury's orbit; the maximum elongation of Venus is 48°. The existence of maximum elongations for these inner planets accounts for their never being seen very long after sunset or before sunrise, for they must follow the sun down in the west fairly promptly, when east of it, and cannot precede the sun very greatly at sunrise, when west of it.

Special designations are also given to other configurations of interest. One of these is *conjunction,* in which the elongation of planet from sun is 0°; in other words, at conjunction the right ascensions (or longitudes) of sun and planet are the same, though generally their declinations (or latitudes) differ. A *superior conjunction* occurs when the planet is beyond the sun from the earth. Each of the planets is periodically at superior conjunction. The two inner planets may also sometimes be at *inferior conjunction;* the planet is then between the earth and the sun.

The outer planets, those with greater mean distances than the earth, are not limited to maximum elongations as are Mercury and Venus. When one of these planets attains an elongation of 90°, it is said to be at *quadrature.* When the planet's elongation becomes 180°, it is said to be at *opposition;* then the planet rises as the sun sets and vice versa.

The time interval between two successive superior conjunctions of any planet is known as the *synodic period* of that planet. This is to be distinguished from its *sidereal period,* which is the length of time required for the planet to traverse its orbit once. The two are not equal because the synodic period depends upon the relative positions of sun, planet, and revolving earth whereas the sidereal period depends upon the positions of the sun, planet, and fixed stars. Thus the number of revolutions any planet makes about the sun in a given time depends upon its sidereal period; on the other hand, the frequency with which a planet is visible to us at a given time of night depends upon its synodic period.

For example, the two planets nearest us, Venus and Mars, have the longest synodic periods though not the longest sidereal periods. This is due to the fact that since their sidereal periods are more nearly equal the earth's than any of the rest, the one can manage to overtake us only slowly while the other will be but slowly left behind. Mercury, by contrast, finds the earth no match and hustles around the sun, leaving us far out of the race. At the opposite extreme, Pluto proceeds at a celestial snail's pace (an average of about $1\frac{1}{2}°$ per year in our sky); but little extra time is required, therefore, to return it to conjunction. For comparison, the sidereal and synodic periods of the planets are given in Table 5.

table 5

PLANET	SIDEREAL PERIOD		SYNODIC PERIOD	
	Years	Days	Years	Days
Mercury	0.2409	87.969	0.3173	115.877
Venus	0.6152	224.701	1.5987	583.920
Earth	1.0000	365.257	. . . . . .	. . . .
Mars	1.8809	686.980	2.1354	779.935
Jupiter	11.8622	. . . .	1.0921	398.885
Saturn	29.4577	. . . . . .	1.0352	378.091
Uranus	84.0153	. . . . . .	1.0121	369.658
Neptune	164.7883	. . . .	1.0061	367.485
Pluto	247.6968	. . . .	1.0041	366.736

The relation between synodic and sidereal periods is quite simple. For example, let us take P to be the sidereal period of Mercury, E the earth's period of revolution about the sun, and S Mercury's synodic period. Mercury will on the average move $1/P$ revolutions each day while the earth moves $1/E$ revolutions in pursuit. Mercury's net daily gain on the earth is therefore $1/P - 1/E$ revolutions. Since Mercury gains one whole revolution on the earth in one synodic period, it will gain an average of $1/S$ revolutions per day. In other words, we must have

$$\frac{1}{S} = \frac{1}{P} - \frac{1}{E}, \quad S = \frac{EP}{E - P}, \quad \text{or} \quad P = \frac{ES}{S - E}.$$

Since the earth overtakes the outer planets rather than being overtaken by them, we modify the equation correspondingly; for an outer planet like Jupiter

$$\frac{1}{S} = \frac{1}{E} - \frac{1}{P}, \quad S = \frac{EP}{P - E}, \quad P = \frac{ES}{S + E}.$$

During its synodic period each planet goes through a fixed cycle of configurations. For an inner planet, the sequence of events following superior conjunction are these: (1) direct motion to maximum eastern elongation; (2) decelerating direct motion and then retrograde motion to inferior conjunction; (3) continued retrogression followed by accelerating direct motion to maximum western elongation; and (4) direct motion to superior conjunction. During phases (1) and (2) the planet is an "evening star"; during phases (3) and (4) it is a "morning star."

An outer planet behaves somewhat differently. The sequence after superior conjunction is thus: (1) decelerating direct motion that is slower than the sun's until some time after western quadrature is reached; (2) accelerating retrograde motion until opposition; (3) decelerating retrograde motion for an equal time after opposition; (4) direct motion accelerating (though always less rapid than the sun's) until superior conjunction. Between the times of superior conjunction and western quadrature, the planet will be visible some time between midnight and dawn; at the time of its opposition, the planet is visible the whole night through; between eastern quadrature and conjunction the planet can be seen only during part of the hours from sunset to midnight.

THE DEVELOPMENT OF THE COPERNICAN THEORY

The ancients invented a variety of explanations for these apparent motions of the planets, as well as for those of the sun and moon, which to them were also planets. In devising their theories, most of them saw no reason to suppose anything other than that the earth is stationary and at the center of the universe. Because of this latter assumption, their theories are described as *geocentric theories*. Of all the theories, the most important was that set forth by the Alexandrian astronomer Claudius Ptolemy in the second century A.D. His work was highly regarded by the Arabs, who dominated the south Mediterranean shores and the Near East after the collapse of the Roman Empire, and to it they gave the name Almagest (corrupted from its original Greek title "Megiste Syntaxis").

Ptolemy's explanation of the planets' apparent motions was suggested by their relative motion curves (Fig. 38). To be sure, Ptolemy did not know the planets' distances from the earth, but he could observe their changing brightnesses and he concluded, correctly, that decreased brightness was the result of increased distance; by this argument he was able to construct relative motion curves qualitatively similar to our own. His system placed the earth at the center of the universe. The earth was surrounded by a concentric crystal sphere on which the stars were set. Within this sphere the sun, moon, and planets moved about the earth. Mars, Jupiter, and Saturn (the only outer planets then known) had a motion that was compounded of two motions (Fig. 42): Each of these planets circled in an *epicycle* about a point called the *fictitious planet*. The fictitious planet was situated on a larger circle about the earth called a *deferent*. The rotation of the deferent was presumed to carry a fictitious planet eastward at a uniform rate, once around the sky in one sidereal period of the planet. The simultaneous rotation of the epicycle about the fictitious planet in one year would then produce a loop and retrograde motion every synodic period.

A similar arrangement was postulated for Mercury and Venus except that their respective fictitious planets were to be always on the straight line from earth to sun; then and only then would these two planets swing back and forth from one side of the sun to the other. Only the motions

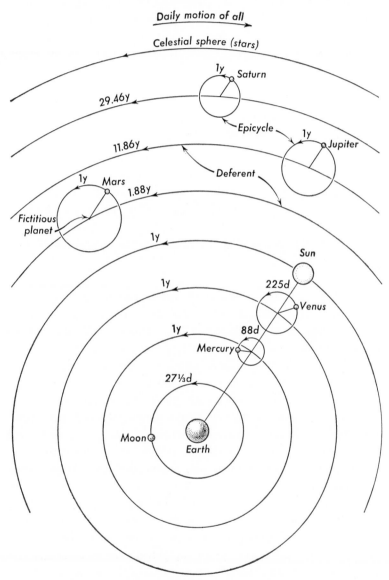

Figure 41. The figure shows schematically the simplest form of the Ptolemaic theory. Refinements of the simple system would replace the planets with further epicycles.

of the sun, moon, and stars were not epicyclic. However, the motions of all bodies were circular or combinations of simultaneous circular motions, for the ancients seemed obsessed with the "perfection" of the circle and the obligation of heavenly bodies to observe "perfection" in every detail.

We have sketched only the rudiments of the Ptolemaic system. To the details devised by Ptolemy himself, his successors in the next 14 centuries found it necessary to add a mountain of others, encumbering the system with epicycles upon epicycles as the system's failures to predict the planets' motions accurately became too obvious to overlook. But there was no end to the Ptolemaic system's failures. Finally, wonder that the

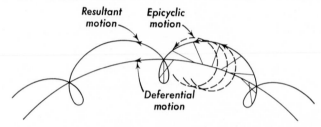

Figure 42. Simultaneous motion of the epicycle and deferent carry a point on the epicycle along a looped path. The epicyclic radius from fictitious planet to true planet is shown in a number of positions during the course of a single cycle.

motions of the heavenly bodies could be so complicated began to give way to doubts in the minds of a few that the complications were real and to suspicions that the entire Ptolemaic system might be a false representation of the universe.

Then in 1543 a Pole named Nicholas Copernicus revived the idea, once considered by the ancient Greeks and long since discarded, that the sun, not the earth, is the center of the universe. His advocacy of a *heliocentric* theory was in his day a rash if not dangerous act. However, he died (of natural causes) so soon after the publication of his radical "On the Revolutions of the Celestial Bodies" (in Latin) that he was spared the probable punishment and humiliation that might otherwise have befallen him.

While adhering to the "perfection" of circles, Copernicus supposed a rotating earth to be but one of a family of planets revolving about the sun. He could then explain in the same general way that we do now the direct and retrograde motions of the planets, the sun's annual motion on the ecliptic, and the diurnal motions of all celestial objects. He could not offer proof of his hypotheses, however, and his principal defense was that his system was much simpler than the intricate and unsuccessful Ptolemaic system. But arguments of this nature carried little weight with the authorities of his day, and those of the church, in particular, were prone to see the Copernican theory as blasphemy; they placed his work on the Index of Prohibited Books, where it remained until 1835.

A Danish nobleman, Tycho Brahe, sought to reach a rational decision as to the relative merits of the Ptolemaic and Copernican systems. Like Ptolemy but unlike Copernicus, Tycho was an excellent observer of the heavens, undoubtedly the greatest before the invention of the telescope. Of several decisive tests between the Ptolemaic and Copernican theories, the only one Tycho could conceivably attempt to apply with the means available to him was that of measuring the nearby stars' annual parallactic displacements. He attempted the test, his results were negative, and he therefore rejected the Copernican hypothesis. He could hardly have guessed how much beyond the power of the unaided eye it is to discern so minute an effect. But neither could Tycho accept the Ptolemaic system, whose difficulties and defects were becoming ever more apparent. Hence he devised a *Tychonic system* having a central stationary earth about which revolved the sun; all the other planets circled about the sun, as in the Copernican theory.

The Tychonic theory, though actually short-lived, was soon to assume an added significance, for the Ptolemaic system presently received the blow that was finally to dispose of it. Since according to the Ptolemaic system the planets Mercury and Venus were always to be between the earth and the sun, then from the earth they could never appear fully illuminated, as they would if they were to pass around to the far side of the sun and as they could according to either the Copernican or Tychonic systems. The great Florentine physicist and astronomer, Galileo, was the first to put the Ptolemaic system to this test, being the first to use a telescope for astronomical observations. In the years following 1610 he watched Venus go through all phases like those of the moon—waxing from crescent to full, then waning. This was decisive evidence against the Ptolemaic theory, in which the "full" phase of Venus was impossible. The choice was now between the Tychonic and Copernican systems, and Galileo favored the latter. The Copernican system recommended itself with particular force after his seeing Jupiter, for he saw the planet accompanied by four satellites which circled about it, all in nearly same plane; it was a miniature solar system.

But the Copernican theory had defects, as did every other theory which insisted on circular orbits for the planets. The details of the planets' motions were still unaccounted for by any system when, in the hope of describing them accurately, Johannes Kepler undertook the staggering task of analyzing by the most elementary mathematical means the very extensive lifetime's observations of Tycho Brahe, his predecessor as royal astronomer and mathematician to the court of Rudolf II in Prague. Through correspondence with Galileo, Kepler was encouraged to consider the heliocentric theory of Copernicus. The results of his work are already known to us in his three laws of planetary motion and represent many years of painstaking trial and error. Kepler's estimate of his final triumph can be judged from his own statement: "The die is cast, the book is written, to be read now or by posterity, I care not which. It can await its reader. Has not God waited six thousand years for an observer?"

The presumption in favor of the heliocentric theory was finally clinched by Sir Isaac Newton, who deduced the law of gravitation from his own three laws of motion and Kepler's laws of planetary motion. The law of gravitation has shown itself to have a range of validity that has justly earned it the title "universal." The Tychonic system is quite incompatible with the law of gravitation and Newton's laws of motion. Since Newton's day, a continual increase in general scientific knowledge and the greater power of new and improved instruments have provided the answers to all the various and sundry objections which originally seemed to make anything but a geocentric theory of the universe both absurd and contrary to all experience.

It is difficult to appreciate in full in our day the significance of the step from geocentricism to heliocentricism. It is one of the most notable steps that men have taken in their perennial efforts to disenslave themselves from dogma. It encouraged a new and more exciting conception of how the universe is constructed. It gave men a radically different perspective of their place in the physical universe. Since Copernicus' day the universe has continually "expanded," apace with increasing knowledge. At present we cannot assign any point as its center, for its boundaries, if any, are unknown. But none of the changes made since Copernicus challenged the geocentric theory has been suggested at such peril or had so much effect.

C. THE EARTH-MOON SYSTEM

> "... Roaming Cynthia bestirs the tides
> Whereby the surf, deserting now the kelp
> Along the shore, exposes shoals of sand."
> —EDMOND HALLEY

So far we have been so preoccupied with a consideration of the earth as an astronomical observing station that we have quite neglected the fact that the earth is really only the senior partner of the earth-moon system.

There are two particular results of this partnership that we shall consider; they are (1) the tides and (2) precession.

Tides

Tides are the result of a distortion of the earth's water surface by the differential gravitational attraction of both the moon and the sun. The distortion is a result of the fact that those parts of the earth nearest the moon (or sun) will, by the law of gravitation, be more strongly attracted by it than the rest. This difference in the moon's or sun's attraction upon the near and far sides of the earth is a force known as the tide-raising force. Because the tide-raising force is inversely proportional to the cube of the distance between the earth and "tide-raiser," the moon's being about four hundred times nearer the earth than is the sun gives it an advantage which more than compensates for the sun's immensely greater mass. The moon is therefore two to three times as effective as the sun in raising tides on the earth. Let us consider briefly the way in which the moon produces the tides; the same will apply separately to the sun, though the sun's effect is less.

Ideally, the moon's tide-raising force produces two bulges of water in the oceans, the cap of one bulge lying at that point of the earth's surface nearest the moon, the cap of the other being at a point diametrically opposite the first. As the continents rotate into the tidal bulge, they will encounter progressively higher parts of it, like a man walking into a deepening snowdrift; in other words, a rising tide will then be experienced along the seacoast. When the highest point of the tidal bulge has been passed, the tide will ebb.

The reason for the very existence of the two tidal bulges can best be explained by a closer consideration of the moon's gravitational attraction upon the earth. The one bulge is produced on the side nearest the moon because the points of the earth nearest the moon are subject to a *stronger-than-average* attraction by the moon; this is exactly equivalent to a tide-raising force directed *toward* the moon. The other tidal bulge is produced on the side away from the moon because the points of the earth farthest from the moon are subject to a *weaker-than-average* attraction by the moon; this is equivalent to a tide-raising force directed *away* from the moon (Fig. 43).

Whatever part of the tide-raising force at any point is vertical will be more than overbalanced by the downward pull of the earth's gravity there. Any remaining locally horizontal component of the tide-raising force will, however, be unopposed. It is this part of the moon's gravitational attraction which marshals the bulges in the earth's hydrosphere, for the oceans, which are free to flow, will be shaped by the action of these forces, whereas the earth's solid crust (of which the continents are a part) can yield but little to them.

Approximately twice monthly the sun, moon, and earth are nearly in line, and at these times the sun and moon combine their tide-raising

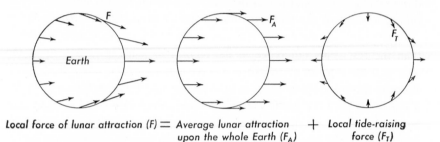

Local force of lunar attraction (F) = Average lunar attraction **+** Local tide-raising
upon the whole Earth (F_A)   force (F_T)

Figure 43. The moon's different gravitational attractions over various parts of the earth may be compounded of an average value, the same everywhere, and a residue which is the local tide-raising force.

forces to produce the greatest tides, called *spring tides.* Midway between-times, sun and moon act in opposition, therewith producing the lowest tides, called *neap tides.*

Since the moon rises approximately 50 minutes later each day, tides will occur an average of 50 minutes later daily. In addition to this

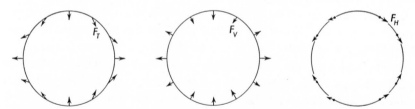

Local tide-raising force (F_T) = Locally vertical force(F_V) **+** Locally horizontal force (F_H)

Figure 44. The local tide-raising force may be resolved into its vertical and horizontal components.

complication, there are numerous others which combine to make predictions of tides a difficult and complicated computational task. For the convenience of shipping, however, accurate predictions of the times of high and low tide at all important harbors are made in the United States by the Coast and Geodetic Survey of the Department of Commerce. In this it is important, of course, to know the positions of the moon and sun.

Because the continents continually "collide" with the tidal bulge of the oceans, the tides act to brake the earth's rotation. In this way tidal braking is gradually lengthening the day at a rate of about one second per 100,000 years. Although this rate of change may seem preposterously small, its effects are cumulative. Thus, if the day were 0.001 second longer than it now is, the difference would accumulate to 36.5 seconds in the course of a century. Such an increase would be easily detectable in the times of occurrence of celestial phenomena such as eclipses.

We note in passing that tides occur also in bodies other than the earth; for example, we find evidence of tides in the members of mutually close-enough double-star systems. Their explanation is the same as for those on the earth.

Precession

A second effect of the moon upon the earth is the phenomenon of the *precession of the equinoxes,* often spoken of simply as *precession.* It

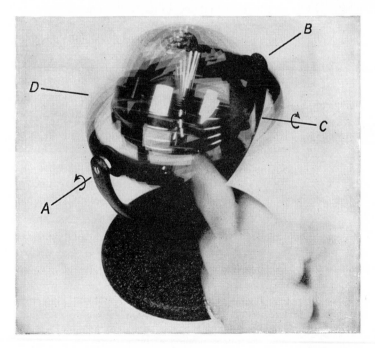

Figure 45. GYROSCOPIC PRECESSION. By a series of interrupted exposures such as this it is possible to see that rotation of the gyroscope ring about the axis *AB* produces a precession of the gyroscope wheel about the axis *CD*. (Courtesy H. R. Rymer.)

consists of a slow circling of the earth's axis of rotation about the poles of the ecliptic (celestial latitude ±90°). As a result, the plane of the earth's equator will always be inclined 23½° to the plane of its orbit though

their points of intersection, the equinoxes, are continually shifting. The earth's precessional motion is therefore like that of a dying top (Fig. 46), whose axis of spin circles about the vertical. The earth's precessional motion is very slow, requiring approximately 26,000 years for the earth's axis to trace out one complete circle.

As in the case of the tides, precession is due primarily to the moon, secondarily to the sun (and to the planets in a still lesser degree). Precession due to the moon, for example, comes about because the moon is usually north or south of the earth's equatorial bulge. In effect, the bulge provides a "handle" by which the moon can gravitationally grasp the earth and attempt to tilt it so that the bulge will come directly under the moon, i.e., approximately into the plane of the ecliptic.

This the spinning earth will not allow, for by virtue of its spinning about its axis it is a giant gyroscope and, with a gyroscope's characteristic perversity, resists any effort to tilt its axis. Instead, the axis yields in a direction perpendicular to the expected motion; that is to say, the earth's axis *precesses,* at the same time maintaining its original *inclination* to the ecliptic though continually changing its *orientation* in space. Since the moon's efforts to tilt the earth's axis are unceasing, so is the earth's motion of precession.

It should not be difficult to see now why this motion is also called "precession of the equinoxes"; we have only to consider its effect. First we note that the ecliptic maintains unchanged its position *among the*

Figure 46. PRECESSION OF THE GLOBE. This model globe is set on a pivot and may be spun on the mounting in top-like fashion. This sequence from a movie-film strip shows how the tilted spinning earth precesses about the vertical direction to which the force of gravity would right it were it at rest. The dark band is about the equator and may be compared in its effect to the earth's equatorial bulge. (Courtesy H. R. Rymer.)

stars, for precession in no way affects the orientation of the earth's orbital plane. On the other hand, the earth's axis circles slowly about the perpendicular to this plane. Therefore, since a change in the direction of the earth's axis produces a like change in the position of the celestial poles, we conclude that the celestial poles are circling about the poles of the ecliptic. But the position of the celestial poles determines the position of the celestial equator, and as the former circle about the poles of the ecliptic, the latter will necessarily follow them around. The result will be

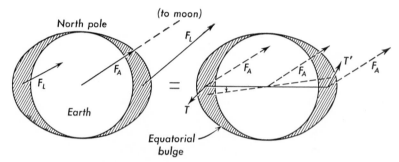

Figure 47. The pair of forces T and T' constitutes a *torque*. The tendency of the torque to tilt the earth's equatorial bulge into the moon's orbital plane is resisted by the gyroscopic precession of the rotating earth.

that the moving celestial equator will cut the fixed ecliptic in two moving equinoxes which circle once around westward in 26,000 years; the equinoxes therefore precess westward 50″.2 per year.

We have already noted one effect of precession, namely, that the westward motion of the vernal equinox results in the sun's meeting it before quite completing one whole round of the ecliptic. This makes the tropical year slightly shorter than the sidereal year, which is the earth's true period of revolution. For exactly the same reason, it makes the sidereal day .^008 shorter than the earth's true period of rotation, since the vernal equinox is time reckoner for sidereal time. But, to astronomers, perhaps the result of most practical importance is that the right ascensions and declinations of all the stars change as the equinox slides slowly westward (Fig. 48), for the equinox serves as the standard reference point on the celestial equator. Precession is thus the source of a considerable nuisance.

One visible effect of precession is to be found in the positions of the constellations of the zodiac. Since ancient times, the zodiac has been sectioned at intervals of 30° along the ecliptic, and each of these sections is referred to as a *sign of the zodiac.* Each sign bears the name of the

constellation which occupied it in the second century B.C. Precession
has since shifted each constellation forward one sign; thus, while the sun

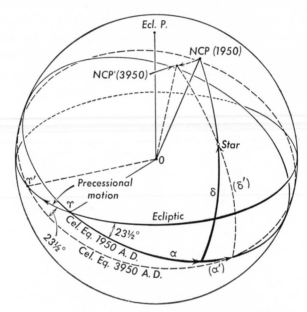

Figure 48. The westward precession of the equinoxes slowly alters the equatorial
coordinates of all stars. Note how the celestial pole circles the ecliptic pole.

is said to enter the *sign* of Aries at the vernal equinox, it is then in the
constellation of Pisces.

QUESTIONS

1. Cite a proof of the earth's roundness. Point out how it precludes the earth's
   being (*a*) a plane of infinite extent, (*b*) a flat thin disk, (*c*) a cylinder,
   (*d*) a torus (doughnut-shaped figure), (*e*) a cube.
2. Outline the method by which the size of a spherical earth could be determined. How does the application of this method show that the earth is not
   spherical? How does it show that the earth is spheroidal? Precisely what
   size and shape has the earth?
3. (*a*) If, on another planet having the same diameter as the earth, one's
   weight were double its present value, what would this indicate about the
   planet's mass? (*b*) If, on a planet having half the earth's diameter, one's
   weight were half its present value, what could be concluded about the
   planet's mass? (*c*) Taking the moon's diameter as approximately one-
   fourth the earth's and its mass as one-eightieth of the earth's, determine the
   weight of a 150-pound man at the moon's surface.

4. The problem of weighing the earth is also known as the problem of determining the *constant of gravity, G,* which appears in the formula

$$F = -G\frac{m_1 m_2}{d^2}$$

expressing the universal law of gravitation. Show that these problems are equivalent by showing that they lead to the same experiment for their solution.

5. In what ways is our atmosphere necessary to life other than as a supply of oxygen to breathe? How is it an obstacle to astronomical research?

6. What is the true direction of a star seen just on the horizon? If the sun appears above the horizon more than half the hours of the year, we must receive more sunlight than if it were above the horizon exactly half the hours of the year; whence does the additional sunlight come?

7. What causes the sun and moon to appear flattened near the horizon? Will they look more flattened or less flattened to a fish than to a fisherman in a boat nearby?

8. What causes the stars to twinkle? Does the sun twinkle? Under what conditions might a diver see the sun twinkle?

9. Distinguish diffusion from reflection, refraction, and dispersion. Explain how diffusion accounts for the blueness of the sky. What would be the appearance of the sky if the atmosphere did not diffuse at all? To what extent are your expectations borne out by the experience of mountain climbers and balloon ascensionists?

10. The smoke from a campfire or burning pile of leaves is bluish when seen with the sun at one's back, reddish when seen with the sun in one's face. Why?

11. How does the atmosphere produce twilight? What part, if any, does refraction have in producing twilight?

12. Compare twilight on the earth with twilight on Mars, where the atmosphere is considerably thinner. Compare a sunset on the earth to a sunset on the moon (which has no atmosphere).

13. The glare of the headlights of approaching cars is unusually troublesome when one's windshield is dusty. Why? What bearing has this phenomenon on the practice of locating astronomical observatories far from large cities, often at high altitudes?

14. Cite a phenomenon which proves the earth's rotation. Would it serve equally well everywhere on a cylindrical earth whose axis of rotation coincided with the axis of the cylinder? On a cubical earth whose axis passed through its center and perpendicular to one face?

15. How does the earth's rotation account for its equatorial bulge? If the earth were cylindrical, would it have an equatorial bulge? If the earth were to rotate from east to west instead of from west to east, what effect (if any) would this have on the present equatorial bulge?

16. From a stationary earth, what would be the radial velocity of a stationary star? How would it depend on time? How would revolution of the earth modify this star's apparent radial velocity? How would the velocity vary

in time? How would uniform straight-line motion by the star modify terrestrial observations of the star's radial velocity? How would it vary with time? How would orbital motion by the star itself modify terrestrial observations of the star's radial velocity?

17. Compare the effect of the earth's orbital motion upon the observed radial velocities of stars in different quarters of the sky. How does their mutual relation change with time? What have their variations in common?

18. Why are all the proofs of the earth's revolution comparatively modern?

19. What determines the position of the equator? What determines the position of the prime meridian? What are the terrestrial coordinates measured from each? Define them. Distinguish between astronomical and geocentric latitude. What is the occasion for more than one kind of latitude?

20. Approximately how many miles are there to a degree of latitude near the equator? Near the poles? Approximately how many miles to a degree of longitude near the equator? Near the poles?

21. Compare qualitatively the differences of direction in the lines of sight of observers in London and San Francisco as they simultaneously look at (a) a particular auroral streamer, (b) a definite point on the surface of the moon, (c) a small sunspot, (d) the star Vega, (e) the vernal equinox on the celestial sphere.

22. Define and point to or trace out the following: (a) zenith, (b) nadir, (c) astronomical horizon, (d) celestial poles, (e) celestial equator, (f) hour circle, (g) celestial meridian, (h) diurnal circle.

23. Define and illustrate the measurement of: (a) right ascension, (b) declination, (c) altitude.

24. At a certain point on the earth's surface the north celestial pole appears to be 48° from the zenith. (a) What is the pole's altitude? (b) What is the observer's latitude? (c) How far from the zenith does the celestial equator cut the observer's celestial meridian?

25. A star whose declination is $\delta = +18°$ crosses a certain observer's meridian 26°35′ south of his zenith. What is the observer's latitude?

26. Determine whether or not in latitude 40° N the following stars would be (a) always visible, (b) above the horizon more than half the time, (c) above the horizon less than half the time, or (d) never visible:

STAR	DECLINATION
Vega	+38°
Dubhe	+62
Sirius	−17
Canopus	−53
Procyon	+5

27. What defines the ecliptic? Devise a method by which one could initially determine the position of the ecliptic among the stars. Is this position fixed? Does the ecliptic maintain a fixed position in any given observer's sky?

28. What two factors are responsible for the occurrence of seasons? How?

When does each season begin? What is the lag of the seasons and what is its explanation?

29. If the obliquity of the ecliptic were changed to 32°, would this have any effect upon the seasons? For what obliquity would there be no seasons? Describe the seasons if the obliquity of the ecliptic were 90°.

30. What arguments prove that the seasons are not the result of the earth's varying distance from the sun? Under what circumstances might the seasons depend, at least in part, on a variation of the earth's distance from the sun? Under what circumstances might the seasons depend wholly on a variation of the earth's distance from the sun?

31. Define (a) apparent solar noon, (b) apparent solar day, (c) mean solar day, (d) hour angle, (e) local apparent solar time, (f) local mean solar time. When does the mean sun coincide with the apparent sun? Under what circumstances would the mean sun and apparent sun always coincide? Why are the largest negative values of the equation of time greater numerically than the largest positive values of the equation of time?

32. Why is it necessary to describe certain kinds of time as "local"? What disadvantages would there be in the use of local apparent solar time? Local mean solar time? What is standard time? How is it free of the disadvantages of other kinds of solar time?

33. On April 15 a sun dial in longitude 87° W reads 3:27 P.M. at a certain instant. What is the local apparent solar time at the position of the sun dial? What is the local mean solar time? What is the standard time?

34. On May 1 at the same standard time as above what will the sun dial read?

35. The local mean solar time of a certain locality is 5^h42^m ahead of Greenwich time. What is the longitude of the place? How is its standard time related to that of Greenwich?

36. If the standard time at a certain place in longitude 174° W is 3:30 P.M., November 9, 1951, what is the standard time in longitude 176°30′ E?

37. Is it possible to "make time stand still" by flying westward through 15° of longitude per hour?

38. What is sidereal time? By what rule or rules can it be determined? Of what use is it?

39. Vega's right ascension is 18^h35^m. What is the sidereal time when Vega's hour angle is 3^h48^m E?

40. When the local mean solar time is 10:32 P.M. on March 21, what is the approximate local sidereal time? What is the approximate local sidereal time at the same hour on March 26? June 22? July 1?

41. What is the approximate local mean solar time on September 23 when the local sidereal time is 5^h41^m? On October 1?

42. How many sidereal days are there in one tropical year? From this and the number of mean solar days in one tropical year, determine how much shorter the sidereal day is than the mean solar day.

43. Upon what kind of year is the calendar based? Why is the calendar not based on the earth's true period of revolution?

44. What is the fundamental difficulty in calendar construction? What results if the length of the year is taken to be exactly 365 mean solar days?

$365\frac{1}{4}$ days? What is the complete leap-year rule of our present calendar? How accurate is it? What would be the leap-year rule if the length of the year were $365\frac{1}{5}$ days? $364\frac{2}{7}$ days? 370.1111 days?

45. What objections can be raised against the present calendar system? Outline the features of the most important alternative calendar systems that have been proposed. Indicate the respects in which each is superior to the Gregorian calendar and to each other. What factors militate against any calendar reform in the near future?

46. Name and give the symbols of the six elements of a planet's orbit. Define each. Identify that characteristic of the orbit which is fixed by each. What purpose does a knowledge of a planet's orbital elements serve?

47. How are the orbital elements of any body obtained? For what kinds of astronomical bodies can orbital elements be given? To what extent is the usefulness of a set of orbital elements limited by change with time?

48. Sketch a qualitatively correct relative motion curve of one of the outer planets. What would the relative motion curve of the earth from the same planet look like? Compare the earth's relative motion curve from Jupiter with Mercury's relative motion curve from the earth.

49. Define (a) direct motion, (b) retrograde motion. Is such motion relative to the sun or the stars? How does each come about?

50. Name the principal configurations of an inner planet. What are the corresponding configurations of the earth seen from the planet? Do the same for an outer planet.

51. Under what circumstances would a planet's sidereal and synodic periods be equal? How does Mercury's synodic period from the earth compare with its synodic period from Jupiter? How does Saturn's compare?

52. Indicate the part of the sky where one would expect to see the following planets at the times specified: (a) Jupiter at opposition, 10:00 P.M.; (b) Mercury at maximum western elongation, 6:00 A.M.; (c) Mercury at maximum western elongation, 6:00 P.M.; (d) Mars at eastern quadrature, 7:00 P.M.; (e) Venus at elongation 30° W, 12:00 noon; (f) Saturn at superior conjunction, 2:00 A.M.

53. Describe the essentials of the Ptolemaic system of the universe. Demonstrate how the Ptolemaic epicyclic theory was able qualitatively to account for the various planets' alternate direct and retrograde motions. How satisfactory was it quantitatively? How was the Ptolemaic system decisively disposed of?

54. What was Copernicus' contribution to astronomy? What objections were raised to Copernicus' system immediately after it was put forth? What defense of the Copernican system could be offered in Copernicus' day? What objections can we find to the original Copernican system in the present day? How has it been modified?

55. Why is the moon more effective than the sun in producing tides?

56. How is the presence of tidal bulges in the oceans responsible for the occurrence of tides? How does the gravitational attraction of the moon create two opposite tidal bulges?

57. What is the average length of time between high tides? What determines this interval?

58. What is the period of rotation of the tidal bulges? (*Hint:* One bulge is, ideally, directly under the moon.) How does this fact affect the rotation of the earth as a whole? How is such an effect detectable?

59. What is precession? What is its explanation? How does it affect the right ascensions and declinations of stars? How does it affect the celestial longitudes and latitudes of stars? How rapid are such effects?

chapter 3
The Moon

...

> *"Which is more useful, the Sun or the Moon? The Moon is the more useful since it gives us light during the night, when it is dark, whereas the Sun shines only in the daytime, when it is light anyway."*
>
> —GEORGE GAMOW

Next to the earth and the sun, the moon is the most familiar astronomical body. It is the earth's *satellite*. Mercury and Venus have no satellites; very probably Pluto does not either. All the rest of the planets have moons, numbering from two for Mars and Neptune to twelve for Jupiter.

Astronomically speaking, the moon is very companionable, being the nearest permanent body to the earth and sharing with the latter a motion about the sun. Consequently it can be studied directly in more detail than any other body outside the earth.

The Motions of the Moon

Perhaps we can most logically first discuss the moon's general behavior. Like everything else in the sky, the moon appears to rise in the east and set in the west, but like nothing else in the sky, its eastward motion among the stars is at an apparent rate of over half a degree an hour on the average. This apparent motion stems from its relative motion of revolution about the earth. To be sure, earth and moon are actually moving about their common center of gravity, which, in all strictness, is what moves about the sun in obedience to Kepler's laws. Then, too, the earth, moon, and sun are three bodies, and their relative motions will present all the complications of the famous three-body problem. But for the most purposes, it suffices to regard the moon's relative motion as one of revolution about the earth.

THE MOON'S ORBITAL MOTION

To a first approximation, the moon's relative orbit about the earth is an ellipse with the earth at one focus, and in its motion the moon obeys

Kepler's laws. The plane of its orbit has an inclination of 5°9′ to the ecliptic, the eccentricity of its orbit is 0.0549, and its major semi-axis is 238,850
miles. From the mean distance and eccentricity we can very easily calculate
that at *perigee* (its point of nearest approach) the
moon is 225,700 miles from the earth, at *apogee*
(the point of greatest distance) 252,000 miles.
The moon's sidereal period is 27.32166 days or
27^{d}7^{h}43^m and 11.^{s}5.

But these data are true only in an average
sense. The attraction of the sun upon the moon
retards the moon with respect to the earth at
times of conjunction and opposition (new and
full moon, respectively), increases its period as
much as 2 hours when the earth approaches perihelion, causes very considerable changes in the
orbital eccentricity, makes the inclination fluctuate slightly, advances the line of apsides (the line
joining perigee and apogee) once around in 8.85
years, and is responsible for a westward regression
of the nodes through 360° in 18.6 years. In view
of the largeness of these perturbations, one is
likely to be very sympathetic to the view that the
earth perturbs the moon's motion about the sun
rather than that the sun perturbs the moon's motion about the earth.

If we consider the moon's motion in space
rather than its motion relative to the earth, the
latter view is literally true, for the sun's attraction
upon the moon is more than twice the earth's, and
the motions of both earth and moon are governed
in the main by the sun. Because the attraction of
the sun for the earth or the moon is greater than
the earth's or moon's attractions for each other,
the earth's and moon's greatest accelerations will
always be toward the sun, and therefore the orbits

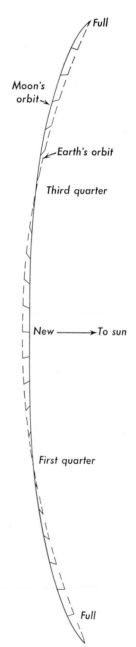

Figure 49. The moon's orbit is always concave toward the sun because the attraction of the sun upon the
moon is greater than the attraction of the earth upon the
moon. No other satellite in the solar system has an orbit
always concave to the sun.

of both will at all times be concave toward the sun (Fig. 49), a fact which is commonly overlooked when one considers only the moon's relative motion about the earth.

The revolution of the moon about the earth and the fact that the moon is illuminated by the sun are together responsible for the moon's showing phases, waxing from new to full, then waning to new again. It is easy to see why the various phases occur (Fig. 50). It is because only half the moon can be illuminated at one time and this half will generally

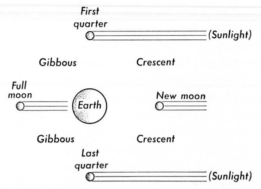

Figure 50. The earthward hemisphere of the moon shows varying proportions of illumination as the moon revolves about the earth. The sequence of different illuminations constitutes the phases of the moon.

not coincide except in part with the half of the moon which faces the earth; their common part is what we see from the earth.

Thus, when the sun and moon are in conjunction, the illuminated hemisphere of the moon will face directly away from the earth; at this phase the moon is *new*. About two weeks later, when the moon is at opposition, the illuminated hemisphere of the moon faces directly toward the earth; at this phase the moon is *full*. Between times, the moon's illuminated and visible hemispheres overlap by increasing or decreasing amounts according as the moon is waxing or waning. When the western half of the moon's disk is lighted, it is *first quarter* phase; when the eastern half is lighted the phase is *last quarter* (or third quarter). Between quarters and full the phase is *gibbous,* while between quarters and new the phase is *crescent.*

Just as the moon exhibits phases when seen from the earth, the earth will exhibit phases when seen from the moon, the only difference being that when the moon is full the earth is new, and vice versa. Hence the dark part of the crescent moon will receive sunlight from the gibbous earth. In the illumination of this *earthlight* we see the dark part of the moon as "the old moon in the new moon's arms."

THE MOON'S ROTATION

As our satellite revolves about us, it also rotates on its axis in a counterclockwise sense. Its period of rotation is precisely equal to its period of revolution. Hence a sidereal day on the moon is $27\frac{1}{3}$ mean solar days and the mean solar day on the moon is $29\frac{1}{2}$ of our mean solar days—necessarily the same as its synodic period of rotation or revolution.

It is preposterously improbable that the perfect equality of the moon's periods of rotation and revolution is coincidental. It is much more reasonable to suppose that the moon's period of rotation has been adjusted by some agent such as the tidal force of the earth upon the moon. It is this same tidal force, presumably, which has caused the moon to be bulged an estimated $\frac{1}{3}$ mile along one diameter.

In fact, the bulge is along a diameter which is always directed toward the earth or nearly so. For the moon always turns the same face toward the earth because of (1) the equality of its periods of rotation and revolution and (2) the fact that both motions are from west to east. To see that this is so, we may consider the separate effects of revolution and rotation upon the appearance of the moon from the earth. If the man in the moon were to stare squarely toward any one point among the stars, he would be forced to look away from us during part of his revolution (Fig. 51). In particular, his gaze would be diverted from us by as many degrees as his revolution had carried him from the line of sight which includes the earth. On the other hand, to keep his eye on us he would need to turn his head precisely this many degrees, which for one revolution requires one rotation of his head. It is obvious, moreover, that the periods of the two motions must be exactly equal, for the effect of even a very minute difference would accumulate over centuries so as to show us the man in the moon's profile rather than full face.

And yet during a month it is possible to see somewhat more than an exact 50 per cent of the moon's surface by taking advantage of the opportunities afforded by librations (literally "balancings"). Librations are slight apparent oscillations of the moon and are of four kinds. One of them (diurnal libration) is due to the earth's own rotation, which carries any observer halfway around the world in 12 hours, thus allowing him to view the moon from positions far enough apart to show slightly different hemispheres, i.e., a little around each edge. This libration is thus really an oscillation of the observer, not the moon, though the apparent effect is all the same.

A second type of libration (latitudinal libration) results from the lunar equator's being inclined about 1½° to its orbit, 6½° to the ecliptic. As a result of this inclination we shall see first one pole tipped earthward, giving us a view beyond it, then the other, half a revolution later.

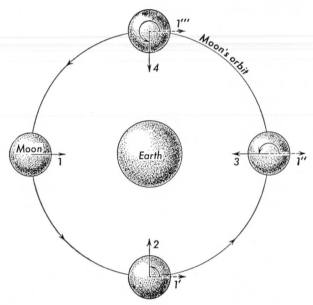

Figure 51. The arrows 1, 1′, 1″ and 1‴ all point in the same direction. The arrows 1, 2, 3, and 4 point toward the earth and are therefore rotated from the directions 1, 1′, etc., by the angle through which the moon revolves.

The most important libration (longitudinal libration) is equal to the difference which usually exists between the number of degrees through which the moon has rotated and the number of degrees it has revolved in its orbit. There is a difference between them because the moon rotates at a uniform rate whereas in accord with the law of areas the rate of revolution is variable. The resulting libration in longitude will disclose about 8° on each limb which would otherwise be invisible. Diurnal, latitudinal, and longitudinal librations combine to show us 59 per cent of the moon's surface. Of course, only 50 per cent is visible at any one time, though 41 per cent is never invisible from the earth, and the visibility of 18 per cent is subject to librations.

Actually, the moon's rate of rotation on its axis is not absolutely uniform, although it is very nearly so. Because of longitudinal and latitudinal librations, the moon's slight bulge fails to be always turned directly toward the earth. The earth's attraction upon the excess which forms the bulge is thereby able to produce a very small true oscillation of the moon's longest diameter. This is called physical libration; it permits a view of an additional mile of the moon's equator on either side. The portion of the moon's surface not visible from the earth has been photographed from a lunar rocket. The quality of the reproductions suffices to show only the grossest features, however, and these appear not to differ in any essential respects from those of the portion of the surface theretofore visible.

THE MOON'S APPARENT MOTIONS

The period of the moon's phases is the moon's period with respect to the *apparent* sun; this is, as we know, its synodic period. The length of the moon's synodic period is 29.530588 days, or $29^d12^h44^m$ and 2^s8, to within less than a tenth of a second. The excess of synodic over sidereal period of the moon is the time required by the moon to move from where it last passed the sun to the sun's new position.

Inasmuch as the moon moves farther east of the sun daily, its time of transit will be delayed and by an average amount of 50^m47^s of mean solar time. But the same causes which produced a variation in the length of the apparent solar day, namely, inclination of the apparent path to the celestial equator and nonuniform orbital motion, operate to produce deviations in the amount of delay of the moon's transits; the actual delay may be any amount between 38 and 66 minutes.

Though it may seem strange, the delay in the moon's rising time on successive nights is not necessarily equal to its delay in time of transit, though to be sure, their averages are equal. The explanation of this fact is exactly the same as the explanation of the fact that although the apparent sun never transits more than 14^m slow or 16^m fast, the times of sunrise and sunset can vary by several hours in the course of a year. If on any day the moon's position at time of rising is north of that of the preceding day, for example, it will rise earlier in the northern hemisphere than it would have had it kept the same declination. The reason is that on the second day the moon is nearer the visible celestial circumpolar cap, with the result that it rises earlier and sets later. On the other hand, when the moon is moving southward on the celestial sphere, its rising is delayed an amount in addition to the delay in time of transit.

In particular, since the sun is crossing the celestial equator southward at the time of the autumnal equinox, a full moon then would be crossing the celestial equator northward. There would therefore be a minimum delay in the moon's rising time from one night to the next, and at this time there occurs the maximum number of evenings with full moonlight in the early evening. In recognition of this fact, the full moon occurring

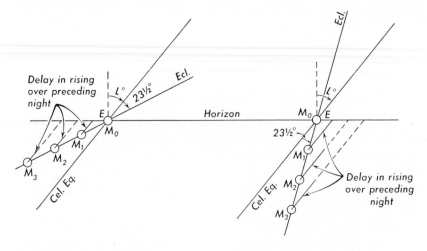

(a) Time of Autumnal equinox   (b) Time of vernal equinox

Figure 52. One day after the moon is seen to rise in the east at sunset (as at M_0), the moon will be at M_1. Twenty-four hours later it will be at M_2, the next day at M_3, etc. The additional time required to reach the horizon is the delay in rising. In the northern hemisphere, this delay will be a minimum at the autumnal equinox [as in (a)], a maximum at vernal equinox [as in (b)].

nearest the date of the autumnal equinox (September 23) is called the *harvest moon.* In latitude 40° north, its delay in rising may be as little as 13 minutes. The full moon following harvest moon is called the *hunter's moon;* it suffers only slightly greater delay in times of successive moonrises. Of course at the time of the vernal equinox the state of affairs is reversed and the full moon's daily delay in rising is a maximum—as much as 1 hour and 20 minutes in latitude 40° N. In the southern hemisphere, these phenomena are turned about.

It is also of some interest to note that the full moon rides highest and is therefore up for the greatest number of hours during the winter, when the nights are longest. This is because the sun is farthest south in the winter and full moon will occur when the moon is farthest north.

Eclipses

As the moon goes around the earth, the shadow it casts will sometimes fall on the earth; at other times the earth's shadow will fall on the moon. From the earth these occurrences will be observed as an eclipse of the sun (solar eclipse) and as an eclipse of the moon (lunar eclipse), respectively.

THE CONDITIONS FOR ECLIPSE

If the moon moved along the ecliptic as the sun does, there would be one eclipse of each kind every synodic period of the moon, for then the

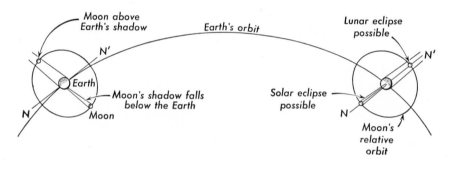

Figure 53. In order that an eclipse occur, the line from earth to sun must nearly coincide with the line from earth to moon. This is the case when the line of nodes, *NN'*, is directed toward the sun (as at the right); such times are called *eclipse seasons.* Several months later (as on the left), the line from earth to moon may be directed as much as 5° above or below the line from earth to sun.

moon would come squarely between us and the sun at each new moon, and the earth would come squarely between the sun and moon at each full moon. But this does not take place, and it does not for the reason that the moon does not follow the ecliptic but rather an orbit inclined 5° to it. Hence the moon can sail above or skirt below the sun in the sky at the time of new moon and in the same manner dodge the shadow of the earth at full moon. As a result, the combined number of eclipses can never exceed seven in any year and may be as few as two.

The specific condition to be met in order that an eclipse take place is that the sun be sufficiently near a node of the moon's orbit. The nodes are common to the apparent paths of both the sun and the moon and could

conceivably be simultaneously occupied by both the moon and the sun
(or by the moon and the earth's shadow, which is opposite the sun). But
it is not even necessary that the moon and the sun (or moon and earth's
shadow) have *exactly* the same position on the celestial sphere at the time
of an eclipse. Both appear as disks of about half a degree in diameter; these
disks will appear to overlap to some extent even though their centers may
be half a degree apart. For a solar eclipse, this can be the case only when
both sun and moon are within $18\frac{1}{2}°$ of the same node; for a lunar eclipse,

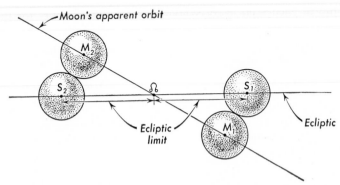

Figure 54. As it would appear on the celestial sphere, the sun's position at S_1 is
the extreme western position at which it could make contact with the moon, as at
M_1; similarly, the sun's position at S_2 is the extreme eastern position at which the
sun could make contact with the moon, as at M_2. Beyond these limits, the sun and
moon would miss each other. The distances of S_1 and S_2 from the node are therefore
the ecliptic limits.

this can be the case only when the sun and moon are within $12\frac{1}{4}°$ of opposite nodes. These angular distances are called the *ecliptic limits* for the
most favorable circumstances.

   It is not difficult to see that twice a year the sun must be within the
ecliptic limit for a solar eclipse. What is more, it will be within the ecliptic
limit of each node for more than a month, since its average rate of motion
along the ecliptic is not quite $1°$ per day. Since the sun is within the ecliptic
limits for a length of time greater than the moon's synodic period, there
cannot fail to be a new moon at some time during this interval. Hence the
sun must suffer an eclipse of some sort at least twice a year—once near
each node.

   By supposing extreme conditions, we can see how there might be four
solar eclipses in one year. If the new moon were to eclipse the sun just
as the latter first comes within the ecliptic limits, the moon can catch the
sun again before the sun shall have had time to pass beyond the ecliptic

limit of that node. Consequently two solar eclipses may occur within a month of each other and be followed by a second pair after half a year.

But there may sometimes occur even a fifth solar eclipse in a single calendar year. This is possible because of the regression of the moon's nodes. As we have seen, the nodes of the moon's orbit move westward about 20° per year. As a result, the sun will reach a given node just 346.62 days (an *eclipse year*) after its last conjunction with that node. Therefore, in any year during which an eclipse takes place in the first 19 days of January, the sun may again be within the ecliptic limit of the first node before the calendar year is out. In this way, five eclipses of the sun can take place in one calendar year; this is the greatest possible number.

By an exactly similar argument we can determine that as many as three lunar eclipses can fall in one year. This lesser number is due to the fact that, on account of the smaller lunar ecliptic limits, lunar eclipses can never occur in pairs. In no case can there be more than seven eclipses in a year; these may be either five solar and two lunar or four solar and three lunar. For example, in 1935 there were five solar and two lunar eclipses, while in 1982 they will be divided four and three. There were only two eclipses in 1933 and these were, of course, both solar eclipses.

THE GEOMETRY OF ECLIPSES

It might at first sight seem surprising that the ecliptic limits for solar eclipse are greater than the ecliptic limits for lunar eclipse, for we expect the earth's shadow to be as much larger than the moon's shadow as the earth is larger than the moon; therefore we might expect the frequency of lunar eclipses to be correspondingly greater than the frequency of solar eclipses. We shall be able to see why this expectation is not borne out if we consider the simple geometry of eclipses (Figs. 55–56; these figures are only diagrammatic, since they could not conveniently be drawn to scale).

The shadow which the earth (or moon) will cast in the light from any point such as A on the sun's disk will evidently be a cone-shaped volume GAH, whose vertex is at the point A and whose surface is tangent to the earth (or moon); everywhere within the cone GAH on the side of the earth away from the sun, the point A is obscured by the opaque earth. Suppose we consider points such as A and B at the extreme edge of the sun's disk. The shadow cones for these points will have a certain volume in common; for the whole set of points about the limb of the sun's disk, their common volume is likewise a cone (CED), tangent to the earth and with vertex away from the sun. This volume is known as the earth's (or moon's) shadow cone, or *umbra*. Within the umbra, light from all parts of the sun is cut off, since it is common to the shadow cone of them all. The vertex *E*

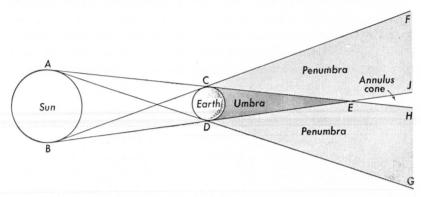

Figure 55. The compound shadow cone generated by the spherical earth (or moon) in the light of all points of the sun's surface from limb *A* to limb *B* consists of an umbra (the region common to the shadow cones of all points of the sun's surface), an annulus cone (the region common to points about the center of the sun's disk), and a penumbra (the region common to some but not all points on the limb of the sun's disk).

of the earth's shadow cone is on the average 859,000 miles from the center of the earth; the moon's shadow cone averages 232,000 miles in length.

Beyond the vertex *E* of the umbra is a conical volume *JEH* which is not a part of the shadow cone of any point on the sun's limb but in which

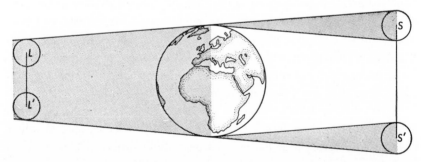

Figure 56. The moon will produce a total solar eclipse when it comes anywhere within the limits *S* and *S'* whereas it must be within the lesser limits *L* and *L'* to be totally eclipsed. This explains the difference between the ecliptic limits for solar and lunar eclipses. (Globe after a drawing by Richard Edes Harrison for *Fortune.*)

the center of the sun's disk is invisible. This region is called the *annulus cone,* since within it only a ring or annulus of points about the edge of the sun's disk can be seen. The remainder of the region of partial shadow

(*FCEJ* and *GDEH*) is the *penumbra* or semishadow. Within the penumbra a part of the sun's limb will be obscured.

From Fig. 56 we can now see why solar eclipses are more frequent than lunar eclipses and why the ecliptic limits are larger for solar than lunar eclipses. It is simply because the region of space from which the moon's shadow will fall on the earth (the region from *S* to *S'* in the figure) is larger than the region which the moon must enter to be eclipsed (the region from *L* to *L'* in the figure); the former is about 10,000 miles across at the moon's distance whereas the latter is only about 5700 miles across.

THE CIRCUMSTANCES OF SOLAR ECLIPSES

An observer anywhere in the umbra of the moon will see a *total eclipse* of the sun; in the annulus cone he will witness an *annular eclipse,* and in the penumbra a *partial eclipse*. Because the penumbra is so much more extensive than either the umbra or annulus cone, partial eclipses of the sun and moon are more frequent and can be seen from a much larger area of the earth's surface than can total or annular eclipses. In fact, the average number of exclusively partial solar eclipses per century is 83.8, while 77.3 are at best annular, 65.9 are total, and 10.5 are both annular and total.[1]

Besides there being more partial than total eclipses, even an eclipse which appears total in some localities will be seen as partial in a much larger neighboring region. Hence it is not surprising that though a total eclipse of the sun will on the average be observed only once in 360 years in any particular locality, a partial eclipse is not too uncommon a sight.

A total eclipse of the sun is both the most interesting and the least frequent kind of eclipse. Its occurrence requires that special conditions be met. For, since the size of the moon's apparent disk is very nearly equal to that of the sun's, both sun and moon must consequently arrive at a node almost simultaneously. It is also most favorable for total eclipse that the moon's apparent size be a maximum, the sun's a minimum, though this is not strictly necessary. The former condition is met when the moon is at perigee, the latter when the earth is at aphelion. Under these most favorable circumstances the solar ecliptic limit is 18°31′. The earth will

---

[1] An eclipse may begin and end as an annular eclipse and yet be total for a short time during mid-eclipse. This will occur whenever the moon's umbra falls short of the earth's surface at the beginning and at the end of the path of the eclipse, being just long enough, however, to reach the nearest points of the earth's surface. An eclipse of this sort took place on April 28, 1930. The path along which it was visible extended from Polynesia nearly to the British Isles, but only from California to Montana was it seen to be total and then only for 1½ seconds.

then cut deepest into the moon's longest possible shadow cone, and the moon will appear enough larger than the sun to keep it covered entirely for nearly 7½ minutes in any one locality; this is the greatest possible length for totality.

Under the most unfavorable circumstances (moon at apogee, earth at perihelion) the solar ecliptic limit is only 15°21′. The moon's umbra then

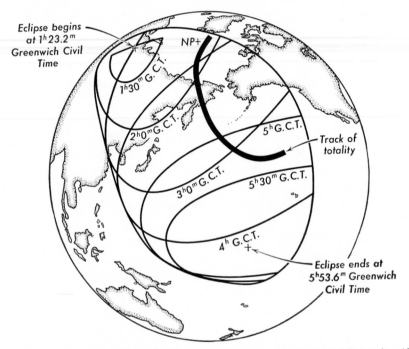

Eclipse begins
at 1ʰ23.2ᵐ
Greenwich Civil
Time

NP+

1ʰ30ᵐG.C.T.

2ʰ0ᵐG.C.T.

5ʰG.C.T.

Track of
totality

3ʰ0ᵐG.C.T.

5ʰ30ᵐG.C.T.

4ʰ G.C.T.
+

Eclipse ends at
5ʰ53.6ᵐ Greenwich
Civil Time

Figure 57. The map shows the progress of the total solar eclipse of September 12, 1950. (Globe after a drawing by Richard Edes Harrison for *Fortune.*)

falls 20,500 miles short of the earth, and the earth experiences an annular eclipse in which the apparently smaller moon is unable to cover completely the apparently larger sun.

But even at best the earth's surface cuts so near the vertex of the moon's umbra that the circle of complete shadow is always less than 167 miles in diameter. About this circle for as far as 3000 miles is the region of the penumbra, in which not all the sun's disk is covered and the eclipse is seen as partial.

Since the eastward traveling moon is overtaking the sun from the west, its shadow will fall first on the west limb of the earth, where the sun is just rising. The shadow will move eastward across the earth's surface as the moon moves eastward in front of the sun. It finally leaves the east limb of the earth, where the sun is just setting. Consequently every eclipse will begin at sunrise at some point and end at sunset about halfway around the earth. Actually, the path of an eclipse spans somewhat less than half the earth, since the earth turns in the same direction the shadow moves, and at the end of the eclipse the point where the eclipse began is no longer on the west limb of the earth.

The minimum speed at which the moon's shadow moves across the earth's surface is equal to the moon's speed in its orbit (about 2300 miles per hour) minus the earth's rate of rotation in the same direction. This can result in a net rate as low as 1100 miles per hour at the equator when the moon is overhead. On the other hand, the shadow may travel as fast as 5000 miles per hour over parts of the earth's surface where it falls obliquely.

The area over which the moon's umbra or annulus cone sweeps is called the *path* of the eclipse. Because of the speed at which the umbra traverses the eclipse path and the fact that the umbra is never more than 167 miles across at the earth's surface, it is easy to see that totality can never last long—7½ minutes at most. An annular eclipse may last somewhat longer, while the partial phase of either total or annular eclipse may last more than 4 hours.

THE CIRCUMSTANCES OF LUNAR ECLIPSES

Eclipses of the moon are less frequent than eclipses of the sun in about the ratio three to four. The circumstances of a lunar eclipse are also rather different. A total eclipse of the moon takes place whenever the whole moon enters the umbra of the earth's shadow, which at the moon's average distance is about 5700 miles across. The greatest length of time the moon can spend in the umbra is 1 hour and 40 minutes, a considerable length of time compared with the brief duration of a total eclipse of the sun.

In spite of their less frequent occurrence, total eclipses of the moon are much more commonly observed than total eclipses of the sun. Whereas an eclipse of the sun can be seen as total only along the narrow eclipse path, a total eclipse of the moon can be seen from any point of the hemisphere of the earth turned toward the moon. If the moon can be seen at all, it will be seen in eclipse; the same is not true of the sun in a solar eclipse. Not only that, but during the time of totality an additional part of the earth will be rotated into a position from which the eclipse may be viewed (and an equal part rotated out), so that actually more than half the earth will be able to view a single total lunar eclipse.

THE PREDICTION OF ECLIPSES

To most people it never ceases to be astonishing that the time of an eclipse can be predicted to within a second or two and that its path can be forecast to within a quarter of a mile. What is required is a very detailed knowledge of the motions of the moon and sun. From the accurately

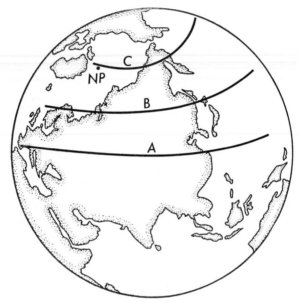

Figure 58. The changing character of eclipses of the same saros cycle is brought out by an inspection of the paths of totality of the eclipses of (A) July 7, 1842, (B) August 8, 1896, and (C) September 12, 1950. (Globe after a drawing by Richard Edes Harrison for *Fortune.*)

computed positions of sun and moon as they would appear at the earth's center it is possible to determine a set of quantities called the elements of the eclipse; from these the conditions of an eclipse can be found for any point on the earth's surface. The calculation of the elements and general circumstances of eclipses is done in the United States at the Naval Observatory, Washington, D. C. Approximate calculations of the elements of all eclipses between 1207 B.C. and A.D. 2162 have been made by Oppolzer, an Austrian astronomer of the nineteenth century.

Incidentally, the calculations for a prediction of an eclipse of the moon are very much simpler than those for a solar eclipse. For one thing, the instant of eclipse is the same for all parts of the world where the eclipse is visible. For another, the predictions need not be so accurate, for immersion of the moon in the earth's umbra is not the abrupt sort of phenomenon that totality in a solar eclipse is.

Of great use in predicting eclipses is a knowledge of the cycle of the *saros*. The cycle of the saros was known to the ancient Chaldeans (whose word "saros" means "repetition"). The saros is a series of intervals of 18 years and $11\frac{1}{3}$ days ($10\frac{1}{3}$ calendar days if the interval contains 5 leap years). This period of a little over 18 years very nearly contains evenly 19 eclipse years and 223 synodic months. Hence this long after one eclipse, another will occur, for the sun returns to the same node after any integral number of eclipse years, and the moon is again at new phase after any integral number of synodic periods. For example, the eclipses of January 14, 1907, January 24, 1925, and February 4, 1943, belong to the same saros cycle. Other eclipses of this period belong to other cycles or series.

Because of the third of a day in the saros, any eclipse of a cycle will occur one-third of a day later, i.e., one-third of the way farther around the

table 6

DATE	WHERE VISIBLE	MAXIMUM DURATION
February 5, 1962	Borneo, Gilbert Islands, South Pacific	4
July 20, 1963	Maine	1
May 30, 1965	New Zealand, South Pacific, Peru	5
November 12, 1966	Central South America, South Africa	2
November 2, 1967	Sandwich Islands, Weddell Sea	
September 22, 1968	Arctic and Central Asia	
March 7, 1970	Florida	3
July 10, 1972	Bering Sea, Northwest Territory, North Atlantic	3
June 30, 1973	Guiana, Central Africa, Indian Ocean	7
June 20, 1974	South Indian Ocean	
October 23, 1976	Congo, Indian Ocean, New Zealand	5
October 12, 1977	North Pacific, Hawaii, Colombia	3
February 26, 1979	Pacific Northwest	3
February 16, 1980	Central Africa, India	4
July 31, 1981	Caspian Sea, Central Asia, Japan	1
June 11, 1983	Indian Ocean, Java, Coral Sea	5
November 22, 1984	East Indies, South Pacific	2
November 12, 1985	South Pacific, Antarctic Ocean	
October 3, 1986	North Atlantic Ocean	1
March 9, 1987	Siberia, Arctic Ocean	3
March 18, 1988	Sumatra, South China Sea, North Pacific Ocean	3
July 22, 1990	Finland, Arctic Ocean, Aleutians	3
July 11, 1991	Marshall Islands, Central Mexico, Brazil	6
June 30, 1992	South Atlantic	
November 3, 1994	East Indies, Australia, Argentina	4
October 24, 1995	Iran, India, Malay, Central Pacific	3
February 26, 1998	Central Pacific, Venezuela, Atlantic Ocean	4
August 11, 1999	North Atlantic, Balkans, India	2

earth than the preceding eclipse of that cycle. Therefore every third eclipse of a series should occur in the same region on the earth, and so it does, approximately. That it does not do so exactly is due to the fact that 19 eclipse years is actually 0.46 days longer than 223 synodic months; consequently the sun will be about 28' west of its previous eclipse position at the time of a new eclipse. This gradually changes the character of the eclipses of a cycle.

Each saros series is a cycle of 68 to 75 solar eclipses over a period of some 1200 years. Approximately 25 of these are partial and 45 annular or total. There are in progress now 12 saros series whose eclipses are total. The series having eclipses in 1919, 1937, and 1955 is remarkable for the near-maximum duration of totality; the eclipse of June 8, 1937, had the greatest duration of totality of any eclipse in 1200 years.

During each saros cycle there will occur a series of lunar eclipses also, but inasmuch as the lunar ecliptic limits are smaller than the solar, the series will last only 870 years. During this time there will be 48 or 49 lunar eclipses, about 23 of them total.

ECLIPSE PHENOMENA

The phenomenon of a total eclipse of the sun is said to be one of the most awesome sights of nature, and it is small wonder that solar eclipses usually bring consternation to superstitious peoples. An eclipse begins as partial, the moon moving slowly from the west across the face of the sun. Unless one knows to look at the sun at the time the moon's east limb makes first contact with the west limb of the sun, he would probably not be aware of anything unusual until the sun's disk were half or more obscured. As the crescent of the sun's visible disk continues to diminish, the sunlight will change in quality as well as become less intense, for light from the sun's limb has less blue in it than that from the center of the disk. In the last stages of the partial phase, birds, animals, and even plants behave as they would at sundown, and a dew or frost may form as the temperature falls. Images of the crescent sun appear in the shadows of leaves and "ripple shadows" appear on white surfaces. Finally the last few rays of direct sunlight will come to us through the serrations and irregularities of the moon's limb, reducing the vanishing crescent to a string of "Baily's beads." The beads vanish almost at once, and their disappearance marks the beginning of totality.

In totality it seems strange enough to see the stars and planets during midday, but the most remarkable feature of the eclipsed sun is its corona (Fig. 137); we are at all other times blinded to it by the diffused bril-

Figure 59. TOTAL SOLAR ECLIPSE. The totally eclipsed sun gave this appearance at the eclipse of May 28, 1900. One sees here only the glowing gases of the parts of the sun's atmosphere known as the chromosphere and inner corona. (Courtesy Yerkes Observatory.)

liance of the sun's disk. The corona is a pearly halo of light two to three times the diameter of the sun and estimated to be altogether about half as bright as the full moon, a millionth as bright as the sun itself. It is variable in shape, the variations being due to the absence or the presence and arrangement of coronal streamers. Until the comparatively recent invention of the coronagraph, the corona could be seen only at times of total eclipse.

After a few minutes or seconds of totality, the moon has moved far enough east to begin uncovering the sun's west limb. First Baily's beads will appear—this time at the west limb. Then all the phenomena of the beginning of the eclipse will occur in reverse order.

A total lunar eclipse is not nearly so spectacular. The atmosphere of the earth causes the earth's shadow to be ill-defined, and the penumbra will produce very little noticeable effect on the moon's brightness except in the neighborhood of the umbra. The umbra is likewise not sharply

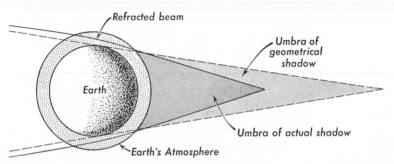

Figure 60. The earth's atmosphere, like a drop of water, focuses the sunlight which passes through it and effectively shortens the umbra of the earth's shadow cone.

defined as compared with the moon's umbra. When the moon passes into the umbra of the earth's shadow, its brightness is greatly reduced, but unless clouds on the earth prevent the passage of sunlight through the zones of sunrise and sunset (west and east limbs of the earth), the moon never becomes completely invisible. By refraction, the earth's atmosphere bends the sunlight which passes through it toward the axis of the shadow cone, effectively focusing some of the sun's rays on the moon even when the moon is in the geometric umbra. The color of the moon when it is visible in total eclipse is a dull coppery red; the light which has passed through the sunrise and sunset zones has been reddened by diffusion.

THE IMPORTANCE OF ECLIPSES

From a scientific point of view, total eclipses of the sun are of considerable importance. They permit otherwise unobtainable visual and radio observations to be made of the outer layers of the sun (p. 254) and of its corona. In the past, eclipses have given opportunities to search for a suspected planet nearer the sun than Mercury, and for satellites to Mercury and Venus; none was found. And, finally, because of the abruptness of the

compared with the base line $\overline{AB}$ and so nearly equal to each other in length. In the case of the earth and the moon, for instance, $\overline{AM}$ is at least some 30 times longer than $\overline{AB}$; the ratio for all other astronomical bodies is even more extreme.

The near equality of AM and BM suggests that a circle centered at M with radius $\overline{AM}$ would very nearly pass through B. Then, with $\overline{AM}$ so much larger than $\overline{AB}$, the length of the chord $\overline{AB}$ would be very little different from the length of the arc AB; in fact, if the angle at M is less than $1°$ (which it will almost always be), the difference between arc and chord is less than one-thousandth of 1 per cent. Herein is the simplification, for it is easy to determine the distance $\overline{AM}$ at which an *arc* of length AB would subtend any given angle; it is determined from the formula

$$d = \frac{3438 \times b}{p},$$

in which d is the distance from A to M, b the length of the base line $\overline{AB}$, and p the angle at M expressed in minutes of arc. The distance d will have the same units (miles, meters, etc.) as the base line b.

This formula may be readily derived. We need only observe that the entire circumference C of the circle with radius AM ($=d$) will be as many times greater than the arc AB (closely approximated by the base line $\overline{AB} = b$) as a full $360°$ is greater than the angle at M ($= p$). Written down, this proportion takes the compact form

$$\frac{C}{b} = \frac{360°}{p°}.$$

We now substitute $2\pi d$ for C, convert degrees to minutes of arc by multiplying by 60, and solve the resulting equation for d. We shall get the equation for the distance as given above.

As a rule, the angle p will be so small in problems of astronomical interest that it is most convenient to express it in seconds of arc. In this case we use the formula

$$d = \frac{206,265 \times b}{p},$$

where d and b are in the same units, and p is in seconds of arc. It is obtained as before, except that degrees have been converted to seconds of arc by multiplying the number of degrees by 3600.

But just how is the angle p measured? It is found quite directly by taking advantage of the fact that the angular difference of the moon's apparent position as seen from A and B and gauged with respect to the stars is the required quantity (Fig. 62). For, recalling our very elementary geometry, we see that the apparent difference of the moon's position in the sky as seen from A and from B will be the angle PMQ; this is exactly equal to the angle $AMB = p$.

It might seem that the measurement of the angle PMQ would require an admirable cooperation among observatories strategically placed on the earth's surface. While cooperation among astronomers of all nations (and scientists generally) is commonplace, the desired angle could even be measured by one observer alone, without outside assistance. That is possible since the earth will very accommodatingly rotate any point of the earth's surface to a new position after the lapse of a few hours. Hence observations made 12 hours apart will be made literally "half way around the earth" from each other. Of course due allowance must be made for the moon's actual motion in the meantime.

For the sake of uniformity, all observations of the sort we have been discussing are adjusted so that they will correspond to the use of the earth's equatorial radius as base line. The angle subtended by the earth's equatorial radius at any particular distance is called the *equatorial horizontal parallax* at that distance. The equatorial horizontal parallax at the moon's mean distance is $57'2''.7$; it is customary to refer to this simply as the *parallax* of the moon. Using our definition of parallax, p, and inserting the value of 3963.34 miles (the earth's equatorial radius) for the length of the base line, we can use our formula for distance to determine that the moon has a mean distance of

$$\frac{3438 \times 3963.34}{57.045} = 238,850 \text{ miles.}$$

Let us pause for a few statistics. It is interesting to observe, for example, that with this mean distance, the moon must have an orbit whose circumference is approximately one and a half million miles. Dividing this by the number of hours in its sidereal period will tell us how fast the moon moves in its orbit, and we find that this is about 2290 miles per hour or $\frac{2}{3}$ miles per second. It is also of interest that at the moon's distance of about 60 earth's radii, a free body would fall only $\frac{1}{20}$ inch toward the earth in the first second after its release. (At the earth's surface the distance is 16 feet.) It is rather startling to consider that each second the moon travels $\frac{2}{3}$ miles and in this distance deviates only $\frac{1}{20}$ of an inch from a straight-line path.

THE SIZE OF THE MOON

Turning from such comparisons and convinced that we know how far away the moon is, our next task is to try to discover how large or small the moon may be. To this end we note that our original triangulation formula is versatile and we make it do double duty by giving us now the moon's size. Solving the adapted equation

$$d = \frac{3438 \times D}{\beta}$$

for D the moon's linear diameter, we find that

$$D = \frac{\beta \times d}{3438}$$

where D and d are in the same units and β is in minutes of arc. Since the moon's angular diameter β is 31'5".2 at its mean distance of 238,850 miles, we can determine that its linear diameter is

$$D = \frac{31.087 \times 238,850}{3438} = 2160 \text{ miles.}$$

The moon's diameter is thus 27 per cent of the earth's. The moon therefore has only 7.4 per cent as much surface area as the earth, only 2 per cent as much volume.

One would suspect that with so much smaller a volume, the moon's mass would likewise be smaller. There is a way to put this conjecture to the test and to determine the moon's mass. That is simply to discover the position of the center of gravity of earth and moon together. The moon is as much farther from this point than the earth as the earth is more massive than the moon.

To be able to find how far the earth-and-moon's center of gravity is from the center of the earth, we note again that it is the center of gravity which is moving about the sun, obedient to Kepler's laws. While the center of gravity is smoothly going about the sun in an ellipse, the earth and moon waltz about it, one on each side. As a result, the center of the earth is sometimes (at first quarter) ahead of the center of gravity, sometimes (at last quarter) behind it. At these respective times the sun will appear behind or ahead of its proper position on the ecliptic; the greatest amount is 6".4. But this is precisely the parallax the sun would have with a base line of 2886 miles (Fig. 63). In other words, the center of the earth is this many miles from the center of gravity of moon and earth.

Evidently the moon's center is 235,964 miles from it or 81.8 times farther. The earth is therefore this many times more massive; which is to say that the moon's mass is 1/81.8 as much as the earth's.

Evidently the moon "weighs" less in proportion to its size than the earth does, for its volume is one-fiftieth while its mass is not even one-eightieth. Its average density is, in fact, about three and a third times that of water.

If earth and moon were the same size, a person standing on the moon would be pulled by gravity only one-eightieth as strongly as on the earth

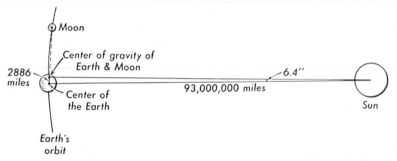

Figure 63. The parallax of the sun, some 93,000,000 miles distant, is 6″4 when one uses a base-line equal to the separation of the earth's center from the center of gravity of earth and moon. The base-line is therefore 2886 miles in length, 1/82.8th part of the mean distance of the moon from the earth.

by the mass only one-eightieth as great. But because the moon's surface is 3.67 times nearer its center than we are to the earth's, the force of lunar surface gravity will be $(3.67)^2/80$ that at the earth's surface, or approximately one-sixth as much. A fall of 18 feet on the moon would be no more serious than a fall of 3 feet on the earth and a 180-pound man would weigh only 30 pounds on the moon.

THE ABSENCE OF A LUNAR ATMOSPHERE

But for his buoyancy the man in the moon has paid a price. Just as it is much easier to jump higher on the moon, it is also easier to escape entirely from the moon's gravitational control. Thus, whereas a molecule of our own atmosphere would need to have an outward speed of 7 miles per second to leave the earth permanently, the velocity of escape from the moon is only about one-sixth as great, or 1½ miles per second. This is a sufficiently common velocity for molecules of atmospheric gases at ordinary temperatures that they have long since been lost to the moon. So far, not a trace of lunar atmosphere has been observed either at times of total solar eclipse or at the occultation of stars, when diffraction and diffusion by a lunar atmosphere would produce effects of the same sort as on the earth. Furthermore, there is no detectable twilight zone. The absence of such atmospheric effects makes it possible to estimate that if any atmosphere exists on the moon, it must be less than a ten-billionth as dense as the earth's.

Inasmuch as the moon is unable to retain an atmosphere, it will have no water, for water vapor would be lost just as other gases are. With no water, there are no oceans, lakes, rivers, or glaciers to erode the moon's surface. The sky is always cloudless.

With no atmosphere, there is nothing to prevent large and rapid rises of temperature during the half-month day and large and rapid drops of temperature during the half-month night. Thus the temperature of the moon varies from 214° F (2° above the boiling point of water) to −243° F— a range of over 450° F. These temperature determinations were made with an instrument called a vacuum thermocouple, which permits measurement of the amount of heat radiated per unit area of lunar surface. The intensity of such heat radiation is determined by the temperature of the surface.

Without an atmosphere on the moon, the lunar sky will appear black, stars will be visible at midday. All is calm and silence, for there is no air to transmit sound or blow a gale. Sunrise and sunset are abrupt, and there is no protection from the sun's ultraviolet rays or from meteors. In view of these conditions, we must conclude that the moon is a rugged desert devoid of life, more barren and inhospitable than any on earth.

LUNAR SURFACE FEATURES

The unaided eye attests to the existence of lunar surface markings, for they form the features of "the man in the moon." Much more can be seen with only a pair of binoculars, and a small telescope will give a view of all the major features.

Those features most conspicuous to the naked eye are large plains, called *maria,* which are darker in color than the rest of the surface and cover about half of it. The term "maria," from the Latin *mare* meaning "sea," is obviously inappropriate for any feature of the arid lunar surface. It is descended in usage from the first few astronomers who systematically observed the moon telescopically and to whom these areas appeared to be bodies of water. The approximately 30 maria have received fanciful names such as Mare Serenitatis (Sea of Serenity), Mare Crisium (Sea of Crises), Sinus Iridum (Gulf of Rainbows, though of course a rainbow could never exist to be seen by anyone on the moon), and Lacus Som-

Figure 64. THE FULL MOON. The moon's coloration features such as the maria (dark areas) and rays (network of bright lines about several of the craters) show most conspicuously at the full phase. South is at the top, as it would appear in an astronomical telescope. (Courtesy Yerkes Observatory.)

Figure 65. THE MOON 9¾ DAYS AFTER NEW. The moon's western hemisphere is shown about two days after first quarter phase. Note that those relief features nearest the terminator (sunrise line) show to best advantage. (Courtesy Yerkes Observatory.)

125 . . . .

Figure 66. THE MOON AT EIGHTEEN DAYS. The moon's eastern hemisphere is shown several days before last quarter. (Courtesy Yerkes Observatory.)

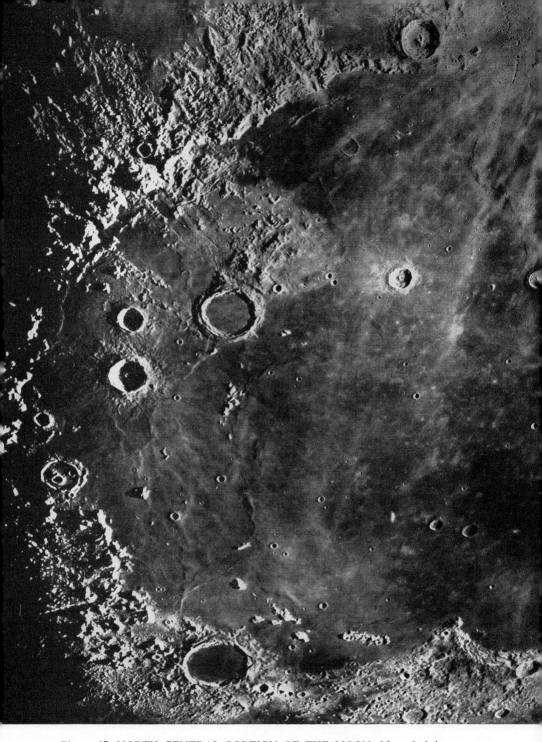

Figure 67. NORTH CENTRAL PORTION OF THE MOON. Mare Imbrium gives the appearance of being one of the flattest regions of the moon. It is ringed by the Appenines (above, left), Caucasus Mts. (extreme left, center), and Alps (lower left). The smooth-floored crater near the bottom is Plato, the one near the center is Archimedes. (Courtesy Yerkes Observatory.)

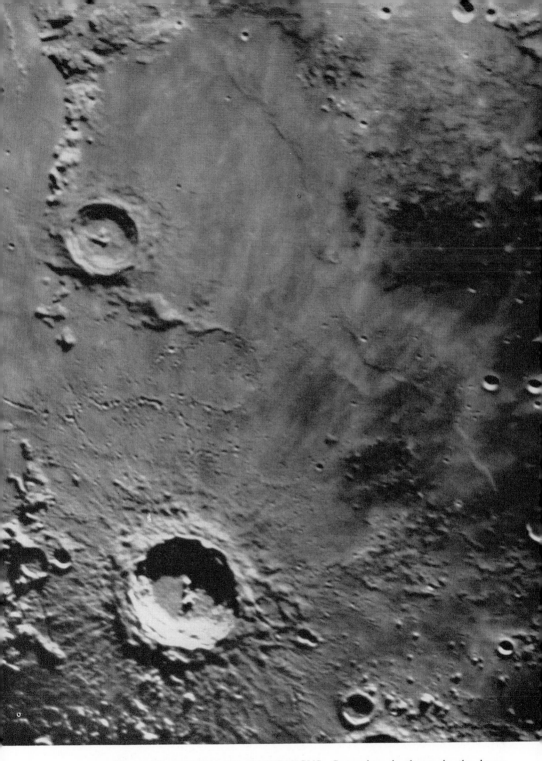

Figure 68. REGION OF COPERNICUS. Copernicus is shown in the lower left; Eratosthenes is above it. Note the drowned crater about midway between them. The ridges which run diagonally across the center of the photograph are presumably a flow pattern in once molten lava. (Mt. Wilson-Palomar Observatories Photo.)

Figure 69. REGION OF CLAVIUS. Clavius, near the center, is the largest crater on the moon. It is near the moon's south pole. (Mt. Wilson-Palomar Observatories Photo.)

niorum (Lake of Dreams). The largest of the maria is Mare Imbrium (Sea of Showers), which in its greatest dimension is about 750 miles across.

Most numerous and characteristic of the moon's features are its craters. The craters are ring-walled pits, usually nearly circular in outline. Though a few of the pits are filled to a level above the surroundings, more than 99 per cent have bottoms below the level of the adjacent surface, some of them thousands of feet lower. It is common to find a peak or group of peaks near the exact center of the crater. The highest such peak rises 7500 feet above the floor of the crater Moretus.

The largest craters are more aptly termed *walled plains,* for they are as large as 146 miles across (the crater Clavius) and greater in area than some of our smaller states such as Maryland or New Jersey. In fact, the rim of Clavius would be below the horizon and therefore invisible to an observer at its center. The walls of such craters commonly have altitudes as great as 20,000 feet. Large craters are relatively shallower than small ones; craters less than 20 miles in diameter have walls whose height is about 10 per cent of the breadth of the crater, whereas the height of the walls of the largest craters may be only 3 per cent of the diameter of the crater.

About 150 craters have diameters of more than 50 miles. Successively smaller craters are increasingly numerous. The smallest that can be seen in the largest telescopes are about one- or two-tenths of a mile across. There are an estimated 200,000 to 1,000,000 craters within reach of the largest telescopes.

Craters occur randomly over all parts of the moon's surface, though less than 10 per cent occur in the comparatively smooth maria. In the rougher regions of the moon, notably the area about the lunar south pole, they exist in profusion, often overlapping. It is commonplace to find smaller craters within or on the rims of larger ones, though the overlapping of craters is never reciprocal.

The 300 to 400 largest, most conspicuous, and most interesting craters have received the names of ancient and medieval astronomers or philosophers. For example, Tycho and Copernicus are present, as well as Plato, Archimedes, and Ptolemy; less familiar are such as Eudoxus, Piccolomini, and Arzachel.

There are on the moon also ten ranges of mountains. Highest among them is the Doerfel range on the moon's rough southern limb. This range has peaks well over 20,000 feet high; comparable terrestrial peaks would have altitudes of more than 15 miles (as compared with Mt. Everest's 5½ miles). Presumably, lunar mountains are well preserved, for they are not subject to erosion as are terrestrial ranges; they are also probably steeper. They differ further in being arcuate and therefore probably not formed by processes like the ones which created linear terrestrial ranges.

A number of lunar mountains are isolated peaks standing in the midst of the lunar plains. Some have been given names. The height of a peak is determined from the length of the shadow it casts. It is a simple matter to calculate the sun's position in the lunar sky at any time and thereby the angle at which a beam of sunlight strikes a peak. For a given angle, there is only one altitude a peak may have and cast a shadow of given length.

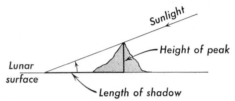

Figure 70. The height of a lunar peak can be found from the length of the shadow it casts.

Comparatively inconspicuous features of the moon's topography are the *clefts*. These are narrow valleys ranging in length from 10 to 300 miles but generally not more than 2 miles wide. They are thus comparable in dimensions with the Grand Canyon. A majority are found in the moon's more elevated areas.

Least common of the moon's relief features are the *fault scarps,* huge embankments rising 1000 to 2000 feet above the adjacent plain and extending as far as 70 miles. They stand out when the sun illuminates the face of the scarp squarely, cast a shadow when illuminated from behind.

Unique to the moon are the *lunar rays.* The rays are streaks on the moon's surface, running almost radially out from several of the craters. Some rays are over 1000 miles in length, but none is more than 10 or 12 miles wide. These odd markings are conspicuously lighter in color than the surrounding surface and extend with little apparent change across maria, mountains, and craters. They are not relief features, for they cast no shadows. The most conspicuous ray systems surround the craters Tycho, Copernicus, and Kepler, probably the last few major craters to have been formed on the moon. The ray systems strongly suggest the blast pattern created by bombs and shells and, more particularly, by small-scale laboratory explosions made expressly for the sake of comparison. They probably consist of splashes of dust.

The rays and the maria—coloration features—are best seen at the time of full moon when the overhead sun casts no delineating shadows and color contrast alone can be appreciated. On the other hand, relief features such as the craters, mountains, clefts, and scarps stand out most boldly at times when they occupy the neighborhood of the terminator; their shadows then show clearly and starkly that they are three-dimensional.

The surface of the moon offers a thoroughgoing contrast with that of the earth. Familiar geological processes will not explain the physiognomy of the moon. What, then, is its orgin? An answer to this question may be sought for in the origin of the craters, which form the dominant feature on the moon.

The term "crater" suggests kinship with terrestrial volcanic cones. It is true that gases in the lunar crust have produced some small blowholes, and some small craterlets appear to be of igneous origin. Nevertheless, not one single example of a true volcanic cone is to be found on the moon.[3] Terrestrial volcanoes are distributed along long, narrow fault zones, lunar craters are distributed randomly. The central peaks of lunar craters never attain the level of the surrounding plain. Only 4 per cent of the large lunar craters have central peaks with summit craters. The peaks of lunar craters are very near the center of the crater; most terrestrial double craters are nonconcentric. And finally, to produce craters of the size of the largest on the moon, forces of a far greater magnitude are required than those which produce terrestrial volcanic craters. Large meteorites provide the only known source of sufficient energy. Let us compare lunar craters with terrestrial meteor craters.

Lunar craters appear much deeper than they really are. In actual proportions they are much like terrestrial meteor craters such as the Arizona Meteor Crater; these latter are nearly always circular, with slightly upraised rims and depressed bottoms. Like the lunar craters, the volume of the rim material is almost the same as the volume of the pit. Lunar craters are surrounded by a jumble of fractured rock and often show radial markings characteristic of an explosion. It therefore seems almost certain that lunar craters are the result of the infall of relatively large solid bodies long ago in the moon's history.

Let us try to imagine the effect upon the surface of the earth or

[3] The discovery of a cloud containing carbon molecules in the vicinity of the crater Alphonsus in 1958 is an observation of highly enigmatic significance. No other authenticated change on the surface of the moon has ever been recorded.

Figure 71. The features marked on this map of the moon's surface may be identified from the key below. (Adapted from drawing, courtesy Adler Planetarium, Chicago Park District.)

Maria	*Craters*	*Craters*
A. Mare Crisium	11. Cleomedes	38. Maginus
B. Mare Fecunditatis	12. Hercules	39. Clavius
C. Mare Nectaris	13. Theophilus	40. Longomontanus
D. Mare Tranquilitatis	14. Catharina	41. Wilhelm I
E. Mare Serenitatis	15. Cyrillus	42. Bullialdus
F. Palus Somnii	16. Maurolycus	43. Landsberg
G. Mare Vaporum	17. Zagut	44. Copernicus
H. Sinus Medii	18. Stofler	45. Timocharis
J. Sinus Aestuum	19. Apianus	46. Aristarchus
K. Mare Imbrium	20. Regiomontanus	47. Kepler
L. Sinus Iridum	21. **Walter**	48. Gassendi
M. Oceanus Procellarum	22. Albategnius	49. Schickard
N. Mare Frigoris	23. Hipparchus	
P. Mare Nubium	24. Pallas	*Mountain*
Q. Sinus Roris	25. Archimedes	*Ranges*
	26. Autolycus	a. Liebnitz
Craters	27. Aristillus	b. Altai
1. Langrenus	28. Eudoxus	c. Pyrenees
2. Proclus	29. Aristoteles	d. Caucasus
3. Taruntius	30. Plato	e. Appenines
4. Petavius	31. Eratosthenes	f. Alps
5. Vendalinus	32. Lalande	g. Haemus
6. Frascatorius	33. Ptolemy	h. Carpathian
7. Piccolomini	34. Alphonsus	j. Riphaean
8. Posidonius	35. Arzachel	k. Cordilleras
9. Plinius	36. Purbach	l. d'Alembert
10. Macrobius	37. Tycho	m. Taurus

moon of the impact of a body a mile or so in diameter. It would be brought to rest in a fraction of a second. If its speed were 4 miles per second, its energy of motion would be six times that of an equal weight of high explosive. This enormous energy could not immediately be imparted to the surrounding surface; the meteorite and the column of material just beneath it would become extremely compressed and very hot. It would therefore explode with enormous violence, casting debris far and wide, possibly rebounding elastically to form a central peak. The explosion of inert missiles with impact velocities of 4 to 5 miles per second, for example, has been demonstrated experimentally. The fact that such a collision produces an explosion would inevitably imply a nearly round crater even though the fall of the object may not have been vertical.

The size of the meteorites needed to produce large craters is comparatively modest. The object which produced the Arizona Meteor Crater was probably less than 50 feet in diameter; to create a crater 80 miles across, a meteorite not over half a mile in diameter would be needed. These dimensions are less than those of the smallest known asteroids (see p. 175).

An especially large meteorite—up to 100 miles in diameter, say— might have a somewhat different effect than simply producing a correspondingly larger crater. Its deceleration would not be so sudden, its penetration would be somewhat greater, and its kinetic energy would be transformed into heat that could raise the material to a temperature of several thousand degrees Fahrenheit. In this way, a comparatively large amount of molten matter would be created. The symmetric outward advance of plastic lava, engulfing and dissolving nearly all pre-existing surface features, would result in mare-like areas. Their limits of flow would be marked by piles of unassimilated debris, the lunar mountain ranges. The maria could reasonably be expected to be more or less round in shape. High-velocity fragments of the collision would cleave deep gashes in the environs; significantly, the clefts about Mare Imbrium are distributed radially with respect to its center. The events which shaped the surface of the moon must have taken place long ago, early in the history of earth and moon.

The moon must have formed as a cold body, not a molten one, for if the moon had once been molten, it would have retained enough heat at its center that it could not now be rigid there. It would thus be unable to support the weight of its present tidal bulge and would have long since adjusted its shape to be in equilibrium with present tidal forces.

Major changes on the surface of the moon are a thing of the distant past. Only two rather minor weathering agents can be working slow changes on the moon. One is a cracking of the surface materials because of extreme and rapid temperature changes. The other is meteoric bombardment, which there is no atmosphere to prevent. The two have probably covered the moon with a layer of dust. This would explain its low reflecting power (7 per cent) and its slower-than-expected rate of cooling during a lunar eclipse.

Artificial Satellites

Since October 4, 1957, the earth has possessed a variable number of artificial satellites. These have been launched by rockets to heights of 100 or more miles, where they have then been given the final impulse which would place them in some desired orbit. All thus far have had limited life expectancies, none exceeding about 100 years; several expired within a few months' time.

Such satellites are of astronomical interest for several reasons. First, they are forerunners of vehicles for extraterrestrial research; the photograph of the moon's far side is a vivid illustration of their value in this respect. Secondly, the satellites provide new information about the earth as an astronomical body. Perturbations of satellite orbits have given the most accurate measure of earth's equatorial bulge (see p. 43), have suggested that the north polar radius exceeds the south polar radius by 100 feet.

Artificial satellites have given new data on interplanetary dust, solar radiations and corpuscles, and the importance of solar radiation pressure in perturbing the orbits of small bodies. It would be difficult to estimate or exaggerate the potential value of artificial satellites to astronomers in the near future.

QUESTIONS

1. What is the moon's relative orbit with respect to the earth? What is the moon's orbital motion with respect to the sun? Which body dominates the moon's motion? How can the paths of both the earth and the moon be always concave toward the sun?
2. Demonstrate how the moon can rotate on its axis and yet keep the same face always toward the earth. From the earth, what would be the moon's apparent behavior if it did not rotate? If it rotated in the opposite direction?
3. By means of a sketch, show how the phases of the moon come about. There is a small difference between first quarter of the moon and eastern quadrature. Why?
4. What are librations? What additional amount of the moon's surface is made visible by them? What is their explanation? What would be necessary if the moon were to show no longitudinal librations? No latitudinal librations?

5. Why does the strength of earthlight on the moon steadily decrease as the moon waxes?

6. How many diurnal revolutions does the sun make in one synodic period of the moon? How many apparent revolutions does the moon make in the same time? From these, determine the average daily delay in moonrise.

7. Why is the daily delay of the moon's times of transit variable? What additional factor affects the moon's daily delay in rising time? When is the delay a minimum for the full moon? Why? When is the delay a minimum at first quarter?

8. Why does a solar eclipse not occur each new moon? What are the conditions necessary for a solar eclipse? A lunar eclipse? Indicate why, as a result of these conditions, the minimum number of solar eclipses per year is two, the maximum five. Show how the number of lunar eclipses may be none to three. How many of each kind will there be in the current year?

9. Assuming that both the sun and moon have an angular radius of $\frac{1}{4}$ degree, what is the greatest inclination of the moon's orbit to the ecliptic which would require solar and lunar eclipses every month?

10. If the nodes of the moon's orbit remained stationary, what would be the length of the eclipse year? What would be the maximum number of solar eclipses possible in one year? Lunar eclipses? All eclipses?

11. If the earth and moon were as close to the sun as Venus, there would be no total solar eclipses. Why?

12. What are the various parts of the shadow cast by the earth and moon? Describe the kind of eclipse witnessed in each.

13. What type of solar eclipse is most common? Why? What type of solar eclipse is most widely seen? What conditions are most favorable for a total solar eclipse? An annular solar eclipse? Why are there no annular lunar eclipses?

14. Describe the progress of a total or annular solar eclipse across the face of the earth. What is the maximum width of the eclipse path? What is the maximum duration of totality?

15. Describe the progress of a lunar eclipse. What is the maximum duration of totality? Why is a total lunar eclipse seen more often than a total solar eclipse even though total lunar eclipses occur less often?

16. Explain the saros and its usefulness. Why do individual cycles not continue indefinitely? Calculate the dates of the next three total eclipses in the cycle containing the eclipse of June 8, 1937. If this eclipse was seen in longitude 130° W, determine the approximate longitudes in which the eclipses of the three calculated dates will be visible.

17. Determine the distance of an object which subtends a parallax of 25′ from a base line of 6 feet. Assuming that one's eyes are 3 inches apart, what is the parallax of an object 100 feet away?

18. By what procedure can the moon's parallax be measured? How great is it?

19. Find the linear diameter of an object whose angular diameter is $\frac{1}{3}$° at 1000 feet. At what distance will a button of $\frac{1}{2}$-inch diameter have the same angular diameter as the moon?

20. How is determining the mass of the moon like weighing with a beam scale?
21. What observations indicate that the moon has no atmosphere? Why does it not? List the various ways in which the conditions on a body with no atmosphere would differ notably from conditions on the earth. What special difficulties will the first lunar explorers have to anticipate?
22. Describe the principal categories of lunar surface features. Under what conditions of illumination may each be seen best? Which have terrestrial counterparts and which are probably unique to the moon? Summarize the evidence that the lunar craters are of meteoric origin.

chapter 4
The Planets and
Their Satellites

• • •

"Fools have said
That knowledge drives out wonder from the world;
They'll say it still, though all the dust's ablaze
With miracles at their feet."

—NOYES

Mercury

The planet Mercury is named for the messenger of the Olympian gods, and his caduceus or wand has been conventionalized to ☿ , the planet's symbol. The namesake is, aptly, the swiftest of the planets, for it is the nearest to the sun; its orbital velocity varies from 36 to 23 miles per second as its distance from the sun varies from 28½ million miles at perihelion to 43½ million miles at aphelion.

For so small an orbit (the mean distance of Mercury is 0.39 astronomical unit) this range of distance from the sun is very considerable, indicating a fairly eccentric orbit. In fact, Mercury's eccentricity of 0.2056 is appreciably more than that for any other planet except Pluto. Mercury speeds once around the sun in 88 days, a little less than 3 months. It will therefore seem to us to swing back and forth about the sun in 116 days, its synodic period. Half of this time it will be a morning star, the other half an evening star. Some of the ancients did not realize that these morning and evening "stars" were one and the same and called the planet Mercury when seen after sunset, Apollo when seen before dawn.

The large eccentricity of Mercury's orbit is responsible for Mercury's maximum elongation varying from 18° to 28°, depending on whether maximum elongation occurs at the time of Mercury's perihelion or aphelion. For example, Mercury was at greatest eastern elongation on February 21, 1947. Since perihelion occurred only 15 hours before, this elongation was one of the most unfavorable, amounting to only 18°7′. The following April

5 it was at greatest western elongation, 27°48′ from the sun, and those who rose a little before dawn could have seen it low in the southeast.

It is plain that this little planet is elusive, never straying far from the blinding sun in whose glare it hides most of the time. As a result, comparatively few people have ever seen Mercury, although at times it appears brighter than any of the stars we see in this latitude save one (Sirius). For visual observation, the necessary trick is a knowledge of when and where to look, information readily gotten from the *American Ephemeris and Nautical Almanac*.

Telescopic observations of the planet are usually made in broad daylight, for it can then be studied at its greatest height above the horizon. Surface markings are not pronounced and are very difficult to detect, for when the planet is nearest the earth, we see practically none of the illuminated half of its surface. Even at such times it is 50,000,000 miles or more from us, and its disk has an apparent diameter of only 13 seconds of arc. Most observations have to be taken under considerably less favorable circumstances.

Observations made in spite of these difficulties indicate, according to the most reliable observers, that Mercury rotates counterclockwise on an axis which is nearly perpendicular to its orbital plane. Its period of rotation seems to be exactly that of its period of revolution, 88 days. Therefore, just as the moon keeps one face toward the earth, Mercury must keep the same face toward the sun. Again, as with the moon, Mercury experiences librations in longitude, but they are much greater since the eccentricity of Mercury's orbit is much greater than that of the moon's. The librations amount to 23°7 about Mercury's mean orientation, so that the sun never sets over 132°6 of longitude, sometimes sets over two zones of 47°4 width in longitude; there is perpetual night over the remaining 132°6 of longitude. Imagine how strange it would seem to have the sun rise slowly in the east so that after three weeks it would reach a height corresponding approximately to its position at midmorning in our sky. Stranger yet would be the sight of its setting then, again in the east. This is what a Mercurian would see in one of the 47°-zones; in the other he could watch the sun rise and set slowly in the west.

Because Mercury's equator is so nearly in the plane of its orbit, the sun will appear to move north or south hardly at all in the course of a revolution, and seasons cannot be brought about as they are on earth. Yet there will be seasons of a sort, for at aphelion Mercury is half again as far from the sun as at perihelion and the sun's radiation will therefore be less than half as intense as it was at perihelion.

However, it is unlikely that we would enjoy the Mercurian climate on the sunlit side at any season. In winter it is very hot, in summer very much hotter. Mercury at its mean distance receives $6\frac{2}{3}$ times as much solar radiation per square foot as does the earth. This and the fact that one face is always toward the sun make it very credible that the temperature of Mercury in the center of the sunlit side is higher than that of any other planet, estimated as about $+770°$ F at perihelion, at which temperature lead would be molten. In extreme contrast, the temperature of the side away from the sun must be extremely low, not much above absolute zero,[1] i.e., some 300 to 400 degrees below Fahrenheit. Thus, very possibly Mercury is both the hottest and the coldest of the planets. Not even distant Pluto is as cold as the perpetually dark face of Mercury. Though some heat from the very hot face of Mercury will be conducted to the very cold face, thereby diminishing both extremes, the amount of heat conducted from the one side to the other must be very small, since it must flow through the body of the planet itself.

There is little or no atmosphere whose currents could rapidly transport heat as well as temper by reflection and absorption. Thus we see no diffusion or refraction effects which we might expect to see at inferior conjunction if Mercury were surrounded by a layer of gases. Then, too, Mercury's velocity of escape is only about $2\frac{1}{2}$ miles per second, since its surface gravity is only about a third the earth's. This is quite certainly not great enough to hold permanently most of the more rapidly moving atoms and molecules of a much hotter atmosphere which the planet may have once possessed. An occasional faint haze suggests, however, that small amounts of a few of the heavier gases may constitute a Mercurian atmosphere which is less than 0.003 times as dense as the earth's.

Our estimation of the surface gravity of Mercury presumes a knowledge of the mass and diameter of the planet. Its diameter is 3100 miles, a figure easily obtained, since its distance and apparent angular diameter are known. The mass is more difficult to determine, for it has to be estimated from the small effects of Mercury's feeble pull on Venus or on an occasional comet or planetoid. The best guess at present gives Mercury a mass one-eighteenth of the earth's, whence its average density is 5.46 times that of water.

---

[1] Absolute zero is the lowest conceivable temperature. Physicists have been able to achieve temperatures within a few thousandths of a degree of absolute zero but have never attained absolute zero itself, which is at $-459°$ F.

Of scientific interest are Mercury's transits of the sun. A transit is a passage of the planet across the disk of the sun. As in the case of our own moon, a transit does not occur at every inferior conjunction but only at those when the sun is near a node (in May or November), again because of orbital inclination. There are 13 transits per century on the average, but they are not evenly spaced; the intervals between transits at any one node are 7, 13, and 46 years, since these intervals very nearly contain 22, 41, and 145 synodic periods, respectively. The last transit of Mercury was on November 7, 1960; the next will be on May 9, 1970. Transits of Mercury and Venus are of scientific interest because they offer a means of determining accurately the positions, and hence the motions, of these planets.

The motion of Mercury was for a long time puzzling in one detail. The axis of its orbit was observed to turn slowly, advancing the position of its perihelion by about 574″ per century, some 43″ per century more than could be accounted for. This phenomenon is now explained by the theory of relativity, which predicts almost exactly the observed rate of advance over what can be expected from the perturbations of the other planets. The motion of Mercury thus offers one of the few instances [2] of an observable divergence between classical and relativistic mechanics; it gave the first observational confirmation of the relativity theory.

Venus

Venus, namesake of the goddess of beauty, has been given the symbol ♀ representing a looking glass, perhaps on the strength of the apothegm "Vanity, thy name is woman." [3] As an inner planet, it will appear to swing back and forth about the sun. For 220 days (over seven months) after superior conjunction, it works slowly east of the sun in the sky until it is at its maximum eastern elongation of 48°. Then, in a brief 72 days, it moves west to inferior conjunction, on to greatest western elongation in another 72 days, then slowly back to superior conjunction in 220 days more, the whole requiring 584 days, its synodic period. We see that Venus alternates every 292 days between roles of morning and evening

---

[2] Venus' motion will not do because the orbit of Venus is so nearly circular that the position of perihelion cannot be determined accurately enough. In recent years, a slow (4 seconds of arc per century) relativistic advance of the earth's perihelion has been detected. There is also prospect of noting the effect in Mars' motion. For the more distant planets, however, the effect is too small to observe, since it decreases with distance from the sun.

[3] With apologies to Shakespeare.

"star." Like Mercury, Venus was in consequence given a split personality by the ancients, being Phosphorus before dawn, Hesperus after sundown.

Though at first surprising, it is obvious why Venus requires more than three times longer to go from greatest western elongation to greatest eastern elongation than it requires to return; it has really that many more miles to go, as can be seen from Fig. 40. The arc traversed in going from western to eastern maximum elongation is considerably longer than that traversed from eastern to western maximum elongation.

Like Mercury, Venus shows all phases from new at inferior conjunction to full at superior conjunction. Also like Mercury, but unlike the moon, its distance from the earth varies greatly as the phases change. Unfortunately we see little or none of its illuminated face when it is nearest us, see the whole of it only when it is farthest from us. The two effects of varying phase and simultaneously varying distance evidently work at cross-purposes, with the result that Venus appears brightest to us 36 days before or after inferior conjunction.

At its brightest, Venus may be seen in broad daylight by anyone who knows where to look. It is then 15 times brighter than Sirius, the apparently brightest star in the sky, and is capable of casting a noticeable shadow after dark. It is the brightest of the planets.

At inferior conjunction Venus comes nearer the earth than any other planet, being then only 26 million miles from us. Its mean distance from the sun is 67 million miles. The eccentricity of its orbit, 0.0068, is the smallest of any. The mass of Venus has been determined, by methods similar to those used on Mercury, to be 0.81 as great as the earth's. With a diameter of 7700 miles it thus has a surface gravity 90 per cent as great as the earth's, a density of 5.1.

Aside from its phases, Venus shows little of interest in the telescope. Only the most skilled observers have been able to detect any markings on its dazzling silvery disk, and these are ill defined and impermanent. These vague markings show much more distinctly on photographs taken in ultraviolet light. Because these markings are temporary and since ultraviolet light is unable to penetrate a layer of gas to any appreciable depth, it has been concluded that Venus is surrounded by a cloud-covered atmosphere. The photographs register clouds in the upper layers of the atmosphere.

The presence of an atmosphere on Venus is also shown in another way. Near inferior conjunction the horns of the crescent planet extend more than halfway around it, forming a complete ring when Venus is

Figure 72. VENUS. This photograph shows Venus in the crescent phase. The photograph was taken in blue light and shows the absence of surface markings. (Mt. Wilson-Palomar Observatories Photo.)

very near the sun in our sky. This ring is the result of diffusion in the planet's atmosphere.

A spectroscopic analysis (pp. 222–25) of the composition of the atmosphere of Venus above its cloud layer indicates that there cannot be even a thousandth as much free oxygen or a tenth as much water vapor as in the earth's atmosphere. However, carbon dioxide is abundant in comparison. Faint atmospheric airglow indicates the presence of molecular nitrogen (N_2) and the color of sunlight that has penetrated Venus' atmos-

143 . . . .

phere gives a strong indication of the presence of nitrogen tetroxide (N_2O_4).

Since at Venus' distance from the sun, sunlight is twice as intense as it is at the earth, the temperature may be expected to be somewhat higher than on the earth. Measurements of the heat received from Venus show that the temperature of the visible layer must be about $-10°$ F as compared with a temperature of about $-65°$ F at the top of our own stratosphere. This suggests that the Venusian clouds may be of crystals of nitrogen tetroxide, which takes the form of white granules at temperatures below $-13°$ F. In support of this suggestion is the observation that the clouds of Venus are not as white as clouds of water crystals or droplets; solid nitrogen tetroxide becomes yellow in color as its temperature is raised.

Because of the perpetual clouds, the surface of Venus has never been seen, and one can only speculate as to the specific conditions there. The strength of radio wavelength radiation seems to imply a surface temperature of about $600°$ F. Such a high temperature may be achieved because oxygen, which prevents the sun's ultraviolet radiation from reaching the earth's surface, is scarce on Venus, and at the same time the re-radiated infrared radiation of the planet is efficiently trapped by carbon dioxide, abundant on Venus but present only in small quantities in the earth's atmosphere. The high surface temperature undoubtedly explains the scarcity of oxygen in Venus' atmosphere, for oxygen readily enters into chemical combination with most other elements, and the rate of its reaction is greatly accelerated by high temperatures. It may therefore be that conditions on Venus have resulted in the removal of free oxygen from its atmosphere by the extensive formation of oxides. The earth, too, might be in this predicament but for the action of plants which release oxygen in the process of photosynthesis.

Temperature measurements of the light and the dark sides of Venus give the same result for both. This may indicate that Venus does not keep one face turned sunward, like Mercury. If this is the case, its period of rotation cannot be as great as 225 days, its sidereal period of revolution. On the other hand, it cannot rotate in less than two or three weeks because its atmosphere does not, as shown by the motion of the cloud markings. The true period is unknown.

The fact that Venus is so nearly like the earth in size, mass, density, gravity, and the possession of an atmosphere has earned it the name "the earth's twin." For all we know, the climate on parts of Venus may be comparable to that of some of the earth's desert regions, though probably it is much hotter. Next to the earth and Mars (p. 145), Venus seems to be the planet most congenial to life, though to be sure any organism on that planet would have to be adapted to the scarcity of oxygen and water vapor and the abundance of carbon dioxide. But of the weather on Venus we are certain; the prediction is monotonously "windy and cloudy today and tomorrow."

Much less frequently than Mercury, Venus transits the sun. These transits currently occur in pairs, one pair per century, on the average. A transit always takes place within a day or so of June 7 or December 9. The last pair occurred in 1874 and 1882; the next will be on June 8, 2004, and June 5, 2012. With only a smoked glass, the interested reader can then observe them.

Earth

The next planet in order is the earth, about which little more need be said. Its symbol ⊕ represents a sphere with meridian and equator. As a planet it is noteworthy for its sustaining life and for the fact that its mean density of 5.5 is the greatest of any of the planets. It has also the satellite which is the largest in comparison to its primary.

Mars

Ruddy Mars, named for the bloody god of war, has the symbol ♂, a shield and spear. Of all astronomical bodies, Mars is the object of greatest popular interest because of the question of the possibility of its supporting some form of life. This subject has been greatly capitalized upon in pseudo-scientific fiction. The most outstanding instance of its hold on the public mind is to be found, of course, in any account of the serio-comic reactions to Orson Welles' broadcast of 1938, "The Men from Mars."

Inasmuch as it is an outer planet, Mars is best seen from the earth at the times of its opposition, when it is nearest us. It may then be brighter than any planet but Venus. Oppositions of Mars occur every 780 days (2 years, 50 days), its synodic period. In spite of the fact that at its nearest to earth Mars lacks nearly 9 million miles of coming as close as Venus, it is nonetheless the best observed of any of the planets; Venus is at "new" phase when nearest, and we can see nothing of it. Mars, of course, does not show all phases like Venus but does appear decidedly gibbous at times. Mars shows the least percentage of illumination when at quadrature; from Mars the earth would then appear at its greatest elongation of 47°.

Not all oppositions of Mars are equally advantageous. Mars' orbit is rather eccentric ($e = 0.0933$) as planets' orbits go, and an opposition which occurs at the time of Mars' perihelion is markedly more favorable than one at the time of its aphelion. In fact, Mars' opposition distance can vary from 34,600,000 miles to 62,900,000 miles—by nearly a factor of two—on this account. The most favorable oppositions occur at in-

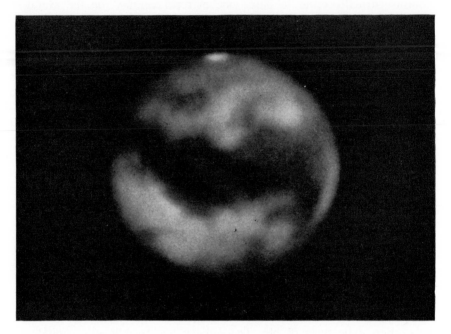

Figure 73. MARS. This photograph of Mars is made from a composite of eleven negatives taken of the planet in 1941 at the Pic-du-Midi Observatory in France. It shows clearly the large surface markings as well as a polar cap. (Courtesy B. Lyot.)

tervals of 15 or 17 years (as in 1939, 1956, 1971) and always in August or September, for the earth is nearest Mars' perihelion on August 28. Unfortunately, Mars will be south of the celestial equator at any August opposition, to the disadvantage of observers in the northern hemisphere where most of the large observatories and telescopes are located.

Useful telescopic observations of Mars extend back to 1666 and have made possible the measurement of its period of rotation, accurate to a few hundredths of a second. It has been found to rotate eastward in $24^h 37^m 22\overset{s}{.}7$; this is only $41\frac{1}{2}$ minutes longer than the earth's period of rotation. Not so accurately determinable is the inclination of its equator to the plane of its orbit. It is about $24°$, again strikingly like the earth's.

The Martian pole star is Deneb, just as ours will be in A.D. 9000 because of precession.

With an equatorial inclination so nearly like ours, Mars will have climatic zones and seasons (but not climate!) almost exactly like ours. The Martian seasons will be nearly twice as long, however, for Mars'

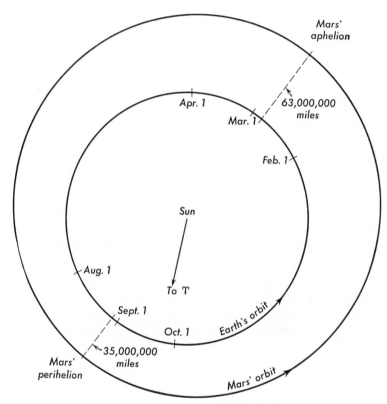

Figure 74. Mars comes nearer to the position which the earth occupies in late August than to any other.

sidereal period is 687 days. And whereas the earth's small variations in distance from the sun produce no noticeable effect on our seasons, Mars' much greater change of distance causes more extreme summers and winters in its southern hemisphere. It also makes the seasons more unequal in length; in the southern hemisphere spring is 199 days, summer 182 days, fall 146 days, and winter 160 days.

At Mars' nearest, its apparent diameter is 25 seconds of arc; its linear diameter must therefore be 4215 miles (with an uncertainty of not over 10 miles). Its mass is much more easily determined than were the masses of Mercury or Venus, for Mars possesses two satellites. From knowledge of the motion of either of these satellites it is a relatively simple matter to determine the gravitational acceleration which Mars produces at their respective distances. There is only one mass which could produce the observed acceleration; a greater mass would produce more, a smaller mass less. By such a method it is found that Mars has a mass of 0.11 the mass of the earth. From the known mass and diameter of Mars we find that its density must be 4.1, its surface gravity 0.38 as much as ours.

From Mars' mass and radius it is also possible to determine that the velocity of escape is just over 3 miles per second. Though less than half the earth's and only twice the moon's, it is sufficient to guarantee Mars some atmosphere. Even so, the light constituents such as hydrogen and helium will have long since taken their leave. Nonetheless, the existence of a Martian twilight zone and the presence of occasional clouds give evidence that the planet does possess a blanket of gases.

Most of the information on the composition of the Martian atmosphere is negative. There is no trace of water vapor, implying that water cannot have an abundance as great as 0.15 per cent of that in the earth's atmosphere. The more sensitive test for oxygen is even more emphatic; the abundance of oxygen on Mars must be less than a thousandth of what it is on earth. Carbon dioxide, however, is thought to be twice as abundant as in the earth's atmosphere.

The Martian atmosphere is thin. It is estimated that the mass of atmosphere above unit surface area is only one-fourth of that above the same area of the earth. The sparsity of the Martian atmosphere is demonstrated by the rapidity with which occulted stars are cut off; they disappear much more gradually behind planets with extended atmospheres, such as Jupiter. It follows that the atmospheric pressure on Mars is only 10 or 15 per cent of what it is on the earth.

The thinness of Mars' atmosphere makes it possible to see the planet's surface distinctly. This is really an exceptional state of affairs; Mercury is the only other planet whose solid surface is visible. Three-fourths of the surface is a bright reddish or orange color. The character of the light reflected from it suggests that it is a mixture of silicates colored by mineral impurities and a ferrous oxide known as limonite. The comparison to terrestrial deserts at once comes to mind. Overall, the surface is comparatively smooth; there are no high mountain ranges.

The remainder of Mars' surface consists of darker areas concentrated for the most part in the vicinity of the equator. They are not of uniform color and have been variously described as blue, green, brown, gray, and black. They are about half as bright as the deserts. Failure to observe bright reflected sunlight from them shows that they are not bodies of water. This fact has not prevented their receiving a nomenclature as fanciful and inappropriate as that of the moon. The Latin names designate seas, bays, lakes, channels, and swamps. The thought of a planet with no oceans dividing land masses into continents is an odd one to inhabitants of the earth.

During the cycle of the Martian seasons there is an alternate advance and retreat of the two Martian polar caps. Either polar cap can creep equatorward to latitudes as low as 40°, the approximate terrestrial latitude of Chicago, New York, Madrid, or Rome. At its maximum, a cap may cover some 4 million square miles. The south polar cap becomes both larger and smaller than the north polar cap, clear evidence of the more extreme climatic conditions in this hemisphere.

Each cap forms in the fall under a cloud blanket. It is assuredly thin, else it could not be melted during the summer. If composed of water, the substance of a polar cap would not fill Lake Erie. Each cap disappears in almost the same way every spring and summer, shrinking and splitting at the same time. The characteristic rifts and fragments probably indicate surface features of different levels, the last-disappearing being colder plateaus. A melting polar cap is outlined by a dark fringe of discontinuous fragments, presumably puddles of some sort.

Mars receives on the average only 43 per cent as much sunlight per unit area as the earth. We therefore expect to find for it a lower temperature. On the average, temperatures on Mars are about 90 or 100 degrees below those of the corresponding points on the earth's surface. The noonday temperature in the Martian tropics may rise to 50° F to 70° F. The poles must attain a temperature above the freezing point in midsummer. In winter, however, the temperature of the polar caps is below −110° F. All temperatures are about 50 degrees lower at aphelion than at perihelion.

Because of the thinness of Mars' atmosphere, there is very little atmospheric blanketing. This makes for a daily temperature range of 150° F or so. The temperature falls rapidly after noon; the nighttime low may drop to −130° F. Mars' climate has been well described as like that of "a terrestrial desert shifted to the polar regions and lifted to stratospheric level."

Mars' equator is bulged by 1 part in 192. This indicates that Mars is not as concentrated toward its center as is the earth; i.e., it is more homogeneous.

Such is a description of the general facts and features of the planet Mars. To these must be added mention of the markings known as canals, discovered at the favorable opposition of 1877 by the Italian astronomer Schiaparelli. They were first seen as a network of fine lines or streaks upon the reddish desert areas. They crisscrossed the face of the planet along straight courses quite unlike those of streams or rivers. Some of these channels (which is the preferable English equivalent of Schiaparelli's term *canali*) were plainly visible, whereas others were of such fineness as to tax the most skilled observer. Their respective breadths must range from 100 to 200 miles down to perhaps 20 miles. Their length and configuration were constant, but the clarity with which they could be seen appeared to vary capriciously from week to week. Curiously, they intersected one another at all variety of angles, and at their intersections there were usually small dark areas, since called *oases*. Every channel originated and terminated in what was then thought to be a sea, lake, or another channel; none broke off in middesert.

At the time of the melting of the polar cap in either hemisphere, arterial channels appear as extensions of the rifts of the retreating polar cap. They darken and press toward the equator at a rate of 50 miles a day, ultimately crossing into the opposite hemisphere. At the same time, many of them undergo a doubling or *gemination;* two parallel canals appear where there had been one. Gemination does not occur simultaneously for all those canals which show the phenomenon, and in different years the second canal may have a different width, intensity, and configuration. The distance between geminate canals ranges from 30 to 300 or 400 miles.

Seasonal changes in the color and form of the dark areas provided one of the first evidences that these areas were not bodies of water, as had been assumed. It was concluded that they were areas of vegetation, for with the approach of summer they changed from a lighter to a darker green, then to yellow and brown. Some changes of a nonseasonal character were also observed. The desert areas remained almost immutable.

Such highly suggestive results encouraged the American astronomer Percival Lowell to advocate the thesis of intelligent life upon the planet Mars. Schiaparelli had already noted, after observing the canals, that "their singular aspect, and their being drawn with absolute geometrical precision, as if they were the work of rule or compass, had led some to see in them the work of intelligent beings." Lowell provided the motive for the canals' construction by calling attention to the scarcity of water on the planet. He noted that the low velocity of escape meant the inexorable depletion of water, a process already far advanced. Only intelligent beings capable of abstract concern could attempt to offset the tide of events with a countermeasure such as a monumental network of artificial watercourses to convey the remaining small reserves of water from their sources in the polar caps to the habitable, arable equatorial regions. The entire economy of the planet must be addressed to the conservation and maximum utilization of the remaining scanty supply of water. To this end, a vast pumping system forces water of the polar cap through the canals and beyond the equator; it must be inferred from this that the Martians are engineers of great skill. As the water becomes available each spring, vegetation flourishes along the canals in a pattern that spreads from pole to equator. Oases like those of our own deserts thrive at the points of distribution.

Lowell's proposition that on Mars there are kindred beings, engaged in a heroic rear-guard action against the forces of a hostile environment has had a curiously intense and widespread appeal. As a result, other explanations of Martian phenomena have tended to languish; the uncertainties in the observational basis of Lowell's theory have not always been as keenly appreciated as the theory has been enthusiastically embraced. What reservations are there?

First, it should be admitted that the observations themselves are of such delicacy that they cannot be considered firmly established or even established at all. Optimum circumstances for observing the planet are limited to only a few months every two years. Even then, Mars appears no larger in a telescope of 75 times magnification than the moon does to the naked eye; the very best view of Mars is no better than that of the moon with a low-power binoculars.

It should be remembered, too, that most features on the Martian surface are accessible to observation for no more than two weeks continuously. Because of Mars' slightly longer day, the hemisphere it presents to view slowly regresses from view at any given hour on the earth, and observation of a particular marking may be interrupted for nearly a month. This factor, in combination with the short useful observing season, implies that to observe a complete cycle of Martian seasons under optimum conditions would require at least 15 years to accomplish. Since much of what the observer hopes to see is at the limit of vision, it is fair to say that it is difficult to follow the particulars of the seasonal cycle on Mars. Lowell's description is not abundantly confirmed.

Even a lingering hope that Mars may nevertheless support vegetation, thereby accounting for seasonal changes of color, has no positive evidence to sustain it. The color from the dark equatorial regions is not what one would expect from green chlorophyll-bearing plants. Martian plant life, if there is any, must be of a low order or of a type quite unlike any on the earth.

The case for the canals is at once better and worse. The existence of some such markings is reasonably well established. Some of the most prominent canals have even been photographed, though the slowness of the photographic plate puts it at a great disadvantage to the retina of a skilled observer. It must therefore be counted heavily against Lowell's theory that some of the most skilled observers fail to see these markings as Lowell did; indeed, with telescopes of aperture greater than 30 inches, the canals are lost. The best prevailing opinion is that the canals are not a crisp, artificial web but a broad, diffuse, disjointed network probably of natural origin. Even Schiaparelli, first to see the canals, said of the theory of the canals' artificial origin that "the examination of these ingenious suppositions leads us to conclude that none of them seems to correspond entirely with the observed facts."

An alternative to the theory of life on Mars has been based upon an ingenious analysis of the Martian surface markings and weather conditions. It has been noted that the absence of oceans on the planet should ensure a prevailing wind pattern not modified by large bodies of water, as on the earth. The entire equatorial regions would thus experience summer monsoons. The more extreme summers and the greater proportion of dark areas in the southern hemisphere would make this season's wind pattern the dominant one. It is these winds which provide the only important weathering agent on a planet with little or no water. The sustained deposition of dust by such a stable wind system might well have created the features of Mars' surface. Why are these features not permanent and uniform? It is further supposed that much of the dust deposited by the Martian monsoons is injected by active volcanoes. Numerous, pointed, dark bays are seen as the deltas of these aeolian rivers; the canals are the airborne plumes from erupting volcanoes. The unpredictability of volcanic activity and the seasonal shifting of the wind belts are presumed to account for most of the other changes that we witness from the earth.

At best, such a theory seems to be no more than a partial answer to the riddle of Martian phenomena, for the present Martian atmosphere is probably too thin to hold any considerable quantity of dust in suspension long enough to deposit it a great distance away. Mars' surface may quite possibly have come about in such a fashion long ago, however. The theory of wind-distributed volcanic ash may thus very well complement yet another theory, which rests upon a spectroscopic analysis of the light from Mars; the latter theory accounts for many of the observations by invoking the presence of various oxides of nitrogen in Mars' atmosphere.

As we have already seen, such oxides are thought to exist in the atmosphere of Venus. They are believed to arise largely by default: All the more active chemical elements have already combined to such an extent that the surface materials are thoroughly oxidized. Yet even after such a state of complete oxidation had been reached, an excess of oxygen remained, possibly augmented by oxygen molecules derived from the dissociation of water vapor by the action of ultraviolet sunlight. Since the hydrogen molecules set free by the photodissociative process would ultimately escape, the oxygen had no other recourse than to form compounds with nitrogen, which is presumably a major constituent of all planetary atmospheres. The most likely compound is nitrogen peroxide, a mixture of nitrogen dioxide (NO_2) and nitrogen tetroxide (N_2O_4). The light reflected from Mars is deficient in blue and violet light in just such a way as might be expected after it had passed through an atmosphere containing nitrogen tetroxide.

Many of the particulars of the Martian phenomena can be readily explained in terms of the properties of nitrogen peroxide. It is known, for example, that the polar caps reflect only 60 per cent as much light as thick fresh snow. It has been inferred from this that they are thin, but it might better be concluded that they are not snow; instead they may well be solid nitrogen tetroxide, which above $-40°$ F is a chalk-white tinged with yellow. At lower temperatures it is tinged with greenish-blue, at higher temperatures tending to dissociate into the dioxide, which is successively yellow and brown.

As a polar cap melts, the nitrogen tetroxide melts, becomes darker and flows toward the equator along clefts seen as canals. The dark line which surrounds the polar cap is a belt of melting peroxide, narrow because the melting and boiling points are not far apart. The equator presents no barrier because the gas is propelled from pole to pole by a difference of vapor pressure. As it passes over old mineral deposits (possibly of volcanic origin), it changes their colors by the formation of reversible addition compounds; the suggestion of such inorganic origin of the seasonal color changes was made as early as 1918.

The occasional Martian clouds also receive a consistent explanation. The atmosphere contains both crystals and vapor of the oxides of nitrogen. When their concentration is sufficient in the high, cold levels of the atmosphere, a white or bluish cloud will form. Such clouds are seen at altitudes as great as 12 miles and are the most frequent at the times of Mars' aphelion when its average temperature is lowest. During cold spells, the vapor is condensed out nearly completely and the atmosphere becomes very clear, just as our own does in the most bitter weather. At such times Mars' surface may be seen in blue light as well as red.

There are also yellow clouds over Mars which hover near its surface. These have been taken to be dust clouds from the deserts; more probably they are clouds of yellow nitrogen dioxide. As we would expect if the latter were true, they are found most often during warm weather, are commonest at Mars' perihelion. They can hardly be dust, for on at least one occasion

Figure 75. HAZE-PENETRATING POWER OF RED LIGHT. These two photographs of the Santa Catalina Mts. near Tucson differ only in that the one at the left was taken in red light whereas the one at the right was taken in blue light. (Courtesy Edwin P. Martz, Jr.)

such clouds covered the entire surface of the planet for a period of three weeks. Keeping that much dust in suspension for that long a time without leaving a visible covering upon the previous surface features seems unlikely. Moreover, the very presence of dust is doubtful, for nitrogen tetroxide does not expand upon freezing, as water does, and will therefore produce no exfoliation or mechanical decomposition of rocks.

If the various observations of Mars are correctly interpreted as evidence of the presence of the oxides of nitrogen in its atmosphere, we may be sure that there is no life on Mars, for nitrogen peroxide is noxious to plants and animals.

The Satellites of Mars

Mars' two little moons were discovered as the fruit of a search conducted during the favorable opposition of 1877. The inner is named Phobos (Fear) and the outer Deimos (Dread), after the fiery steeds of the chariot of the god of war. They can be seen only in the largest telescopes and are estimated from their brightnesses to be respectively about 10 and 5 miles in diameter. The masses of these pygmies are minute by comparison even with our own moon which is one of the smaller bodies of the solar system; consequently their gravitational attractions must be so feeble that an ordinary man would weigh only a few ounces on either satellite.

Phobos is only 5820 miles from Mars' center, or 3715 miles from its surface. This is so near to the planet that it can be seen from Mars' surface over a range of only 138° in latitude, rather than a full hemisphere; thus, if Phobos were over Mars' equator, no Martians whose latitudes exceeded 69° north or south would be able to see it. Deimos is 14,600 miles from the center of the planet.

Because they are so near the planet, Phobos and Deimos revolve about it in short periods—Phobos in only 7^{h}39^m, Deimos in 30^{h}18^m. Phobos' period is shorter than that of any other satellite in the solar system, and Phobos is the only satellite which revolves about its primary in less time than the planet requires for one rotation on its axis. From Mars it would appear to rise in the west every 11^{h}7^m; it could thus rise twice in a single night! Its eastward motion in the Martian sky would be a true motion as well as an apparent one, and is so rapid that Phobos goes through all phases from new to full and back three times in less than a Martian day.

Deimos, on the other hand, revolves only a little more slowly than Mars rotates and so would seem to rise reluctantly in the east, not setting (on the average) until 2⅔ days later, having in the meantime gone through its phases twice.

Seen from Mars, Phobos would have one-third the diameter of our full moon and be only one twenty-fourth as bright. Deimos would have an apparent diameter of only one twenty-fourth the apparent diameter of the full moon and be but one-fortieth as bright as Phobos; it would therefore look much like Venus does to us. Most of the Martian year, the satellites would be visible only in the morning or evening twilight, for they would be either invisible against the daytime sky or immersed in the umbra of Mars. Only in midsummer or midwinter would they avoid Mars' shadow enough to be seen entirely across the sky.

Phobos' present short period is a result of the fact that the satellite is approaching Mars. Some 4.5 billion years ago it probably had a period of 17 hours; in another 35 to 40 million years it may have fallen into the planet. Deimos, on the other hand, is receding from Mars.

One of the most curious items relating to these two interesting little bodies is purely historical. Kepler, often given to fanciful speculation, once wrote to Galileo of the probability of Mars having two small moons. The coincidence is made more remarkable by Voltaire's mention of these two satellites in his imaginative "Micromegas." But the most incredible anticipation of Deimos and Phobos is made by Dean Jonathan Swift, famous satirist and a contemporary of Newton. In his "Gulliver's Travels" he describes the work of astronomers of Lilliput who were possessed of very superior telescopes; they had "discovered two lesser stars, or satellites, which revolve about Mars; whereof the innermost is distant from the center of the primary planet exactly three (1.4) [4] of his diameters, and the outermost, five (3.5); the former revolves in a space of ten hours (7⅔) and the latter in twenty-one and a half (30.3)." This was written in 1726, a century and a half before their discovery!

Jupiter

A little more than five times as far from the sun as the earth is Jupiter, given as a symbol the Egyptian hieroglyph ♃, which represents an eagle, "the bird of Jove." It moves about the sun once in 11.86 years, passing through one constellation of the zodiac each year. Except for Mars at opposition and for Venus, Jupiter is the brightest of the planets and only occasionally is it less bright than Sirius.

The planet deserves the kingly pre-eminence its name implies, for, next to the sun, it is the dominant body of the solar system, being more massive than all the rest together, some 318 times as massive as the earth alone. It is likewise the largest, having an equatorial diameter of 88,640 miles; this is more than 11 times greater than the earth's. Its volume is 1312 times the earth's. It is evidently more voluminous than it is more massive than the earth, so much so that its mean density is only 1.34 times that of water. Its surface gravity, however, is 2.64 times ours. Semipermanent markings on the planet's disk permit quite accurate determinations of its period of rotation; it is found to be 9^h50^m—shorter than that of any other planet. The material at Jupiter's equator whirls about the planet's axis at a rate of 30,000 miles per hour.

What we see of the planet is most certainly not its solid surface, for different latitudes rotate in different periods. Rotation is most rapid at the equator, the period of rotation increasing to about 9^h56^m in some of the higher latitudes. Thus material at Jupiter's equator gains one whole revolu-

[4] Figures in parentheses indicate the true values.

Figure 76. JUPITER. This photograph of Jupiter was taken with the 200-inch telescope in blue light. It shows a number of belts, the great red spot (upper left), the satellite Jupiter III (Ganymede) (upper right), and its transiting shadow (top center). (Mt. Wilson-Palomar Observatories Photo.)

tion over the material in the highest latitudes in about 103 Jovian "equatorial" days. To add to the confusion, the period of rotation does not increase uniformly with latitude but varies erratically; in fact, the periods of like north and south latitudes are usually different. Furthermore, they do not remain constant.

As is to be expected, the rapid rotation produces a considerable equatorial bulge, the equatorial diameter exceeding the polar diameter by

157 . . . .

5760 miles. The planet thus appears to be flattened by 1 part in 15, an effect easily visible on photographs or in the telescope.

In appearance Jupiter is distinguished by prominent belt markings parallel to its equator. The belts are a deep red or brown on a bright creamy white background; their color may be due to traces of impurities such as sodium. They seem to maintain their general arrangement and size, although changes in their cloudlike detail are continually taking place. Occasionally, brighter spots appear over the dark belts, and dark spots show against the bright belts. Most famous of these disturbances is the Great Red Spot, which suddenly appeared in 1878. It became brick red, was 7000 miles wide and 30,000 miles long. It has long since faded but is still discernible; after its appearance, it was traced back to 1831 as a faint marking on drawings and may have been present for 300 years. It has wandered the equivalent of three times around Jupiter.

The belts are undoubtedly currents in the very deep and extensive Jovian atmosphere. The only things in terrestrial experience which are remotely like them are the trade-wind zones.[5] Very probably the different belts are at different levels, and they rotate with different velocities because of vertical currents.

Atmospheric eruptions and bursts of radio emission are correlated with the planet's rotation in such a way as to indicate that their respective sources may be attached to a solid planetary surface which has a true period of rotation of $9^h55^m43^s$. The solid planetary ball is quite unlike the earth, however, for it is made of solid hydrogen. Hydrogen is one of a number of nonmetallic substances which assumes a metallic form under very high pressure; with this change of phase, there is at the same time an abrupt increase in density. Jupiter's average interior pressure, which must exceed 70 million pounds per square inch, is more than enough to cause the hydrogen to become metallic. Though no planet less massive than about 88 times the earth can be made of metallic hydrogen, it comprises most of Jupiter and one-fourth of Saturn. The temperatures in the deep interiors of these two planets have been calculated to be probably a few thousand degrees.

Three gases have been identified in Jupiter's atmosphere—ammonia, methane, and hydrogen. Ammonia (NH_3) is a gas, more familiar dissolved in water and used as a household cleaning agent; methane (CH_4) is commonly known as marsh gas. The methane is in its gaseous state, whereas much of the ammonia must be frozen into crystals, for ammonia becomes solid at $-108°$ F and the temperature on Jupiter as measured is $-216°$

---

[5] It is quite probable that the earth would appear to have belt markings (not necessarily like Jupiter's) if seen from Venus.

poles. These periods have been determined from observation of occasional spots on Saturn's disk, one having appeared in 1876, another in 1903, the most recent in 1933; spot appearances are very infrequent on Saturn as compared to Jupiter. As a check on these determinations of Saturn's period, the spectroscope has been used to find the speed of the planet's spinning, and the period therefrom agrees with the others.

The rapid rotation naturally produces a considerable equatorial bulge; in fact, the equatorial and polar diameters differ by nearly 8000 miles, one part in 9.5; among all the planets, this is the greatest proportional difference. The difference between equatorial and polar diameters and the considerable centrifugal force at the equator result in a 16 per cent difference of surface gravity between equator and pole.

What we see of Saturn is the top of its atmosphere. It appears belted but much more uniformly and not nearly so conspicuously as Jupiter. These belts, too, are thought to be atmospheric currents. The color of most of the ball of the planet is light yellow, but the polar regions are described as having a greenish cast.

Identifiable in Saturn's atmosphere are ammonia and methane, the ammonia being less prominent and the methane more so than on Jupiter. It seems likely that the lower abundance of ammonia is a result of Saturn's lower temperature ($-243°$ F), at which more of the ammonia has frozen out; the greater abundance of methane is thus more apparent than real.

The planet's low temperature is, of course, a result of its receiving only one-ninetieth as much sunlight per unit area as the earth. Unlike Jupiter, though, Saturn will experience marked seasons, for its equator is inclined by 26°45′ to its orbital plane. Each Saturnian season is, however, 7½ years long, or 6300 Saturnian days.

The body of the planet must be largely solid hydrogen, like that of Jupiter. Its deep interior may have a temperature of a few thousand degrees.

Saturn owes both its beauty and its greatest distinction to its system of rings. They were first seen by Galileo in 1610, but their true nature was not suggested until 45 years later by Huygens. They have an over-all diameter of 171,000 miles, and their innermost edge is 6000 or 7000 miles from the planet's surface. Their thickness is too small to be measured at such a great distance, but has been estimated variously between 10 and 20 miles. Supposing their thickness and diameter to be in the ratio of 1 to 10,000, they are much thinner, relatively, than a 10-inch circle of the thinnest tissue paper; Saturn's rings are the flattest and relatively thinnest natural structure known in the universe.

The ring system is in three concentric parts. The innermost section is known as the crepe ring, or C ring; the next section is the bright, or B ring; and the outermost is the A ring. Because it is faint, the crepe ring can be seen only in large telescopes and was unknown before 1850. The 2500-mile gap between the A and B rings is called the "Cassini division," in honor of the Frenchman who was the first to see and describe it in 1675.

The rings appear to be precisely in the plane of Saturn's equator and are therefore inclined by about 28° to the plane of the ecliptic. Since Saturn's equator and its rings maintain a fixed orientation in space, we shall see first one hemisphere of the planet and one side of the rings, then the other as Saturn moves from one side of us to the other. The rings will therefore seem to close and open as we view them first from an angle of 28° above, then on edge, then 28° below. Since Saturn's period of revolution is about 29½ years, the rings will pass through one complete cycle of closing, opening to the other side, closing, and re-opening to the original orientation in this length of time. It is one proof of their extreme thinness that at the times they are viewed edgewise, they cannot be seen at all for a day or two. They appear edgewise twice per revolution of Saturn, or about every 15 years. Actually it takes the better part of a year for the plane of the rings to cross the earth's orbit from one side to the other. The earth may therefore cross their plane once to three times within that interval of time. In 1950, the earth crossed the plane of the rings once. In 1965 and 1966 it will cross three times. When open widest, the rings reflect 1.7 times as much light as the ball of the planet.

It is thought that the rings are composed of a swarm of small particles, probably ice-coated and of the size of ordinary dust, sand, or gravel particles but not so fine as flour. These particles are estimated to occupy less than one-sixteenth the volume of the rings and to have a total mass which is certainly less than one-fourth of our own moon's. Their size is necessarily guessed at from their efficiency of reflection, small particles offering a more efficient and greater total reflecting surface than an equal mass of large particles. Their total mass is estimated from the perturbing effect the rings produce on some of Saturn's inner satellites.

The rings are known not to be continuous surfaces because their inner parts revolve about Saturn in less time than the outer parts. The shorter period of the inner parts has been determined spectroscopically, as was the period of the planet's own rotation; all parts of a solid or liquid ring would have the same period. It is interesting that the periods of the different parts of the ring obey Kepler's harmonic law, the innermost parts having a period of 5^h, the outermost a period of 14^h27^m. Therefore on Saturn the outer parts of the ring would appear to rise slowly in the east, setting in the west, while the inner parts would do just the reverse; a part between them would seem not to move at all!

Each particle of the rings is a tiny satellite of Saturn. The particles' mutual perturbations are negligible and their orbits are virtually independent. The rings must be highly stable; no noticeable changes have occurred in them for as long as they have been observed, and moreover if they were astronomically short-lived, it is highly unlikely that we should have the good fortune to be at hand to observe them during their brief period of existence. If occasional collisions among the particles do take place, it will have the effect of diminishing the size of the orbit of one or both. Thus it may be that the rings are shrinking very, very slowly.

Although the particles of the rings may have little effect on one another, they are subject to appreciable perturbations by the more important of Saturn's nine satellites. In fact, the Cassini division is probably the result of a perturbative effect called *resonance*.[6] A particle in this gap would have a period one-half that of Mimas, Saturn's closest satellite, revolving in practically the same plane as the ring; after every two revolutions of the particle, it would be subjected to identical perturbations by Mimas. The effects would thus reinforce each other and accumulate rather than average out. The resultant changes in the particle's orbit would clear it from the Cassini division. Satellites Dione and Rhea cause the diffuseness of the crepe ring, and all the satellites together bring about the gap between ring and planet.

The ring's origin can, of course, never be determined with certainty, but there is an important theorem from celestial mechanics which is highly pertinent to this interesting problem. The theorem, first demonstrated by Roche, states that the disruptive tidal force of a planet will exceed the cohesive gravitational force of a satellite of the same density everywhere within a distance of 2.44 planetary radii of its center. This distance is known as the *Roche limit*. All of Saturn's ring lies within this limit; the nearest satellite is outside it. The ring is therefore probably formed of material which, because of Roche's theorem, could not coalesce into a single body. Less likely is the possibility that it is made of fragments of a disrupted pre-existent satellite. Whatever its origin, the ring is unique in the whole of the known universe and makes Saturn one of the skies' most beautiful and interesting objects.

[6] A familiar example of resonance is the sympathetic vibration which nearly everyone has observed to take place in small free objects when a musical note of the proper pitch is sounded.

The Satellites of Saturn

Besides the countless miniscule satellites which comprise Saturn's rings, there are nine satellites of the more orthodox variety in the planet's retinue. The first was discovered in 1655, the most recent one in 1899. Their order of discovery is not the order of their distance from Saturn, and therefore to minimize confusion, they have been given names—the nearest Mimas, after it Enceladus, Tethys, Dione, Rhea, Titan, Hyperion, Iapetus, and finally Phoebe.

Mimas is 117,000 miles from Saturn's center, coasts around it in $22\frac{1}{2}$ hours, just 30,000 miles beyond the rings. The rest, except Phoebe, are at distances up to $2\frac{1}{4}$ million miles and have periods up to 80 days; anti-social Phoebe enjoys the isolation of 8,000,000 miles and the more leisurely pace of a 546-day period. Phoebe is further assertive of its independence by revolving retrograde, like Jupiter's four outermost moons; at the time of its discovery, Phoebe was the only satellite known whose motion was retrograde, and it was regarded as something of a curiosity. Unlike Jupiter's outermost satellites, Phoebe's motion about its primary is stable, and the satellite could not be pilfered by the sun even in a direct orbit. Phoebe has the further distinctions of having been the first satellite discovered by photographic means and is the only satellite discovered at an observatory in the southern hemisphere.

Only Titan, whose diameter is about 2600 miles, is larger than our moon; the smallest is individualistic Phoebe, probably only 200 miles in diameter. Besides its size, Titan holds the distinction of being the only satellite in the whole solar system which is known to possess an atmosphere (methane).

It is thought that all the satellites rotate so as to present the same face to Saturn, for they vary in brightness in the same periods as they revolve. Iapetus is remarkable in this respect, changing brightness by a factor of five during each revolution.

A tenth satellite, named Themis, was found on 13 of the plates taken following the discovery of Phoebe. It was credited with a period of 21 days, but it has not been seen since and its existence is in doubt.

Uranus and Its Satellites

Distant Uranus has the distinction of being the only planet to be discovered quite by accident, in 1781. The discoverer was William Herschel, whose acuteness is attested to by the fact that it was later realized that recorded observations of Uranus had been made a score of times in the preceding century, but the planet had always been mistaken for a star. Herschel himself first thought it to be a new comet, but its more nearly circular motion soon marked it as a planet. A considerable number of names for the new planet were proposed, but general acceptance was finally granted to the name "Uranus"; Herschel's own choice was Georgium Sidus ("Georgian Star"), in honor of his king and patron, George III of England. The Uranus of mythology was god of the skies and the planet's symbol is therefore ♁, an arrow directed from earth to sky.

Under the best of conditions Uranus is just barely visible to the un-aided eye; it is no surprise that it escaped notice for so long, however, for there are at least 5000 stars which appear as bright or brighter. The cause of Uranus' being so much fainter than any other of the planets thus far is, of course, primarily its much greater distance; it is over 19 times as far from the sun as the earth, a vast 1,782,000,000 miles. At this distance the earth would always appear within 3° of the sun, sunlight would be only $\frac{1}{368}$ as intense as on the earth, the temperature would be a bitter $-300°$ F, and the year would be a little over 84 times as long as ours.

Uranus is 29,300 miles in diameter (and therefore has 64 times the volume of the earth) and 14.5 times as massive as the earth. Consequently its mean density is 1.56, a value rather like that of the other giant planets, but its surface gravity is, surprisingly, only 7 per cent greater than the earth's.

The planet is greenish in color and shows only occasional very faint markings of the nature of belts like those of Jupiter and Saturn. The green color derives from the high abundance of its atmospheric methane which heavily absorbs the yellow and red from the reflected sunlight. A trace of ammonia is also present, but most of the ammonia must have condensed at such a low temperature as prevails on Uranus.

The absence of distinct markings makes it impossible to determine Uranus' period of rotation from observations of surface detail, as has been done so successfully for Mars, Jupiter, and even Saturn. It has been neces-sary to resort to the more difficult and less accurate spectroscopic method, which has fixed the planet's period of rotation as about 10^h45^m. This result has been latterly confirmed by observations of small periodic fluctuations of the planet's brightness; the period of these fluctuations is 10^h49^m. As we should expect, the rapid rotation produces a considerable bulge, 2000 to 3000 miles.

Probably the most remarkable thing about the planet is the fact that it rotates from east to west, whereas all the rest of the planets go from west to east; what is more, the plane of its equator is inclined by 82° to its orbit, nearly a right angle. To visualize what would be the state of terrestrial affairs corresponding to those on Uranus, imagine this experiment. Let the plane of the earth's equator, now inclined 23½° to its orbit, be tilted still more to 90° and then 8° in addition. At 90° inclination the earth's axis would lie exactly in the plane of its orbit. The additional 8° inclination would cause the original north pole to be directed "below" the ecliptic, the original south pole to be directed "above" it. If north and south were now interchanged so as to conform with their original sense (north in the hemisphere "above" the orbital plane), we should find the United States in the new southern hemisphere, Florida on the west coast, California on the east, and everything reversed. At the times of the equinoxes the sun would still be on the celestial equator and day would equal night. But at winter solstice, the sun would execute a circle 8° from the "south" celestial pole, and at summer solstice the land of the midnight sun would extend to Panama and Central Africa. Each season would be 17,124 days of 10¾ hours; the sun would be reduced to a dazzling point brighter than 3000 full moons. And the final instruction in our recipe is: chill to −300° F. This is what it would be like on Uranus.

Uranus' five satellites, Miranda, Ariel, Umbriel, Titania, and Oberon, are interesting because they revolve very nearly in the plane of the planet's equator and in the direction it rotates, i.e., retrograde and nearly at right angles to the plane of Uranus' orbit. They are 400 to 1000 miles in diameter but very faint because of the great distance of Uranus from the sun. They are from 66,000 to 364,000 miles distant from the planet. Because of the unique orientation of the orbits, we see them sometimes fully open, as in 1945, sometimes edgewise, as in 1924 and 1965.

Neptune and Its Satellites

It might fairly be said that Neptune was discovered on paper and not once but twice. Its existence was predicted independently by a Frenchman and an Englishman. The young Frenchman was Leverrier, the young Englishman was Adams. Working unbeknown to each other, both were attempting to explain by the presence of a new planet certain unaccountable deviations in the observed motion of Uranus. The predictions made for this latter planet simply did not hold, and Leverrier was able to show that its observed motion just could not be reconciled with any possible orbit calculated so as to include only the effects of the then known planets. Later in the same year (1846) he completed an extremely difficult calculation to determine the position of the disturbing body. He communicated his result to the astronomer Galle, in Berlin. Galle, after only half an hour's search on the night of the same day he received Leverrier's prediction, found the new planet, and within 52′ of the predicted position! The accumulated discrepancy in Uranus' motion for 60 years, an amount barely perceptible to the unaided eye, had led to the discovery of a new planet. This remarkable feat is a monument to the exactitude and power of the scientific method in general and mathematical astronomy in particular.

The less fortunate Adams had made a prediction similar to Leverrier's, actually some weeks before, but the astronomer to whom he sent his results failed, for one reason or another, to capitalize on his unparalleled opportunity.

In conformity with immemorial precedent, the new planet was named after one of the ancient Greek gods. It was given the symbol ♆, Neptune's trident.

If Neptune were five times brighter, it would be just at the limit of naked-eye visibility. Its faintness bears witness to its great distance from the sun—30 times the earth's, some 2,793,000,000 miles. Light, whose velocity is 186,000 miles per second, spends 4 hours on its way to Neptune from the sun. In view of the distance Neptune must travel to go once around its orbit, its speed of $3\frac{1}{3}$ miles per second is a laggardly pace, and the trip requires 164.79 years. Since its discovery, it has gone through only about two-thirds of a revolution, will not have made a complete one until the year 2011.

Neptune is rather like Uranus, often called "Uranus' twin." Its diameter is 27,700 miles (compared with 29,300), its mass 17.2 times the earth's (as against Uranus' 14.5), and hence its mean density is 2.47 (instead of 1.56), and its surface gravity 1.41 times the earth's (slightly more than Uranus' 1.07 times). Moreover, it too shows a small green disk (about 2 seconds of arc in diameter) in the telescope. The green is again due to methane, which seems to be the only gas left in any abundance at about $-330°$ F. A spectroscopic determination of its period of rotation gives about 15^h48^m; the general correctness of this figure is confirmed by periodic fluctuations of brightness in half this time.

A Neptunian, if there were such, would get a poor view of the solar system. The sun would appear smaller than Venus does to us when nearest; it would appear only $\frac{1}{904}$th as bright as it does to us, but still some 520 times brighter than our full moon. Mercury, Mars, and even Uranus would require telescopic aid to be seen. Jupiter and Saturn would have elongations of only 10° and 17°, respectively, and would appear as inconspicuous "stars." The earth and Venus would never be farther than 2° and 1½°, respectively, from the sun and could be seen faintly only during an eclipse of the sun by one of Neptune's two satellites.

Neptune's larger satellite is sometimes called Triton. Its distance from Neptune (220,000 miles) is practically the same as our moon's distance from the earth, but because Neptune is 17 times as massive as the earth, Triton's period is slightly less than 6 days. Its size, estimated from its brightness, would make it larger than the moon, perhaps 3000 miles in diameter. Its mass is 1.8 times the moon's. Most interesting item concerning this satellite is the fact that though it is not at a great distance from the planet, its near-circular motion is retrograde, while Neptune's rotation is direct.

Neptune's second satellite is called Nereid, a mythological sea nymph attendant on Neptune. It is too faint to be observed visually with any existing telescope and was found by photography. Its orbital eccentricity of 0.76 is the greatest of any known satellite. Because the eccentricity is so great, Nereid's distance from Neptune varies from 867,000 miles to more than 6,000,000 miles. Its motion is direct in a period of about one year.

There is no reason to suppose that the current list of satellites in the solar system is complete, particularly since one has been discovered as recently as 1951. What others there may be, however, are small and faint and their discovery waits on time and large telescopes.

Pluto

Skulking about the outskirts of the known solar system is Pluto, latest comer into our ken. The circumstances of its discovery are reminiscent of the discovery of Neptune. Unaccounted for perturbations of both Uranus and Neptune suggested the existence of a still more distant planet. Independently, two American astronomers, Lowell and Pickering, attempted the extremely difficult task of predicting its position. Like Adams, Pickering was denied success (in 1919), this time because of a flaw in a photographic plate and the nearness of Pluto to a bright star whose image hid it. Unlike Leverrier, Lowell never lived to see his prediction verified for he died in 1916. But at the Lowell Observatory a search for his trans-Neptunian Planet X was undertaken. The effort was rewarded in 1930 when on January 21 the faint new planet was discovered on a photographic search plate. Its motion was carefully observed for several weeks following to make certain its planetary nature.

An announcement of the discovery was made on March 13, Lowell's birthday and the anniversary of Herschel's discovery of Uranus. The name Pluto was conceded to be most appropriate for the new planet, for Pluto, god of the lower world, reigned over the regions of outer darkness.

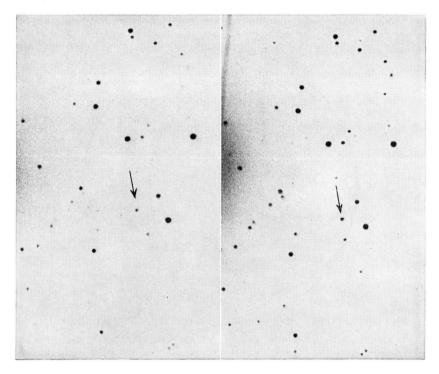

Figure 79. PLUTO. The planet Pluto is indicated on these photographic negatives by the arrows. Its non-stellar character is made evident by its change of position among the stars in one day. Note how many stars in this field alone are brighter than the planet. The dark area at the central left margins is produced by a bright star just outside the field of the photographs. The streak from the one on the right is produced by diffraction from the supporting vanes of the telescope's secondary mirror. (Mt. Wilson-Palomar Observatories Photo.)

Then, too, the obvious symbol ♇ formed of the initials P and L would commemorate Percival Lowell, moving spirit of the posthumously successful search.

One decided difference between the discoveries of Neptune and Pluto is the comparative lack in the latter instance of the directness which characterized the former. This has been the origin of much discussion as to how relevant the predictions may have been to the actual discovery.

Wherever the truth may lie, it can hardly be questioned that the discovery would not have been made when it was but for Lowell.

A determination of Pluto's orbit shows that the planet's mean distance is 39.5 astronomical units, or 3,670,000,000 miles, nearly another billion beyond Neptune. The orbit has the highest inclination and eccentricity of any of the planets, 17° and 0.25, respectively. The large eccentricity

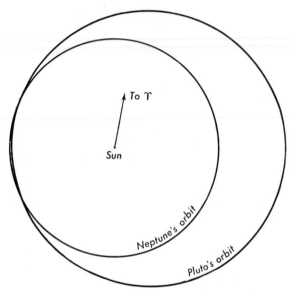

Figure 80. Although Pluto comes within the orbit of Neptune, the two orbits are so inclined that the two planets can never come closer than 240 million miles to each other.

will cause a large difference between aphelion and perihelion distances, the former being nearly 50 astronomical units, the latter 29.7 astronomical units. In fact, when nearest the sun, in 2010, Pluto will be 35 million miles inside the orbit of Neptune; there is no cause for alarm, however, for because of the orbit's considerable inclination, Neptune and Pluto never come nearer each other than 240 million miles.

Pluto is about 4000 times too faint to be seen without a telescope. It gives the appearance of a small yellowish star. Only the 200-inch Hale telescope at Mount Palomar has proved powerful enough to permit measures of the size of Pluto's apparent disk. From these the planet's diameter is determined to be about 4700 miles. Its period of rotation is 6.39 days. Like Mercury, Pluto is not known to have any satellites, and consequently its mass is difficult to determine. From its size, Pluto is estimated to have a mass not in excess of several tenths earth's masses. On Pluto it must be even colder than Neptune, possibly −350° F. Except in temperature, Pluto bears no resemblance to the giant planets but seems to have more in common with the four innermost.

There is no way of knowing whether or not Pluto is the last planet in the solar system. It can only be said that if others exist, they are either very distant or of small mass, for they would otherwise produce perturbations on Uranus and Neptune that could not have been thus far unnoticed. In either case, such a hypothetical object would necessarily be very faint and its discovery therefore most difficult.

QUESTIONS

1. Identify the planets described by the following phrases: (*a*) largest in diameter; (*b*) smallest in diameter; (*c*) hottest; (*d*) coldest; (*e*) densest; (*f*) least dense; (*g*) prominently belted; (*h*) ringed; (*i*) accidentally discovered; (*j*) accurately predicted; (*k*) found after years' search; (*l*) comes closest to the earth; (*m*) best observed; (*n*) most bulged; (*o*) most rapidly rotating; (*p*) possesses much atmospheric carbon dioxide; (*q*) possesses much atmospheric methane; (*r*) possesses much atmospheric free nitrogen; (*s*) rotates retrograde; (*t*) seasons similar to the earth's; (*u*) greatest equatorial obliquity; (*v*) brightest in the sky; (*w*) most eccentric orbit.
2. Why is Mercury seldom seen? When is it most easily seen? How is it best observed?
3. What is Mercury's period of revolution? Of rotation? How great are its longitudinal librations? Latitudinal librations?
4. How are seasons brought about on Mercury? Will seasons be experienced on the dark side of the planet? If any part of the planet were habitable (with respect to temperature), where would it be?
5. Why does Mercury not have an atmosphere?
6. Why is Mercury of particular interest in the theory of relativity? Why is it of more interest in this respect than are the other planets?
7. What justification is there for calling Venus the "earth's twin"? In what respects is the term inappropriate?
8. How does Venus compare with the other planets in our sky as to (*a*) apparent brightness, (*b*) telescopic interest, (*c*) distance from the earth, (*d*) placement favorable for observation.
9. What proofs are there that Venus has an atmosphere? What is known of its composition? Point out two ways wherein Venus' atmosphere may be a decisive factor in determining the climate on Venus.
10. Under what conditions is Mars most favorably placed for observation? What circumstances combine to make Mars the best observed of all the planets?
11. How are the Martian seasons brought about? Compare them with terrestrial

seasons. What is Mars' climate probably like? Contrast it with the climates of corresponding terrestrial latitudes.

12. What novel features would terrestrial geographers, meteorologists, and geologists find on Mars?

13. What was the observational basis of Lowell's suggestion that a highly developed civilization exists on Mars? What are the weaknesses of this theory? What are the alternative explanations of the Martian phenomena?

14. What features of special interest are observed on Jupiter? How do they change with time? What is their interpretation?

15. What is the chemical composition of Jupiter? The physical constitution? Describe the probable seasons and climate on Jupiter.

16. What are Saturn's rings? Cite the evidence which supports your answer. What are the dimensions of the rings? What is their total mass? What is the probable average size of the particles and how is this determined? Why is it unlikely that the rings are a temporary structure?

17. How are the particles of Saturn's rings affected by each other? How are they affected by Saturn's satellites? How does the Roche theorem bear on Saturn's effect upon its rings?

18. Review the circumstances surrounding the discoveries of Uranus, of Neptune, and of Pluto. What is the likelihood of the discovery of still other planets in the solar system?

19. What similarities exist between Uranus and Neptune? How are Uranus and Neptune like Jupiter and Saturn? How do the giant planets differ from the rest (Mercury, Venus, earth, Mars, and Pluto)? What accounts for the characteristic green color of Uranus and Neptune?

20. Why is it more than ordinarily difficult to determine the masses of Mercury and Pluto?

21. Identify the satellite(s) described by the following phrases: (a) largest; (b) smallest; (c) largest with respect to its primary; (d) least dense; (e) possesses an atmosphere; (f) largest orbital velocity; (g) shortest period of revolution; (h) longest period of revolution; (i) retrograde revolution; (j) orbit most inclined to primary's orbital plane; (k) orbit most rapidly perturbed by its primary; (l) largest orbit; (m) smallest orbit.

22. Describe the probable appearance of each of the satellite systems as seen from the primary and point out the features of particular interest in each.

23. In what respect have Jupiter's Galilean satellites been of general scientific interest? In what respect are the retrograde satellites of Jupiter and Saturn of particular astronomical interest? In the light of your answer, explain why Neptune's retrograde satellite is exceptional. Is the same true of Uranus' five retrograde satellites?

24. How probable is the discovery of other planets in the solar system? Other satellites?

chapter 5
The Lesser Bodies
of the Solar System

● ● ●

*"Great fleas have little fleas upon their backs to bite 'em,
And little fleas have lesser fleas, and so ad infinitum."*
—DE MORGAN

A. THE MINOR PLANETS [1]

A minor planet is a small, frequently irregularly shaped, solid body revolving independently about the sun. The largest has a diameter of 480 miles; the smallest ones thus far observed are only 1 or 2 miles in diameter, but presumably there exist some even smaller. All are faint, only one being at times barely bright enough to be seen with the unaided eye.

Their Discovery

Though they were not predicted like Neptune, the minor planets were in a sense anticipated at least a quarter of a century before the discovery of the first of them. This was in consequence of a remarkable and suggestive relation known as Bode's law.[2] In 1772 Bode called attention to the fact that if 0.4 were arbitrarily subtracted from the mean distance (in astronomical units) of each of the then known planets, the resulting sequence of numbers was very nearly equal to the series 0, 0.3, 0.6, 1.2, 2.4, 4.8, 9.6, of which each number after the second is gotten by doubling the number preceding it; in other words, exclusive of the first term, these numbers form a geometric sequence. The notable difference between the two series of numbers was the absence of a planet at distance 2.8 astronomical units to supply the number 2.4 to the second sequence. Why not search for it? The cogency of this question increased greatly

[1] Also called *asteroids,* because of their starlike appearance, or *planetoids* because of their similarities to the planets.

[2] The term "Bode's law" is a complete misnomer; it isn't Bode's and it isn't a law. The relation was first recognized by Titius, publicized by Bode, and has received no detailed theoretical explanation.

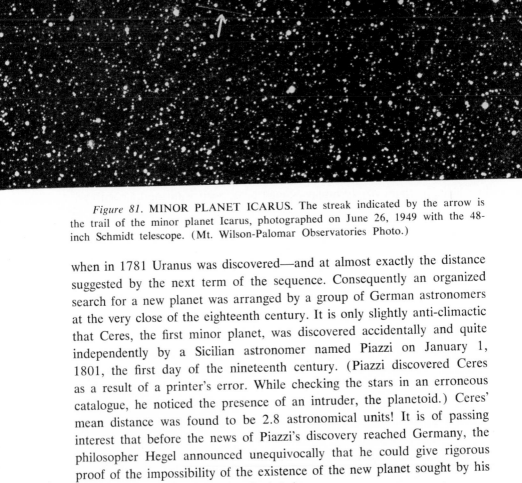

Figure 81. MINOR PLANET ICARUS. The streak indicated by the arrow is the trail of the minor planet Icarus, photographed on June 26, 1949 with the 48-inch Schmidt telescope. (Mt. Wilson-Palomar Observatories Photo.)

when in 1781 Uranus was discovered—and at almost exactly the distance suggested by the next term of the sequence. Consequently an organized search for a new planet was arranged by a group of German astronomers at the very close of the eighteenth century. It is only slightly anti-climactic that Ceres, the first minor planet, was discovered accidentally and quite independently by a Sicilian astronomer named Piazzi on January 1, 1801, the first day of the nineteenth century. (Piazzi discovered Ceres as a result of a printer's error. While checking the stars in an erroneous catalogue, he noticed the presence of an intruder, the planetoid.) Ceres' mean distance was found to be 2.8 astronomical units! It is of passing interest that before the news of Piazzi's discovery reached Germany, the philosopher Hegel announced unequivocally that he could give rigorous proof of the impossibility of the existence of the new planet sought by his countrymen, and he publicly ridiculed them.

After the discovery of Ceres, three other minor planets were found by 1807, then none until 1845. In 1847 three more were discovered and from one to one hundred new ones have been found every year since.

The modern method of discovery is efficient and simple; the planetoids are "trapped" photographically by taking long-exposure photographs of likely regions of the sky. By guiding the telescope or camera carefully, the stars are made to register as points, whereas a planetoid will, by its motion, appear as a streak.[3]

The Motions of the Minor Planets

When an unidentified minor planet has been detected, an attempt is made to secure sufficient observations to determine its orbit. If then its orbital elements distinguish it as a new object, it is assigned a number indicating the order of its discovery, and its discoverer is allowed to name it. (One astronomer is said to have financed an eclipse expedition by selling his rights to the name of a planetoid.) Most all are given feminine names [4] —originally those of mythical goddesses, but the supply of these has been so nearly exhausted that there are now celestial namesakes of astronomers' friends, pets, and favorite desserts! The number of different minor planets catalogued is currently over 1600; the number estimated to be within range of the 100-inch Mt. Wilson telescope is about 55,000. All together are probably not three ten-thousandths as massive as the earth.

The orbits of the great majority of the minor planets place them between Mars and Jupiter, their average mean distance being almost exactly the 2.8 astronomical units suggested by Bode's law; the corresponding period is 4.69 years. While the motion of all is direct, the minor planets differ from the major planets in having more eccentric orbits (average 0.15) more highly inclined to the ecliptic (average $9\frac{1}{2}°$). Significantly, the aphelia of minor planets show a concentration toward the longitude of Jupiter's perihelion.

Even among the minor planets, the motions of some are exceptional. Hidalgo, for example, has an orbital inclination of $43°$ and the longest period (13.7 years) of any. Because of its large orbital eccentricity (0.65), this little whirling fragment comes in to two astronomical units, wanders out nearly as far as Saturn.

At the other extreme is Icarus, discovered in 1949. Its mean distance of 1.08 astronomical units is the smallest among the planetoids. Because

---

[3] The very faintest planetoids, conversely, can be photographed only by trailing the stars at the rate of the planetoid's anticipated motion. A planetoid will then be a point, the stars streaks. Had the planetoid image been trailed, the light from the planetoid would have been spread too thin to be recorded.

[4] It is probably not intentional that the few having masculine names are some of the most interesting.

its orbital eccentricity is 0.83, however, Icarus can penetrate to within a mere 17 million miles of the sun, about half the mean distance of Mercury. Also of interest is the fact that its period of revolution of 409 days is so little different from the earth's that Icarus' synodic period is nearly 9 years and 4 months. Consequently it will pass near the earth only once every 28 years or so.

Their Importance

Astronomically, the minor planets are chiefly of interest, however, on three other counts. For one, they are found to be subject to resonance effects just as were the rings of Saturn. The distribution of periods (and therefore mean distances) of the minor planets exhibits "gaps" in the immediate neighborhood of values which are simple fractions of the period of Jupiter, particularly $\frac{1}{2}$, $\frac{1}{3}$, $\frac{2}{5}$, etc.; the unoccupied regions are known as the *Kirkwood gaps,* after the man who first recognized their existence. In surprising contrast to the nearly vacant Kirkwood gaps is a concentration of minor planets with periods approximately $\frac{4}{3}$ that of Jupiter. The reason for this is unknown.

The second point of interest consists in a demonstration of a celebrated result in the three-body problem. A special solution of that problem predicted that a small third body should, when started off suitably, move so as to be always at the third vertex of an equilateral triangle whose other two vertices were occupied by the two principal masses. The principal masses are here those of Jupiter and the sun. Nearly equidistant from both are several minor planets known as the *Trojan group* (because they are named Achilles, Patroclus, Priam, etc.), one group preceding and another following Jupiter.

Of most practical importance to astronomers (as we shall see presently) are a few planetoids which shave by the earth at only a few million miles or less. The first of these objects to be known was Eros, discovered in 1898. Its perihelion is within 14 million miles of the earth's position on January 22, so that close approaches will occur whenever Eros passes perihelion near this date. The last close approach was on January 30, 1931, when Eros was only 16 million miles from us; the next is in 1975.

Apollo, found in 1932, comes within 2 million miles of the earth. It has a period of 1.8 years and an orbit which passes nearer the sun than Venus. In 1936, Adonis was discovered, and the following year Hermes. Adonis passed not quite a million miles away, while Hermes came within

shortest period, has been observed at more perihelion passages than any other (45 times up to 1957)—every 3.3 years since 1819 except the year 1944. Halley's comet holds second place with 29 reappearances approximately every 77 years since 467 B.C. except in 163 B.C.

The preponderance of parabolic orbits is characteristic. A parabola, it may be recalled, is a conic section whose eccentricity is exactly 1.0; it is open rather than closed and represents the dividing line between closed ellipses (eccentricity less than 1) and open hyperbolas (eccentricity more than 1). Were one to take comet statistics literally, then, it would have to be concluded that perhaps two-thirds of all comets come from beyond the solar system, make a single perihelion passage, and recede forevermore.

This seems almost certainly not to be the case, however, for even among comets ascribed elliptical orbits, hardly one in four has an orbital eccentricity less than 0.99. The orbital ellipses of the rest are extremely elongated. Consequently they are near perihelion a very small fraction of their entire period. It is only near perihelion that they can be observed, however. Aside from the two comets of smallest known orbital eccentricity —comet Schwassmann-Wachmann, which can be kept under almost constant observation in its orbit between Jupiter and Saturn, and comet Oterma, which can be followed entirely around its orbit between Mars and Jupiter—no comet has been observed longer than $3\frac{1}{2}$ years. Most are observed only a few months; two were seen only during the few minutes of totality at a total solar eclipse and never found again; faint comets have been prematurely lost in the glare of moonlight. Complementing the limited duration of the observation of comets is the small proportion of the orbital arc over which nearly all comets are observed. All known comets have perihelion distances less than 5.52 astronomical units (Comet 1925 I), and few can be seen even as far as 4 astronomical units from the sun. This is but a fraction of a per cent of the mean distances of most comets. It is evident, then, that the task of recreating an entire, very elongated orbital ellipse from a minute portion of the arc near perihelion is one of extreme delicacy. Discriminating a highly elongated elliptical orbit from a genuinely parabolic one may well be impossible on the basis of the available observations.

The reality of parabolic orbits is thus open to question. Even more dubious are the hyperbolic orbits. Comet 1883 III possesses the largest known orbital eccentricity, 1.013. The orbit of this comet is so weakly hyperbolic that it seems probably to have become so by the action of planetary perturbations. More typical of the hyperbolic comets is Comet Dela-

Figure 84. COMET DANIEL. (Courtesy Yerkes Observatory.)

.... 184

van (1914 V), whose final orbital eccentricity was 1.0001618. It approached perihelion, however, in an elliptical orbit which originally had an eccentricity of 0.9999781, a period of some 24,000,000 years, and an aphelion distance of 170,000 astronomical units. It fell afoul of planetary perturbations which can be expected eventually to cast almost all comets into hyperbolic outgoing orbits. Of 18 comets receding in hyperbolic orbits, all were found to have approached the sun in orbits that were definitely or probably elliptical.

Present evidence is thus decidedly in favor of the hypothesis that cometary orbits are initially ellipses, not true parabolas or hyperbolas. We are therefore led to conclude that comets are members of the solar system. None is known to have come from interstellar space and if one were to do so, we could reasonably expect its orbit to be strongly hyperbolic rather than just barely so.

Short-Period Comets and the Capture Process

A typical comet has a large, extremely elongated, randomly oriented orbit which it follows in a very long period, as likely in the retrograde sense as direct. Entirely atypical, then, are some 85 comets whose orbits lie entirely within the orbit of Neptune, whose orbital eccentricities are as small as 0.14, whose orbital inclinations are all less than 45°, and of which only six revolve retrograde. These are called the *short-period comets*. Approximately 60 of the short-period comets have periods under 12 years, Jupiter's period of revolution; almost all these have aphelia near Jupiter's orbit. At least 11 of them have been found to have made a close approach to Jupiter shortly before their discovery. Such a relationship can hardly be the work of chance; it is ascribed to a process called *capture.*

A capture of a comet by Jupiter occurs when a comet passes the massive planet in such a way as to be decelerated relative to the sun; its decreased orbital velocity will cause it to follow a smaller orbit and have a shorter period. For example, a decrease of only 25 feet per second in a comet's orbital velocity at 1 astronomical unit from the sun could change its period from 10,000 years to as little as 6500 years. The 60 or so comets whose orbits are presumed to have been reduced in this way by Jupiter are known as Jupiter's *comet family*. The capture of a comet may occur in installments, successive encounters reducing the orbit by stages.

It is also possible that a comet may pass a planet in such a way as to receive a net acceleration relative to the sun; its increased orbital velocity will cause it to follow a larger orbit and have a longer period. For

Figure 85. COMET BROOKS. This photograph of Comet Brooks was taken on September 22, 1911. (Courtesy Yerkes Observatory.)

example, an increase of only 25 feet per second in a comet's orbital velocity at 1 astronomical unit from the sun could change its period from 10,000

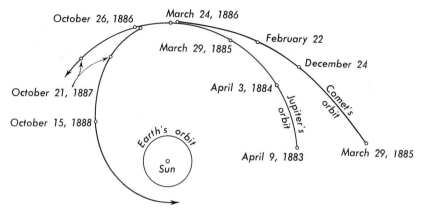

Figure 86. The motion of Comet Brooks before and after its close approach to Jupiter is shown projected upon the plane of the earth's orbit.

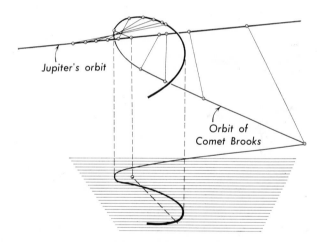

Figure 87. The motion of Comet Brooks is shown in the immediate vicinity of Jupiter, as is the projection of this motion upon the orbital plane of the earth. The lines connect the positions of comet and planet at like times, thereby giving some indication of the nature of the encounter.

years to as much as 18,000 years. A sufficient increase in its orbital velocity will transform the orbit thereafter into a hyperbola and the comet will be expelled.

Both expulsion and capture have been witnessed. Comet Delavan,

as we have seen, was expelled. On the other hand, in 1886 comet Brooks
fell under Jupiter's spell and for seven months dallied at such close range
to Jupiter as to be subject to a stronger attraction from the planet than
from the sun. It passed within about 55,000 miles of the planet's surface.
Its period was changed from 27 years to 6.8 years. Jupiter is responsible
for an estimated 97 per cent of all cometary captures. It has been shown
that capture will at the same time probably reduce a comet's orbital inclination and that capture is more likely for directly revolving comets,
whereas expulsion is more likely for retrograde comets. These likelihoods
are clearly reflected in the statistics of the short-period comets.

The Constitution of Comets

A comet's nucleus is its most important part, for it is from the
nucleus that the head and tail derive. All nuclei are small, though the
nuclei of comets with long tails often appear multiple. Because the brightness of nuclei varies with distance according to the inverse square law,
the nuclei must be solid. This conclusion is reinforced by the observation
that light from the nucleus is qualitatively the same as sunlight and therefore must have been reflected by extended surfaces.

The size of the nuclear solid matter is more difficult to ascertain. From
observations of comet 1884 I as it transited a star field, the conclusion
was drawn that the nucleus must have a diameter of at least 60 miles.
The nucleus of Halley's comet was estimated as 10 to 30 miles. Few if
any nuclei are thought to be greater in diameter than 100 miles, most
only a few miles. It seems likely that many are in several parts. On the
other hand, several comets, like 1886 II, have passed through the outer
fringes of the sun's atmosphere at perihelion. They must there have been
subjected to heat so intense that all bodies less than a foot in diameter
would have completely evaporated, yet these comets did not disappear.

The diameters of comets' heads average 80,000 miles, approximately
the size of Jupiter. They show an extreme variation, however, ranging from
a minimum diameter of 10,000 miles to a maximum thus far of 1,400,000
miles, the size of the head of Holmes' comet of 1892.

The light of the comae of some 70 comets since 1864 has been
analyzed spectroscopically (see p. 223). It is generally characteristic of a
very thin gas constituted of the diatomic molecules and radicals C_2 (carbon), N_2 (nitrogen), CO (poisonous carbon monoxide), CH (methyli-
dyne), CN (deadly cyanogen), NH (nitrogen hydride), OH (hydroxyl),
CH_2 (methylene), and NH_2 (amide). Most of these compounds are pre-

sumed to arise from the disruption of chemically more stable molecules such as CH_4 (methane), NH_3 (ammonia), CO_2 (carbon dioxide), or H_2O (water) by the action of unfiltered solar ultraviolet radiation. The heads of some comets also show traces of sodium, iron, nickel, and chromium, particularly if the comet makes a close approach to the sun.

An exception to the general rule, a small proportion of comets (less than 7 per cent) have comae from which the light is qualitatively like that of the sun, even as their nuclei. This indicates that the coma is composed largely of solid particles, thought to be of the dimensions of dust particles down to a few hundredths or even a few ten-thousandths of an inch in diameter. The head of comet Schwassmann-Wachmann, for example, appears to be composed entirely of dust. The proportion of gas and dust ranges to both extremes in other comets. Oddly, bright comets contain larger quantities of dust and solid particles than do faint comets.

Most comets do not have tails. No faint comets have tails and even a bright comet like Holmes' had none. But for those which have them, the tail may be the most impressive part. The longest on record is that of the great comet of 1843 whose tail had an over-all length of 180 million miles, 2 astronomical units. In 1910 the tail of Halley's comet grew at a rate of about half a million miles a day, became 90 million miles long, and at one time spanned 120° of sky. In cross-section, comets' tails may be up to half a million miles in diameter.

Spectroscopic analysis of the tails shows them to be composed chiefly of electrically positively charged CO and N_2 molecules. Some comets show two tails, the second composed of dust.

Despite the impressive dimensions of comets, their masses are insignificant; they are variously estimated as between a hundred-thousandth and a hundred-billionth the mass of the earth. Comets contain so little matter that their feeble gravitational attractions have not produced a noticeable perturbation in the motion of any other body. For example, Brooks' comet, in its close encounter with Jupiter, appears not even to have perturbed any of the satellites, although it passed within the orbit of Jupiter I and its own orbit was drastically altered. Comets' small masses and great volumes imply very low mean densities—a quarter of a millionth the density of air or less. It is not surprising that they are transparent.

Direct evidence of comets' low densities, and therefore of the smallness of their masses as well, is provided by observations of the tidal disruption of some. For objects of such low density the Roche limit is about 90 million miles from the sun, 9 million miles from Jupiter, and 1¾ million miles from the earth. Comet 1947n passed within about 9 million miles of the sun, and its nucleus was sundered into two parts. The great comet of 1882 appeared to have a single nucleus as it approached the sun, but during its passage around the sun at a distance of less than 200,000 miles from the sun's surface, the nucleus was divided into four

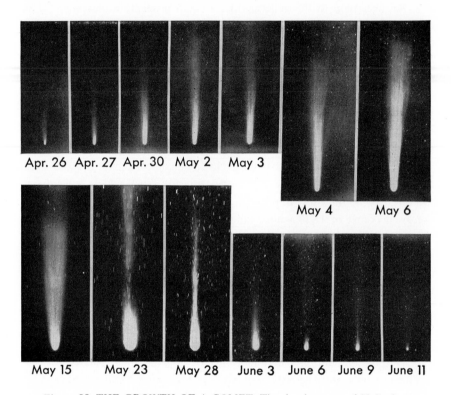

Figure 88. THE GROWTH OF A COMET. The development of Halley's comet during its most recent appearance (1910) is shown in this series of photographs. (Mt. Wilson-Palomar Observatories Photo.)

parts which proceeded in single file. The four, constituting what is called a *comet group,* will return after 664, 769, 875, and 959 years, respectively. Moreover, the original comet is thought to be but one member of a group including comets of 1668, 1843, 1880, and possibly 1887, all of which have nearly identical orbits. Comet Brooks was followed by four fragments after its encounter with Jupiter in 1886. Biela's comet was seen to split into two at its perihelion passage of 1846. At least 19 comet groups are recognized; the existence of many more is claimed. The comets' low densities are a necessary condition for the formation of a comet group.

Further details of comets' constitutions are suggested by these bodies' general behavior. Contrary to widespread popular misconception, comets do not swoop across the sky like flaming firebrands. When first visible, an average comet is very faint and shows only a coma. As the comet comes nearer the sun, its nucleus becomes apparent and the head grows in size. Large comets usually begin to form tails at about 200 million miles from the sun, and even small comets take on a slightly elongated shape. As a comet's distance from the sun diminishes, the comet normally brightens disproportionately, more than an inverse square distance relation

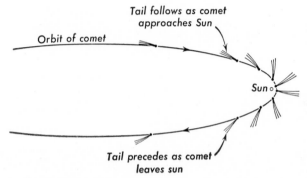

Figure 89. Solar radiation pressure and solar "wind" at all times force the tail of a comet in the direction away from the sun.

would imply. The seeming surplus of light is traceable to the molecules of the coma, chiefly carbon molecules, which absorb light of the sun and re-radiate it as their own. Such fluorescent activity accelerates with the comet's approach.

The coma of an incoming comet grows in size to a maximum which is attained before and after, but not at, perihelion. For example, when Halley's comet was about 300 million miles from the sun, its diameter was only 14,000 miles; this increased to 220,000 miles while the comet was still 180 million miles out and then diminished to 120,000 miles at perihelion. After perihelion it swelled to 320,000 miles and finally contracted to 30,000 miles when last seen.

Comets' tails are generally formed at distances less than 1.5 astronomical units from the sun. They point away from the sun, trailing an incoming comet and preceding an outgoing one.[5] Often the nucleus expels

[5] Comet Arend-Roland, in 1957, showed a sunward-pointing spike; about a dozen similar instances are known. Such spikes are usually seen long after perihelion, last only a few days, appear only when the comet is crossing the earth's orbit. They are dust particles spread in the comet's orbital plane, viewed edgewise from the earth.

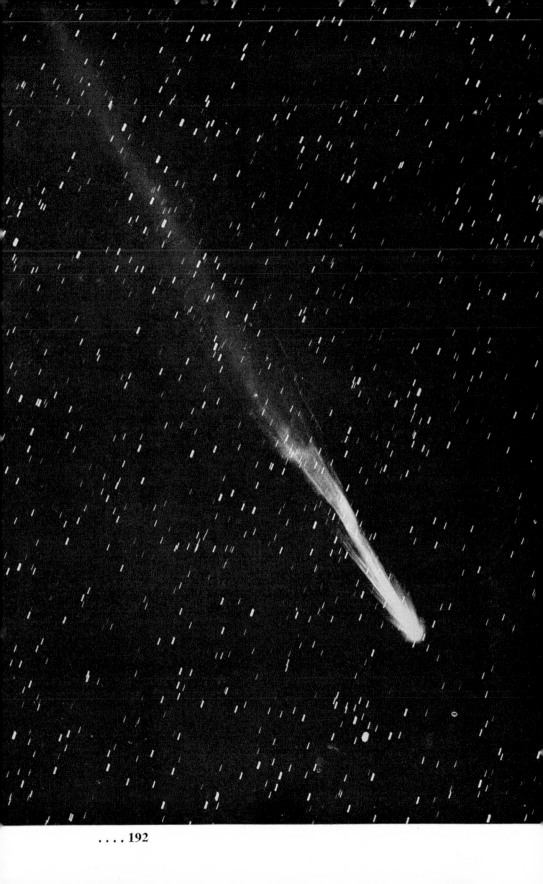

diffuse material in jets or bursts; such matter, passing into the tail, gives it a rippled or filamentary appearance.

On the basis of evidence such as we have summarized, comets are thought to be constituted in the manner of a model facetiously described as a "dirty snowball." The nucleus is pictured as a conglomerate of ices and dust or solid particles. The ices are frozen CO_2, NH_3, and CH_4 as well as H_2O. They may constitute as much as 70 or 80 per cent of the nuclear matter, with dust intermixed. The conglomerate may be in several or many pieces, pieces large enough to survive the solar heat and tidal disruptive force. As the comet approaches the sun, the exterior of the nucleus is warmed by sunlight. The various ices melt and evaporate and the nucleus exhales the gas and dust which becomes its coma. Evaporated molecules are exposed to the sun's radiation. They survive its disruptive effects for approximately 10 hours, on the average, are then broken into constituent atoms; near perihelion their lives are cut even shorter by the stronger radiation. The molecules fluoresce and are therefore visible; the atoms do not and therefore become lost to sight. The coma would soon disappear if it were not continually replenished by evaporation of an estimated 10^{25} molecules per second from the nucleus.

The dust and gas of the coma are evaporated from the nucleus with a speed of a few tens or a few hundreds of feet per second. By diffusion, the coma grows, for the nuclear gravitational attraction is far too slight to check the particles' thermal velocities. The molecules and dust particles now become subject to the pressure of solar radiations. In the first place, light will exert a pressure upon whatever it falls. It produces a calculated pressure of $\frac{1}{11}$ ounce per acre on the earth's surface. Though the effect upon the earth is infinitesimal, the effect is relatively great on small bodies which have proportionately so much more area than mass. The effects are evident even in the motion of artificial earth satellites. They are dominant in the motion of molecules and dust particles in a comet. Radiation pressure upon small, absorbing dust particles exerts a force of repulsion many times greater than the sun's gravitational attraction; the particles are therefore swept back like leaves before a stream of hose water, following convex hyperbolic orbits away from the sun.

In the second place, absorbing gas molecules will be even more

Figure 90. COMET MOREHOUSE. The tail of Comet Morehouse shows an unusual amount of structure and underwent rapid changes. Comet photographs of considerable duration of exposure such as this are very superior to the visual impression that could be had of the same objects even in the largest telescopes. (Courtesy Yerkes Observatory.)

strongly affected than dust. They appear to be accelerated away from the sun by a force sometimes several hundred times as strong as the sun's gravitational attraction. It is almost certain that the radiation pressure on them has been augmented by a violent "wind" of charged atoms emitted from the sun with speeds as high as 1000 miles per second. Such a wind blows the two most long-lived molecules of the coma—CO and N_2—directly away from the sun, as a terrestrial wind blows out a flag. The different wind sensitivity of gas and dust accounts for separate tails of each in some comets. Moreover, it is reasonably well established that many of the seemingly erratic changes in comets' forms and brightnesses (such as the rapid hundred-fold changes in the brightness of comet Schwassmann-Wachmann) are due to fluctuations of the sun's ultraviolet or corpuscular radiation. There is prospect on this account that comets may be used as a sort of solar weathervane.

The conglomerate model of a comet explains the jets and bursts sometimes observed as caused by erosion or disintegration of the surface of the nucleus, suddenly exposing fresh surfaces to evaporation by solar radiation. Possible indirect confirmation of this interpretation is provided by several comets whose orbital motions are anomalous. Encke's comet, for example, has a diminishing period of revolution, as do two others; contrariwise, the periods of comets Winnecke and Wolf are increasing. Such changes could be the effect of systematic rocket-like impulses provided by asymmetric or violent evaporation from the nucleus.

The Origin of Comets

The materials which form the head and tail of a comet are obviously lost to it. The loss of material at a single perihelion passage is small, but it cannot be sustained indefinitely. Halley's comet has shown no obvious signs of wear between A.D. 451 and 1910. On the other hand, comet Faye suffered an almost 250-fold decrease in brightness between 1843 and 1925. We can expect comets with tails to become continually less spectacular as their supply of tail material is dissipated. It is significant that tails are not possessed by any of the short-period comets which come to perihelion frequently.

The mortality of comets poses an interesting problem: How is it that there are still comets for us to see? It is estimated that an average observable comet survives only about 70 perihelion passages. The present short-period comets must then be relative newcomers to the immediate vicinity of the sun. Whence did they come?

Figure 91. HEAD OF HALLEY'S COMET. This photograph of the head of Halley's comet was taken on June 4, 1910, with the 60-inch reflector of the Mt. Wilson Observatory. (Mt. Wilson-Palomar Observatories Photo.)

A clue to their origin comes from a study of comets whose orbits are the most accurately known. The number of comets with small perihelion distances is exceeded by the number with somewhat larger perihelion distances, and the manner of the increase leads one to expect some 5 million comets with perihelia inside the orbit of Neptune. May there not be many more comets at the distances from which these have come? The statistics of long-period comets give ground for expecting that there may, in fact, be approximately 100 billion (10^{11}) comets forming a "comet cloud" about the sun. Such a presumed cloud perhaps extends to a distance of 150,000 astronomical units or more. The radius of the cloud is limited to some such size by the presence of the nearest stars whose attractions would induce more distant comets to desert the sun permanently. As it is, stellar perturbations will serve to "inject" an occasional comet of the cloud into the inner regions of the solar system. Near perihelion, observable comets run the risk of capture or expulsion by Jupiter or one of the other planets. Those captured are thought to make up the current short-period comets. Those which are not captured form the long-period comets. Moreover, since we shall not be able to see any except that very small fraction whose perihelion distances are less than 2 or 3 astronomical units, and since the comets' mean distances are very great, visible long-period comets will be precisely those whose orbital eccentricities are very close to 1.

The number of comets postulated for the comet cloud may seem monstrously, great, yet it is not. Because of comets' very small masses, a hundred billion comets probably have no more than the mass of the earth. The supposition of a great cloud of comets is not only not unreasonable but also appears to account well for most comets' high orbital eccentricities, random orbital inclinations, random longitudes of perihelion, and the existence of short-period comets; the latter are the present "catch" from the vast cometary reservoir.

C. METEORS AND METEORITES

The Nature of Meteors

Almost everyone has seen "shooting stars" and enjoyed their brief displays. They are more properly known as *meteors*. Meteors are small fragments of stone or metal which end their careers in a blaze of glory as they strike the earth's atmosphere at high speed. The particles' outer surfaces are quickly brought to white heat by compression of and friction with the air. Since meteoric particles generate surface temperatures as great as 3000° K, the material of their outer layers melts and is continually swept away in flight, ultimately at the expense of the whole of most meteors.

On the average, five to ten meteors per hour are visible to any observer every clear dark night. The frequency is greater than average after midnight, when the observer is in the unsheltered hemisphere where meteors can be met head-on. For a similar reason, the greatest seasonal frequency in the northern hemisphere occurs in autumn. An estimated 100 million visible meteors strike the earth each day.

Many more meteors which strike the earth cannot be seen. These are very small particles whose surfaces are proportionately so large in comparison with their volumes that they can keep relatively cool by radiating away frictional heat at long wave lengths fast enough to prevent its accumulation. Such particles, from one-thousandth to one-hundred-thousandth of an inch in diameter, are called *micrometeorites*. They are detected

Figure 92. PHOTOGRAPHIC METEOR. This photographic meteor was recorded during an exposure on a section of the Milky Way in Cygnus. Its changing brightness during flight may be seen from the variable thickness of its trail. (Courtesy Yerkes Observatory.)

by the pitting they produce on the surface of rockets and by rocket-borne microphones which pick up the sound of these miniscule hailstones.

Micrometeorites are so small that they are not appreciably altered by their collision with the earth's atmosphere. Sufficiently large bodies will also survive a flight through the air. If not too large, a meteor may be brought by air resistance to a velocity of free fall, landing upon the ground somewhat the worse for wear but not entirely used up. It is then a recoverable *meteorite*. A very large meteor, however, finds the earth's atmosphere almost of no effect as a cushion; it strikes the ground with scarcely diminished momentum. The impact causes it to fragment and vaporize, at the same time creating a crater which may be of considerable size (see p. 208). In general, the larger the meteoric particle, the brighter the meteor. Very bright meteors are called *fireballs* or *bolides*.

197 . . . .

Micrometeorites and meteor debris sift down through the atmosphere to the surface of the earth. Such *meteoritic dust* has been collected from snow, rainwater, sticky surfaces, and collecting tanks; it is probably a constituent of sediments and deep sea oozes. Most clearly indentifiable of the dust particles are spherical ones, droplets of molten meteor which have been shed in its plunge. Their chemical composition differs distinctively from particles of terrestrial origin. From the rate of accumulation of samples, it can be estimated that about 10,000 tons per day are accumulated by the entire earth. This is barely enough to form a layer a few hundred-thou-sandths of an inch thick in 1000 years.

Meteors' Heights and Velocities

Visual observations of meteors were almost the only kind possible until the past two decades or so. Two new techniques now provide observa-tions of far greater accuracy than any heretofore available. Wide-angle,

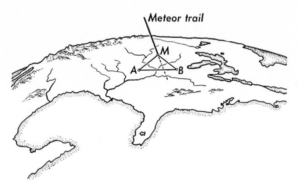

Figure 93. The path of a meteorite *M* may be triangulated by observers as at *A* and *B*. (Map after a drawing by Richard Edes Harrison for *Fortune.*)

high-speed cameras with fast photographic film patrol large areas of the sky every clear night. A comparison of the observations of two such cameras 30 or 40 miles apart will show which meteors have been observed at both places. Each such meteor will be observed to have a somewhat different apparent path amongst the stars as seen from the two stations, just as would a duck viewed by hunters on opposite sides of a river. The intersection of their lines of sight defines the position of the meteor at each instant. The heights of more than 500 meteors have been determined in this way, to an accuracy of a few yards. Meteors appear at a height of 55 to 75 miles, disappear between altitudes of 45 and 60 miles. A rapidly rotating sector

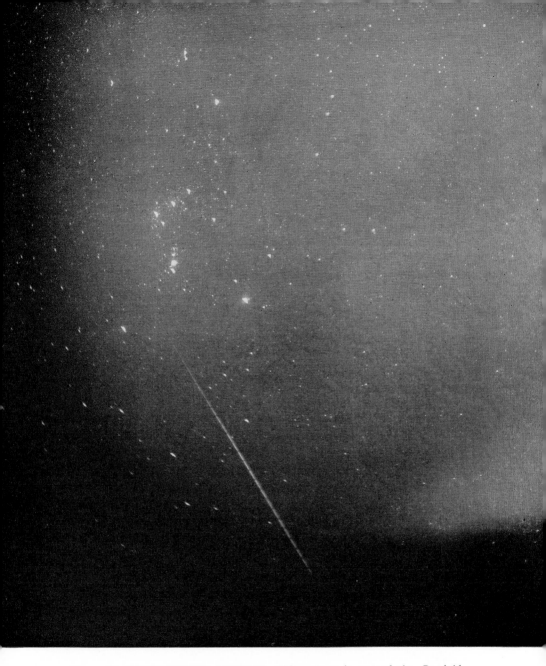

Figure 94. INTERRUPTED METEOR. This meteor is one of the Geminid shower. Its trail has been interrupted every twentieth of a second by a rapidly rotating shutter before the camera lens. By this means its apparent motion has been accurately timed. (Courtesy Harvard College Observatory.)

shutter creates a segmented image of the meteor trail upon the photograph (see Fig. 94); knowing the speed of the shutter, the meteor is thereby timed. Dividing the length of the path by the duration of the flight gives the meteor's speed. Speeds range from 7 to 45 miles per second and are accurate to within about $\frac{1}{3}$ of 1 per cent.

Meteor photography is limited in several respects, however. Only the brightest meteors can be photographed, for the effective exposure time for a short length of trail is only a few ten-thousandths of a second. For the same reason, fast meteors are less often photographed than slow ones. Further, meteor photography is limited to nighttime meteors. The second of the two techniques, radio telescopy, therefore supplements meteor photography in a very valuable way, for radio meteors show a preponderance of high-velocity objects with speeds up to 30 miles per second. Such measures depend upon two stations, as with photography, or may be made by a radar echo-time technique from a single station. The best of these velocity measures are precise to about 1 per cent.

A second advantage of the radio method is that it may be used for observations by day as well as by night. The radio waves in which the meteor is "seen" are broadcast from the ground station and reflected from the column of hot gas created by the meteor. Just as positive and negative charges can be separated by friction when one rubs silk on glass, the friction between meteor and air separates negative electrons and positive molecular ions in the meteor train. Radar pulses are reflected as echoes from the electrons which the meteor leaves in its wake. The visible meteor track of hot gas is only a few feet in diameter. The initial diameter of the ionized radio-reflecting column is probably only a foot or two, though it expands by diffusion of the molecules and ions at a rate of several feet per second to a diameter of several hundred to a thousand feet.

A useful by-product of meteor observations is a determination of the density of the atmosphere at great heights; at 60 miles, the air is a millionth or ten-millionth its density at sea level. In addition, the speed of upper atmospheric winds can be measured by the rate of drift of meteor trails.

The Masses of Meteors

The velocities of meteors are desired for two reasons. First, a knowledge of meteor velocities is needed to estimate meteors' masses; secondly, the velocities are necessary to compute the orbits of meteors. Most meteors have atmospheric velocities which are nearly constant; only some of the brightest, slowest fireballs suffer appreciable deceleration, the greatest deceleration thus far having reduced a velocity to half its initial value at a height of a few miles. The majority of meteors are consumed above a height of 50 miles, where the rarefied air heats the particles efficiently but hinders them little. A meteor's original kinetic energy (energy of motion) is therefore spent primarily in the production of an estimated 99 per cent heat, 1 per cent light, and one-tenth of 1 per cent ionization energy.

The mass of a meteor may therefore be judged from its brightness and velocity. For any given velocity, there is only one mass whose kinetic energy (one-half the mass times the square of the velocity) could supply the observed amount of light as any given proportion of the total (such as 1 per cent). As a check upon estimates obtained in this way, one can also calculate the amount of momentum acquired by the column of gases forming the meteor trail. The meteor train's momentum parallel to itself divided by the meteor's own speed fixes the mass of the particle. It is found that a meteor as bright as one of the half-dozen brightest stars would have a mass less than a hundredth of an ounce, probably much less. A meteor the size of a walnut would appear as bright as the full moon. The small mass of an average meteor implies also a small diameter—a fiftieth of an inch or less.

The Orbits of Meteors

The orbit of a meteor is determinable when the speed and direction of motion of the particle are known (p. 27). The speed alone, after correction for the effect of the earth's gravitational attraction, determines whether the particle is following a closed elliptical orbit or an open hyperbolic one. The critical velocity for a meteor at perihelion colliding head-on with the earth is 45 miles per second. Though older visual observations of meteors seemed to indicate that approximately two-thirds of all meteor orbits were hyperbolic, implying an origin beyond the solar system, the new more accurate photographic and radio data show clearly that less than 1 per cent of all meteors can be hyperbolic. Hyperbolic meteors, if indeed there are any, may be produced by planetary perturbations, like hyperbolic comets. The great majority of meteors follow orbits in the direct sense (97 per cent), with short periods, fairly high eccentricities, and low inclinations. Qualitatively, they bear a strong resemblance to the orbits of the short-period comets. In fact, moribund and defunct short-period comets are thought to constitute a continuing source of such meteors.

Meteors in retrograde orbits have long periods, high eccentricities, and a more or less uniform distribution of inclinations. These orbits bear a strong resemblance to those of the long-period comets. The presumption is that nearly all meteors are of cometary origin, remnants of evaporated nuclear solid material. Bright fireballs and recoverable meteorites represent an exception to this rule, however. The orbits of these bodies are concentrated toward the ecliptic but bear more similarity to the orbits of close-approaching minor planets. The earth would have long since swept up any of the original asteroidal material crossing its orbit, but Mars would not. Presumably Mars perturbs some small asteroids into orbits which intersect the earth's. This seems to be the most likely source of the few brightest meteors.

Meteor Showers

It is established practice to classify meteors observationally as sporadic meteors or shower meteors. *Sporadic meteors* appear at random times and in random directions. *Shower meteors* appear at definite times of the year, have almost identical velocities, and give the appearance of originating from a common point in the sky, their *radiant*. An estimated two-thirds of meteors observed visually and 95 per cent of meteors observed by radio are sporadic.

Meteor showers occur when the earth encounters a meteor swarm or stream. A meteor swarm has been described as a "flying gravel pile," though not a very compact one inasmuch as there is on the average only one meteoric particle per 2 million cubic miles. The meteors of a stream are extended along a considerable arc of their common orbit about the sun. The diameter of a swarm or stream can be inferred from the length of time taken by the earth to cross through it; the Perseid stream is thus judged to have a diameter of about 50 million miles, the Draconids only 400,000 miles.

The particles of a swarm or stream enter the earth's atmosphere along parallel paths. Perspective will therefore cause their trails to appear to converge at the shower's radiant (Figs. 21 and 96). Most showers are named from the constellations which contain their respective radiants. For example, the Lyrids' radiant is in Lyra, the Draconids' in Draco, etc.

Several hundred showers have been catalogued, most of them very inconspicuous. There are at least a dozen major annual showers, produced by streams which the earth encounters every revolution. There are two major periodic showers, the Leonids and the Giacobinids, produced by swarms which the earth encounters only at intervals. Two other periodic showers have disappeared in modern times as a consequence of planetary perturbations which have diverted them to new orbits. Radio meteor observations have led to the discovery of several major annual showers which occur in the daylight hours because the shower radiants are close to the sun in the sky. The number of important showers has been nearly doubled by radio observations.

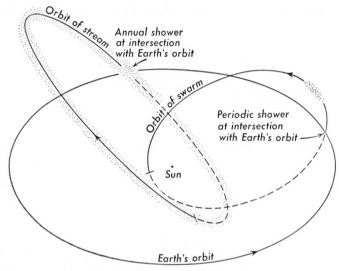

Figure 95. A meteorite stream whose orbit intersects the earth's will provide a shower each year when the earth arrives at the point of intersection. The meteorites of a swarm are more localized and will therefore meet the earth only at average intervals which are the least common integral multiple of the period of the swarm and of the earth.

The orbits of swarm and stream meteors are better known than others. This is due largely to the fact that observations of numerous meteors give a more reliable determination of their common velocity, since the effect of random errors will be minimized. Moreover, knowledge of their radiant serves to define with greater-than-usual accuracy their direction of flight. At least 12 streams follow orbits very nearly identical with those of known comets. The swarm responsible for the spectacular Leonid showers of 1833 and 1866 has an orbit like that of Tempel's comet of 1866; the Andromedids follow closely the orbit of Biela's comet. The inference is plain that shower meteors are a sort of cometary by-product. Conversely, it may be concluded that comets' nuclei contain meteoric particles, albeit 1000 or 10,000 times more concentrated than in a swarm or stream.

Some showers are of long standing. The Leonids have been observed

Figure 96. DRACONID METEOR SHOWER. Forty meteors are recorded on this 12-minute exposure of the sky near the radiant of the Giacobinids in Draco. The photograph was taken during this periodic shower's return on October 9, 1946. The brightest star trail is due to Vega (right center). At the height of this shower, meteors were observed to be falling at a rate of over 5000 per hour. (Courtesy Kenneth Spain, Barnard Observatory.)

at least since A.D. 902. The earth must have intercepted a dense portion of the swarm in the years 1799, 1833, and 1866, for during these showers meteors were reported to be falling at a rate of 200,000 per hour, "like snow." The October Draconids (or Giacobinids) have provided the most recent outstanding display, in 1946, when radio observations recorded falls at a rate of 200 per minute. This same periodic shower has appeared at variable intervals, however, as far back as A.D. 585. Annual showers like the Perseids have been seen for more than 1200 years, and the Lyrids have been recorded for more than 25 centuries.

Presumably all streams begin as swarms. Perturbations induced for the most part by Jupiter will inexorably diffuse swarm particles over a greater and greater length of the orbital arc. For example, the Taurids were probably a swarm following an orbit identical with that of Encke's comet some 13,000 years ago; they are now the most diffuse recognizable stream. The Geminids will probably not be recognizable as a shower in another century. Very diffuse streams of long duration may very well provide a third to a half of all faint meteors. Using diffuseness as an index of age, the Perseids are estimated to be 80,000 years old.

Many, if not most, sporadic meteors may be from streams that have become unrecognizably diffuse over long periods of time. The density of meteoric particles suggests that the number of short-period comets must have been somewhat greater in the astronomically recent past.

Meteorites

A spectroscopic analysis of meteors has shown them to contain the elements hydrogen, oxygen, nitrogen, silicon, sodium, calcium, magnesium, chromium, manganese, iron, and nickel. Meteorites, which can be subjected to more searching laboratory analysis, contain additional elements such as carbon, phosphorus, sulfur, chlorine, potassium, titanium, cobalt, and copper as well as bare traces of rare elements such as gold, silver, and uranium.

Meteors of cometary origin are thought to be made of crumbly material of low density. Ninety per cent of all meteorites, which are of asteroidal origin, are of stony material. About 7 per cent are iron, with 5 to 20 per cent nickel, the rest a mixture of stone and metal. The average stony meteorite consists of 36 per cent magnesium; they are similar to volcanic rocks. Iron meteorites are constituted mainly of the minerals kamacite, taenite, and plessite.

Meteorites' appearances are characterized by the glazed surfaces

which they acquire in their flights through the atmosphere. The durations
of meteorites' falls are so short that the white heat of their surface layers does
not have sufficient time to penetrate inward more than a fraction of an inch.

Careful analysis of the internal structure of stony meteorites indicates

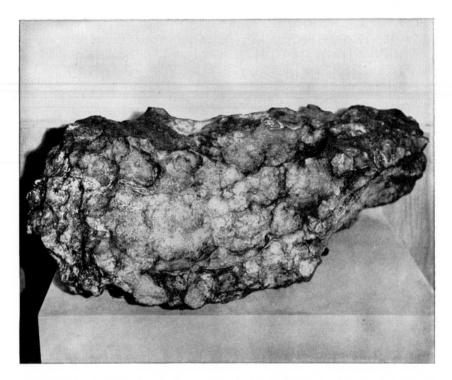

Figure 97. METEORITE. This meteorite, weighing half a ton, was recovered
near the site of the Arizona Meteor Crater (Fig. 99) and is presumed to be a part
of the debris or a small companion to the meteorite or group of meteorites which
produced the famous crater. It is an iron meteorite with about 6 per cent nickel and
now forms a part of the extensive meteorite collection of the Chicago Natural History Museum. (Courtesy Adler Planetarium, Chicago Park District.)

that they have always been at low temperature and pressure. Iron meteorites,
on the other hand, show a characteristic complex crystal structure which
implies that they cooled slowly under high pressure to a temperature of
about 600° F and remained so for at least 50 million years.

An analysis of radioisotopes (p. 283) within meteorites reveals much
about their ages. The oldest stony meteorites appear to be as old as 4.5
billion years, whereas the oldest iron seems to be about 10 billion years.
It is concluded also that the meteorites had formed within 300 million

years of the actual formation of the chemical elements. This is information of the greatest significance for an understanding of the early history of the universe.

Radioisotopic analysis also reveals that meteorites have been exposed to cosmic ray bombardment in interplanetary space for different lengths

Figure 98. CROSS SECTION OF THE WILLAMETTE METEORITE. Sections through two parts of the Willamette meteorite have been etched to show more clearly the interesting crystal structure. (Courtesy J. Hugh Pruett, Evergreen Observatory.)

of time. This is taken to mean that they suffer mutual collisions and are continually subject to pulverization.

The record of meteorite falls dates back to 654 B.C. An estimated 1000 to 2000 falls occur annually. Unfortunately an average of only one recovery per year is made over the whole world. One factor which makes recoveries more difficult is that stony meteorites often fragment in the same way that stones are "exploded" by dropping them suddenly into a campfire. Such fragmentation is the origin of the explosive report which often marks the vanishing of a bright meteor; the reverberations may be heard for a hundred miles in some cases. It also causes stony meteorites to be scattered over a considerable area, sometimes many square miles. The dispersal of

Figure 99, ARIZONA METEOR CRATER. This huge pit nearly a mile in diameter was blasted in the desert by one or a group of meteorites between Winslow and Flagstaff, Arizona. It is exceeded in size only by Chubb Crater in the Ungava region of far northeastern Quebec. Chubb Crater, discovered in 1950, is about 2½ times the size of the Arizona Meteor Crater. (By *Life* Photographer J. R. Eyerman. Copyright *Time, Inc.*)

stony meteorites, their less distinctive appearance, more ordinary density, and lower weathering resistance are responsible for their relatively less frequent recovery. Among witnessed falls, stony meteorites are nearly 20 times more frequent than irons, whereas among finds the irons are 2½ times as common.

Large meteorites embed themselves or blast craters when they strike the ground. The largest known meteorite is an iron estimated to have been originally 80 tons, now sunk about a yard into limestone in South Africa.

There are about a dozen meteorite craters known to be scattered over every continent but unexplored Antarctica. The only large crater formed in modern times was produced by a fall in Siberia on June 30, 1908. The accompanying blast broke windows 50 miles away, was heard for 400 miles, and created a pressure wave recorded in England, 3400 miles from the fall. Trees were blown over for 20 miles around, but the only loss of life was a herd of several hundred reindeer. The site of the fall is marked by ten or so craters which are up to 150 feet across; if the meteorite had arrived 4 hours and 47 minutes later, it would have caused great destruction in Leningrad.

Continually more prehistoric craters are being recognized, some deeply covered by subsequent geological processes. The best known, and second largest, is the Arizona Meteor Crater near Canyon Diablo in northeast Arizona. It is a nearly circular crater 4200 feet across and 570 feet deep in the midst of the desert. Fragments of meteoric material have been found scattered about it for several miles and more have been found in drillings in the crater floor. The drillings show also that the rock beneath has been crushed and pulverized by the impact; some stones have been fused by the heat. The crater has an upturned rim similar to those of lunar craters. Largest in the world is Chubb Crater in the Ungava region of far northeastern Quebec. It has a diameter $2\frac{1}{2}$ times that of the Arizona Meteor Crater. It was discovered only in 1950.

The number and kinds of meteorites may well vary through astronomical ages. There are no fossil meteorites known which antedate the middle Quaternary period of geological history. On the other hand, glass meteorites known as *tektites* fell in uncounted millions upon the earth only during the late Tertiary and early Quaternary periods; none has been observed to fall in historical times. At present, meteorite falls seem to be less common than they were even a century and a half ago and iron meteorites were probably considerably more common in ancient times.

QUESTIONS

1. What is Bode's law? How valid is it? How does it relate to the minor planets?
2. Why were the discoveries of the minor planets so infrequent during the most of the nineteenth century? How is their discovery systematized at present?
3. How do the minor planets differ from the planets in (*a*) diameter, (*b*) mass, (*c*) shape, (*d*) motion?
4. Cite three respects in which the minor planets are of astronomical interest.
5. Contrast comets with the other bodies of the solar system. How can one comet be distinguished from another? Estimate the reliability of this criterion. (*Hint:* Estimate the likelihood that the orbital elements of two distinct comets would all be alike enough to attribute their differences to uncertainties in the elements.)
6. What is the "capture process"? What is its converse? To what comets have

each been applied? What two factors make Jupiter much the most effective captor?

7. Describe the parts of a complete comet. Give the order of magnitude of the dimensions of each. What is the nature and composition of each? Outline the behavior of a comet as it approaches and passes perihelion. Why are comets seen, as a rule, only near their perihelia?

8. What is the nature of a comet's light? What is the source of its luminescence?

9. How are estimates of comets' masses obtained? What are their densities? What independent evidence have we of their very low densities? How is this confirmed by the Roche theorem and the breakup of comets? What is a comet group? Distinguish it from a comet family.

10. Why is radiation pressure so effective upon comets, so ineffective upon planets? How does this fact and the observed motion of comets imply the presence of solid particles in a comet? As repelled molecules recede from the sun, the radiation pressure on them will diminish; at what distance, if at all, will gravitation exceed radiation pressure?

11. When will the next bright comet appear?

12. What origin has been suggested for the comets? How does this suggestion account for their numbers and the character of their motions?

13. Name at least five comets and cite a feature for which each is noteworthy.

14. Explain the inappropriateness of the term "shooting star." What is the source of a meteor's light?

15. How many meteorites are estimated to strike the earth daily? How rapidly is the accretion of meteorites increasing the mass of the earth?

16. Explain how meteorites' masses are estimated. Determine the limit of error in the results for any given limit of error in the assumptions. In view of your result, what may you conclude about the reliability of the order of magnitude of meteorites' estimated masses? About the rate at which the earth is sweeping up meteoritic material?

17. Summarize the principles by which it is possible to determine the orbit of a single meteorite. Compare this with the method for determining the orbit of a meteorite swarm or stream. Why is the latter superior? What is it possible to say at present about hyperbolic meteorites?

18. Where would you look to see the Lyrids? Distinguish between meteorite swarms and meteorite streams. On what grounds may a shower be said to be due to the one or the other? What is their probable origin? What accounts for the disappearance of some? Is it possible to estimate their incidence in the solar system?

19. What is the composition of meteorites? How is this known?

20. What is the likelihood of being struck by a meteorite?

chapter 6
The Sun

• • •

It may perhaps seem strange that a discussion of the sun should be left until all the other bodies of the solar system have been described, for by the sun's radiations the rest are warmed and illuminated, and by the attraction of its mass they are made to revolve about it. One justification that may be given for this topical order is that precisely because of the complete dependence of the rest of the system upon it, it is unique. In almost every feature it contrasts radically with the small, cold, unshining bodies that attend it. In short, we have first dealt with the familiar and the "mildly extreme"; we now turn to the sun for an introduction to some of the radically different conditions and phenomena of the universe.

Our interests in the sun are principally three: (1) Its mass dominates and governs the motion of all other bodies in the solar system, as we have seen in some detail; (2) its radiation is the only important source of energy in the solar system and is the ultimate source of practically every form of terrestrial power; and (3) the sun is a star and as such will be expected to give much information about the stars in general.

What information can we expect to get concerning the sun? What we already have is considerable. It includes such statistics as its distance, size, mass, surface appearance, surface phenomena, and chemical composition as well as some notion of the source of its energy and the conditions and processes in its interior. This still leaves a great many things to be found out about it, some of which we shall note. Let us review our knowledge in detail and see how we come by it.

A. THE SOLAR STATISTICS

"When you can measure what you are speaking about and express it in numbers, you know something about it; but when you cannot measure it, when you cannot express it in numbers, your knowledge is of a meagre and unsatisfactory kind."

—Lord Kelvin

The Distance and Dimensions of the Sun

Before all else we must know the sun's distance. One means of obtaining it is already known to us, namely, that of determining the distance of

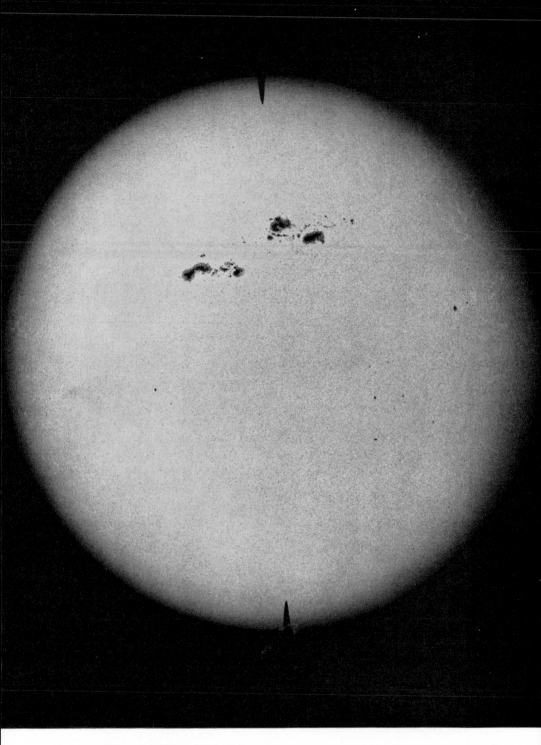

Figure 100. THE SUN. This photograph of the sun was taken under unusually fine observing conditions. It clearly shows sunspots, granulation of the solar surface, and limb darkening. (Mt. Wilson-Palomar Observatories Photo.)

close-approaching planetoids (p. 178). This method has an accuracy of about 1 part in 20,000. It gives the earth's mean distance as 92,913,000 miles. Light requires 8^m20^s to travel this distance.

A newer method, which supplements and will probably supersede previous ones, makes use of the reflections of radar beams from the nearer planets and even the sun itself. By timing the interval required for a radio pulse to propagate from a terrestrial transmitter to Venus and back, the signal time to the planet is gotten directly; since radio waves travel with the speed of light in interplanetary space, the planet's distance is one-half the echo delay multiplied by the velocity of light. A comparison of this figure with the planet's distance in astronomical units shows that there are about 92,875,000 miles in an astronomical unit. The difference in the results of the two methods gives some measure of the uncertainty of the final result. It is hoped that ultimately the radar method will fix any planet's distance to within a few miles.

When the sun's distance has been found, its true diameter can be calculated; the formula is the same one used for the moon. Since the sun has an apparent or angular diameter of $31'59''3$ at one astronomical unit, its linear diameter must be 864,400 miles. This is a diameter nearly 10 times Jupiter's, 109 times the earth's.

The volume of the sun must therefore be 1,300,000 times the earth's. The enormous corresponding mass which this suggests is determinable for the sun, as for any other body, only by a measurement of some gravitational effect which it produces. The most obvious such effect is its acceleration of the earth; as the earth moves forward 18½ miles each second, it is deviated toward the sun ⅑ inch by the latter's gravitational attraction. In other words, the earth "falls" toward the sun ⅑ inch each second; as it happens, a circle of radius 1 astronomical unit also turns in from its tangent by ⅑ inch in 18½ miles, so that the earth thereby "falls" entirely around the sun in a nearly circular orbit.

For comparison, we can calculate how much a body would fall toward the earth each second if it were in a similar circular orbit 1 astronomical unit in radius about the earth. It would be a microscopic three-millionth of an inch. In like circumstances, then, the sun's pull exceeds the earth's by 332,500 times. Consequently the sun must have 332,500 times the earth's mass. This is 2×10^{27} tons. The earth's mass is to the sun's as a tenth of an ounce is to 1 ton.

We obtain the sun's average density by dividing its mass by its volume. Thus it is $332,500/1,300,000 = 0.255$ times as dense as the earth. Since

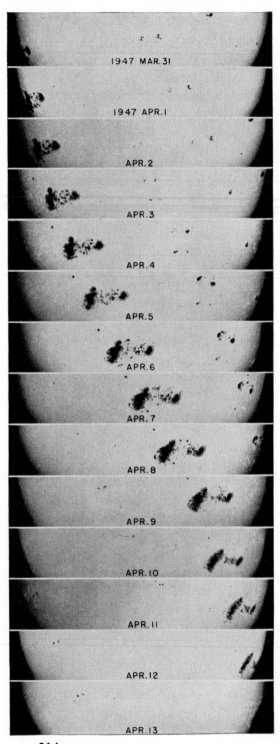

1947 MAR.31

1947 APR.1

APR.2

APR.3

APR.4

APR.5

APR.6

APR.7

APR.8

APR.9

APR.10

APR.11

APR.12

APR.13

Figure 101. ROTA-TION OF THE SUN. Day-by-day photographs of the sun from March 31, 1947, to April 13, 1947, shows how the rotation of the sun carries a large spot group across the solar disk. (Mt. Wilson-Palomar Observatories Photo.)

the earth is 5.5 times as dense as water, the sun must be $0.255 \times 5.5 = 1.41$ times as dense as water.

The sun's surface gravity is not as great as one might at first think. Though its mass is 332,500 times greater than the earth's, its surface is also 109 times farther away. Hence, by Newton's law of gravitation, gravity at the sun's surface will be $332,500/(109)^2 = 28.0$ times the earth's. If a 150-pound man could survive the high temperature on the sun, he would discover that he weighed over 2 tons there; a freely falling body would fall 28 times faster than on earth, 450 feet during the first second after being released. The sun's mass and radius also determine that the velocity of escape from the sun's surface is 383 miles per second.

Observations of semipermanent surface markings on the sun show that it is rotating about an axis inclined slightly more than 7° to the plane of the earth's orbit. It rotates from west to east, like the earth, but in a period of about 25 days at the equator. Strangely, the period is over 28 days in solar latitudes 45° and about 34 days near the sun's poles; its behavior in this respect is similar to that of Jupiter and Saturn. The variable rotation period is probably maintained by a mechanism not yet understood. No measurable changes in the sun's rotation have occurred in the last three-quarters of a century. The rotation is sufficiently slow that the sun is not measurably bulged by it.

The Luminosity of the Sun

The rate at which the sun radiates heat and light is called its *luminosity*. To determine the sun's luminosity, we need to know the strength of the solar radiation received at the earth and the amount by which it is diluted. The former is called the *solar constant*.

The solar constant is determined by measuring carefully the heating effect of the sun's radiation at the earth's surface. Allowance must then be made for the fact that absorption and reflection by the earth's atmosphere reduce the intensity of sunlight by approximately 30 per cent. The value of the solar constant obtained from numerous painstaking measurements is 1.97 calories per minute per square centimeter. A calorie of thermal energy suffices to raise the temperature of 1 gram of water by 1° C; the dietetic calorie is 1000 times greater. Consequently, exposing 1 cubic centimeter of water (1 gram) squarely to full unfiltered sunlight for 1 minute should raise its temperature by 1.97° C (3.55° F). Recent data secured from rockets suggest that the true value of the solar constant may be nearer 2.00 calories per minute per square centimeter. The solar constant may be expressed in somewhat more familiar and mechanical terms as 1.56 horse-power per square yard. Though certain types of radiation from the sun may fluctuate in intensity by a factor of two, they constitute such a small fraction of the whole that the solar constant is believed to be constant to within about 1 per cent.

The factor by which sunlight is diluted in coming from sun to earth can be readily gotten from a simple comparison. The sunlight initially streams out through the surface of a sphere whose radius is 432,000 miles. At the earth's distance from the sun the original radiation is now streaming

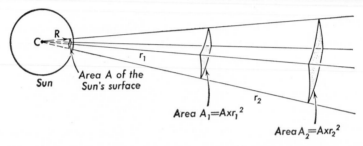

Figure 102. The same total amount of solar radiation flows through areas A, A_1, and A_2. Therefore it must be progressively diluted in strength by the respective ratios $R^2/R^2 = 1:R^2/r_1^2:R^2/r_2^2$.

through an imaginary spherical surface of radius 93,000,000 miles. The sun-light must be spread as much thinner as the ratio of their areas. These are in proportion to the squares of their radii, namely $(93,000,000/432,000)^2$ or approximately 46,200. Hence $1.97 \times 46,200 = 91,000$ calories are radiated by each square centimeter of the sun's surface every minute; this is equivalent to 72,000 horsepower per square yard. This value times the sun's area gives its total output, or luminosity. The final figure is 525×10^{21} (525 sextillion) horsepower or 92.4×10^{24} (92.4 septillion) calories per second.

The Temperature of the Sun

It is clear that the temperature of the sun is not to be had by the usual methods of thermometry. In the first place, the sun is hopelessly inacces-sible. In the second place, since the sun is hot enough to be incandescent, no ordinary glass and mercury thermometer could survive an application to it. Making a virtue of necessity, therefore, we determine the temperature of the sun from the intensity of solar radiation.

For this purpose we invoke a law of physics known as *Stefan's law*. Stefan's law is valid only for a hypothetical source of radiation called a *perfect radiator*. A perfect radiator is one which radiates with the maximum theoretical efficiency. It can be approximated closely by the interior of an enclosure which is maintained at a constant (usually high) temperature. The radiation from such a source is observed through a small aperture in the wall. A perfect radiator is an ideal standard of comparison, for both the quantity and quality of its radiations are independent of the chemical composition, the dimensions, the shape, the density, or any other characteristics of the walls of the source other than its absolute temperature. In particular, the intensity of radiation from the surface of a perfect radiator whose absolute temperature is T will be

$$E = (1.37/10^{-12})T^4 \quad \text{calories/sq cm/sec.}$$

This relation expresses Stefan's law. If T is given, E can be calculated, and conversely, if E is given, T can be calculated. For example, if E is 1520 calories per square centimeter per second, T will have to be 5770° K. For the sun, we have determined that E is in fact 1520 calories per square centimeter per second. By Stefan's law, a perfect radiator with the same surface brightness would have a temperature of 5770° K. We define this to be the *effective temperature* of the sun. We have at this point no assurance that the sun is a perfect radiator. Whether it is or not, the effective temperature may nevertheless be so calculated. We can hope for subsequent evidence that the sun is at least a good approximation, in order that the effective temperature bear a similarity to our customary understanding of the term "temperature."

Matter of a temperature of 5700° K will certainly be in the gaseous state unless perhaps it is also under tremendous pressure—a pressure greater by many orders of magnitude than that at the surface of the sun. This conclusion is reinforced by direct observational evidence. First, the visible surface cannot be solid, since it rotates differentially, the equator more rapidly than the poles. Secondly, the solar surface cannot be liquid, for it is far above its critical temperature; the critical temperature is the limit above which a substance cannot be liquefied, regardless of pressure. Hydrogen and helium, the two preponderant constituents of the sun, have respective critical temperatures of 33° K and 5° K, whereas even a solid such as sulfur has a critical temperature of only 1400° K. The solar surface is gaseous beyond any doubt.

B. THE PHOTOSPHERE

*"Our inborn spirits have a tint of thee,
Even as our outward aspects . . ."*

—BYRON

Qualitative Analysis of the Photosphere

The sun's gaseous surface is what is shown in any ordinary photograph of the sun. It may be regarded as the outermost layer of the body of the sun. It is the layer from which sunlight originates and is therefore called the *photosphere*. The photosphere is surrounded by a blanket of generally transparent gases which comprise the *solar atmosphere*. The solar atmosphere is visible only during total solar eclipse, when the moon masks the body of the sun, or by means of special instruments. These special instruments perform a more sophisticated analysis upon the light of the sun and thereby yield new information about the sun. To understand their usefulness, we must first know something of the nature and origin of radiation and the laws governing its interaction with matter.

THE NATURE OF RADIATION

Radiation (of which light is one variety) is a form of energy known as *electromagnetic energy;* it is called "electromagnetic" because it is capable of exerting electric and magnetic forces on small electrically charged particles such as moving electrons. All forms of electromagnetic radiation are propagated through empty space with a velocity of 186,000 miles per second. Prior to the twentieth century it was not fully appreciated that radiation possesses a dual character, behaving sometimes after the manner of a wave phenomenon and at other times after the manner of a corpuscular phenomenon. As a result, there were advanced two competing theories of its nature. The wave theory of light proposed that it be regarded as an "electromagnetic wave." The graph of such a wave has the appearance of a cross-section view of a ripple on a pond. Such a theory accounts for light's being able to bend around corners slightly just as a ripple can bend around an obstruction; this is *diffraction*. The pattern of "points" on a distant light seen through a screen is produced by diffraction. The wave theory can also best explain interference of light, the phenomenon responsible for the colors of a soap or oil film. In fact, the success of the wave theory together with the results of some decisive experiments performed in the nineteenth century led to the abandonment of the corpuscular theory. The latter was revived in a revised form, however, in the early years of the twentieth century in order

duced by any glowing transparent substance; most commonly such substances are in the gaseous state. A dark-line spectrum is produced by any transparent substance placed between the observer and a more intensely glowing source of continuous spectrum; again, it is most common that substances producing dark-line spectra are in the gaseous state, though this is

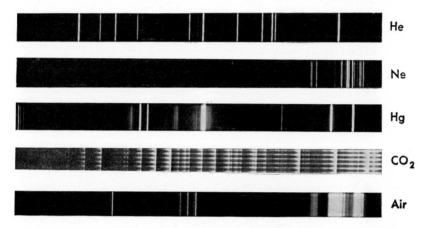

Figure 107. EMISSION SPECTRA. The first three of the emission spectra reproduced here are line spectra of atoms. The clear differences among them make it possible to identify these and the other elements by their unique and characteristic spectra. The fourth spectrum is a band spectrum due to the molecule carbon dioxide. The pattern of horizontal stripes is due to striae in the glowing discharge tube used as a source and is irrelevant to the spectrum proper which consists of numerous bands, each a group of many closely-spaced lines of consecutively lesser intensity. Bands are characteristic of the spectra of molecules as in distinction to atoms. Thus, the spectrum of ordinary air, a mixture of molecules, shows the bands of its constituent gases, strongest among them being nitrogen, as in the fifth spectrum. (Courtesy H. R. Rymer.)

not always the case. At all events, a line spectrum—bright-line or dark-line —identifies the state of its source, whereas a continuous spectrum does not.

There are common enough examples of sources of each type of spectrum. The glowing tungsten filament of an electric light bulb will have a continuous spectrum. A mercury or sodium vapor lamp or an ordinary neon sign produces a bright-line spectrum. And finally, an absorption spectrum is produced by the atmosphere of the sun and every star as well as the atmospheres of the earth and planets.

Line spectra (of either kind) give a great deal more information about the gases in which they originate than do continuous spectra. One of the most important things to be learned from a line spectrum is the chemical composition of the gases which produce it. This is found out simply by a straightforward comparison of the wavelengths of the lines in the spectrum of a source of unknown composition with the laboratory-determined wavelengths of the spectra of the various elements and some of the compounds. The wavelengths present in the spectrum of any element are both unique and characteristic, and while the source of a single line may be ambiguous because of coincidences, the observed positions of a number of lines from a spectrum will serve to delimit the possibilities to the element or elements present. In fact, spectroscopic analysis is used as a fast, extremely sensitive, and comparatively simple method of making qualitative chemical analyses in such diverse fields as criminology and metallurgy.

The Solar Spectrum

The spectrum of the sun is a dark-line spectrum. A number of the dark lines, which vary in strength with the height of the sun in the sky, are plainly due to the atmosphere of the earth and therefore of no further concern to us here. Most observations of the solar spectrum are limited to the visual region of the spectrum, approximately 3500 to 7000 Å. Rocket-borne spectrographs have extended the observations of short wavelengths to the x-ray region and special infrared-sensitive photocells have extended long wave-length observations to some 20,000 Å. Radio telescopes give information on the sun's radiation at very long wavelengths—up to many feet. The spectrum of the sun in the visual region, at least, is virtually constant; very small changes would be readily detectable.

The solar spectrum presents two distinct though related problems—an analysis of the continuous background and an analysis of the dark lines. Both are formed primarily in the photosphere, though some of the lines are modified appreciably by the gases of the surrounding atmosphere. The atmosphere subdivides very naturally into a lower layer, adjacent to the photosphere, called the *chromosphere,* and an extensive outer envelope called the *corona.* The chromosphere extends about 5000 to 7500 miles above the photosphere and the corona to limits which are somewhat arbitrary, possibly as far as the earth. The chromosphere is described as scarlet, a color it owes to the great strength of the red line of hydrogen; the faint corona is yellowish and pearly white. Each of these layers merges into the next; though the boundaries between them are not sharp, the distinction between the layers is real and not difficult to make.

The key to the identification of the dark lines is the fact that the dark lines of an absorption spectrum of any element occur at exactly the same wavelengths as the bright lines of that element. Since this principle was first recognized in 1859, about 18,000 of 26,000 dark lines of the solar spectrum between 2935 and 13,495 Å have been identified, including all intense lines. A total of 67 of the chemical elements is known to be probably present: of these, 55 are certain, 3 are found only in sunspots (see p. 244), 2 are known only in compounds, 4 show only a single line, 3 others are tentatively identified. Of the rest, 6 whose lines are accessible are certainly absent, 9 others do not have lines in the accessible region of the spectrum, and 12 more are not to be expected.

Elements known to be present in the sun include such familiar ones as Ca, Fe, O, H, N, Si, C, and Al. There are no elements in the sun that are not known on the earth, though helium was first discovered in the chromosphere of the sun. Its emission line was observed at an eclipse of the sun in 1868, whence its name from the Greek *helios,* meaning sun. Its isolation in terrestrial laboratories came 27 years later.

The continuous spectrum of the sun is studied in the form of a spectral energy curve. This is a graph in which the horizontal scale is one of wavelengths, the vertical scale intensity of radiation per unit wavelength. Dark lines would appear as indentations. The total intensity of the sun's radiation is the sum of the intensities in all wavelengths and is therefore equal to the

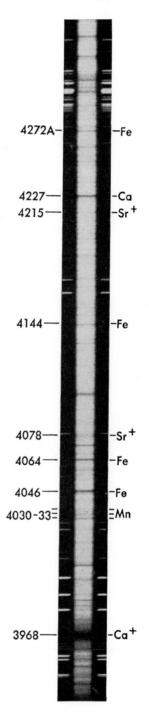

Figure 108. SECTION OF THE SOLAR SPECTRUM. The great richness of the solar spectrum can be seen from this selected portion of somewhat more than 300 Angstroms extent. The line of Ca+ near the bottom is the H line of that ion. This is not a spectrogram of direct sunlight but of diffused sky light. The comparison emission spectrum is of titanium. (Courtesy of the Observatory of the University of Michigan.)

area beneath the spectral energy curve; the amount would be about 10 per cent greater without the notches due to the absorption lines. We have found

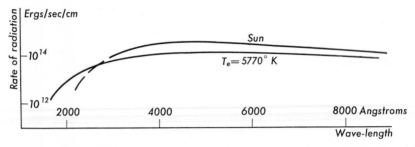

Figure 109. The energy curve for a perfect radiator at 5770° K is compared with the observed energy curve of the sun (neglecting individual line absorption). The near equality of the areas beneath the two curves indicates that the sun's effective temperature is about 5770° K.

that the sun's total intensity is equivalent to the intensity of a perfect radiator at a temperature of 5770° K. It is pertinent, therefore, to compare the sun's spectral energy curve with that of a perfect radiator of the same

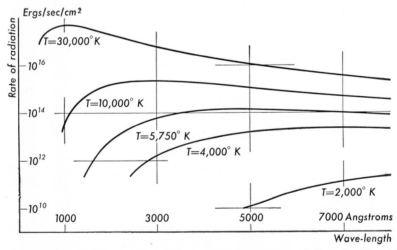

Figure 110. Perfect radiators at the absolute temperatures indicated will radiate the several wavelengths with an intensity specified by the associated curve. The curves are graphs of the equation expressing Planck's law.

effective temperature. This is done in Figure 109, where the indentations of the lines have been ironed out.

The spectral energy curves for perfect radiators are given by *Planck's law,* which states that the energy E_λ radiated in wavelength λ by a perfect radiator whose absolute temperature is T will be

$$E = \frac{3.704 \times 10^{-13}}{\lambda^5 (10^{0.6229/\lambda T} - 1)}$$

ergs per square centimeter per second per angstrom. (To lift 1 pound 1 foot off the ground requires 13,550,000 ergs of energy.) Thus, if $T = 6000°$ K, the intensity of radiation from a perfect radiator is 10,000,000 ergs per square centimeter per second at 4700 Å; conversely, if a perfect radiator is known to radiate 10,000,000 ergs per square centimeter per angstrom at 4700 Å, then its temperature must be 6000° K.

Since the radiations of any two wavelengths from a perfect radiator will indicate one and the same temperature, we may use Planck's law to determine how well or how badly the sun approximates a perfect radiator. We simply determine from the absolute intensity of the sun's spectral energy curve at some wavelength what would be the temperature of a perfect radiator having the same intensity at that wavelength; a temperature so determined is known as a *monochromatic color temperature.* If the monochromatic color temperatures are the same for all wavelengths, the sun is a perfect radiator; to the extent that they differ, the sun differs from a perfect radiator.

In this way, we find that the sun is not a perfect radiator. In the violet and extreme red regions of the spectrum, its monochromatic color temperature is 5800° K, in the infrared 5600° K, in the blue-green 6150° K. However, all these figures are within 5 per cent of the average of the greatest and the least. The approximation is therefore a fairly good one. For many stars other than the sun, the approximation of their spectral energy curves to those of perfect radiators is rather poor. The sun itself is deficient in the ultraviolet and infrared, has an excess in the blue-green.

A part of the reason for the difference between the spectral energy curve of the sun and that of a perfect radiator at 5770° K is the fact that the photosphere and atmosphere of the sun have depth. The top of the photosphere blankets what is below it so that the lower portions are hotter than the upper. The sun's radiation is therefore a composite of radiations from all depths through a layer several hundred miles thick in which the temperature increases inward. Since the relative contribution of each depth is different in every wavelength, it is not surprising that the total radiation in different wavelengths does not correspond to the temperature of one single depth.

The variation of temperature with depth, known as the *temperature gradient,* is responsible for one clearly visible effect, *limb darkening.* Limb darkening is an apparent fading over the sun's apparent disk from the center to edge. It is caused by the fact that one sees to a lesser depth into the sun's atmosphere along a tangential line of sight than along the line of sight at the center of the disk. One therefore looks to a depth at which the temperature is lower and, by Stefan's law, the intensity of radiation

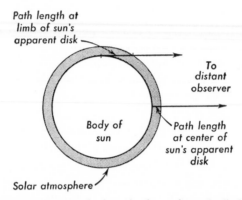

Figure 111. The longer atmospheric path of rays from the limb of the sun causes these rays to suffer a greater absorption than those coming from the apparent center of the sun's disk. The result is an apparent limb darkening on the sun.

less. It is limb darkening and not depth perception which gives the sun its globular appearance.

Quantitative Analysis of the Solar Photosphere

The qualitative analysis of the solar photosphere has in principle been carried out in a straightforward manner. It has not required any detailed knowledge of the way in which the spectrum lines were formed. A quantitative analysis of the sun's photosphere, however, can be undertaken only with the aid of relevant information concerning the way in which atoms absorb and emit radiation. To understand this, we must consider a few rudimentary facts concerning the structure of atoms.

THE STRUCTURE OF ATOMS

All matter in its familiar forms consists of only 92 kinds of chemical elements; eleven other elements have recently been produced artificially by nuclear transmutations. The enormous diversity of common material is a consequence of the almost unlimited number of ways that the 92 fundamental species can and do combine. The smallest unit of any element is an atom of that element; there are evidently 92 kinds of atoms. Needless to say, atoms are of a smallness of size that taxes the imagination; 240 million hydrogen atoms side by side would span only an inch and 1.709 $\times 10^{25}$ of them would weigh but an ounce. Other kinds of atoms are larger and weigh up to about 250 times more than a hydrogen atom.

Although the atom is the smallest unit of a chemical element which can exhibit the chemical properties of that element, the atom is itself

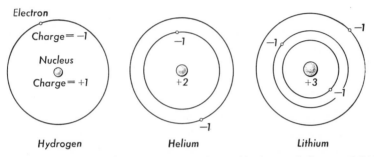

Figure 112. The three simplest atoms are those of hydrogen, helium, and lithium. The greater complexity of atoms of the remaining elements consists chiefly in the possession of additional electrons.

nonetheless divisible. It has been found that an atom consists of a nucleus and electrons. We visualize the nucleus as the relatively massive heart of an atom and suppose the light electrons to revolve about the nucleus just as the planets revolve about the sun, or as mosquitoes swarm about a man's head. They are persuaded to do so by the attraction which the nucleus exerts on them. In contrast to the attractions between the sun and planets, however, the attraction of nucleus for electrons is not primarily gravitational but electrical (for though the particles are very close to each other, they also have extremely small masses); the electron is negatively charged, whereas the nucleus bears a positive charge and, as everyone knows, unlike charges attract. The charge on the nucleus is always some integral multiple of the amount of charge on the electron, this multiple being known as the *atomic number* of the particular kind of atom in question. The atomic number of an atom determines the atom's chemical identity. Thus the atomic number of hydrogen is 1, helium's is 2, lithium's is 3, . . . etc.; the highest atomic number of the natural elements is 92, that of uranium.

Since complete atoms are electrically neutral, each must contain a number of electrons equal to the atomic number of its nucleus; only by the combined charge of this many electrons can the total positive charge of the nucleus be neutralized. Thus the hydrogen nucleus governs one electron, helium governs two, lithium three, . . . , and so on to uranium, whose nucleus controls 92 electrons.

Strangely enough, the electrons of an atom are not free to revolve as they please or as chance might effect, but rather do they assume definite orbits of a special set, just as though they were constrained to tracks like trains. Normally the electrons occupy the innermost (smallest) available orbits of an atom, never more than one electron to the same orbit. The diameter of the outermost occupied orbit is the diameter of the atom.

Such is the naïve mental model which serves for the simple description of many atomic processes. Let us see how the absorption and emission of radiation can be described in terms of it.

THE ABSORPTION AND EMISSION OF RADIATION

When an atom absorbs radiation from a beam of light, it takes from the beam an amount of energy. The abstracted energy does not vanish but is transferred to the *outermost* electron, which in consequence jumps to a larger orbit about the atom's nucleus. The larger the electron's orbit, the greater the electron's energy; in exactly the same way, the earth would move in a larger orbit about the sun if it were somehow given more orbital energy. The remarkable and important thing about this jump or *transition,* as it is called, is that the atom absorbs an amount of energy which is precisely the amount necessary to boost the outer electron from its initial orbit to some one of the larger *permissible* orbits; the atom never miscalculates. The importance of the atom's unerring accuracy lies in the fact that the energy of each photon (see p. 219) it absorbs is determined by the radiation frequency. In fact, the energy in ergs is 6.624×10^{-27} times the frequency in cycles per second.

Here we have the key to the origin of absorption spectra. In selecting the energies it can assimilate, the atom makes a necessary and simultaneous selection of radiation of the associated frequencies (or wavelengths); thus it acts like a radio which possesses only pushbutton tuning. It is at precisely these frequencies (or wavelengths) that the spectrum lines of that atom occur. The missing radiation in the frequencies absorbed has been "swallowed up" by the absorbing atoms.

But, to be sure, an atom cannot retain indefinitely the radiation it absorbs; *as a rule,* it will disgorge all the energy it has ingested after only a hundred-millionth of a second. The electron jumps back from its larger orbit to the original one, and its doing so results in the emission of a photon of radiation of exactly the wavelength it absorbed. This is why the emission and absorption lines of any atom occur at identically the same wavelengths. The notable difference between the absorbed and re-radiated photons is that the re-radiated photon may go not only in the same direction as the original but in any other direction as well. Those which take new directions are lost to the original beam, and its intensity is thereby diminished in that wavelength; hence the lesser intensity of light in an absorption line.

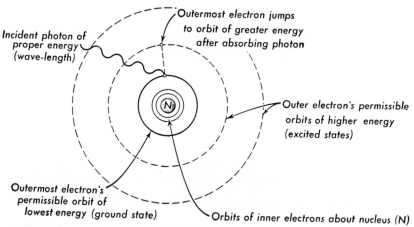

Figure 113. An optical electron (usually the outermost) in any atom may be transferred from its orbit of lowest energy (ground state) to an orbit of greater energy (excited state) by the absorption of a photon of radiant energy. The reverse of such an absorptive transition is accompanied by the radiation of a photon. As a rule, transitions involve only one electron at a time.

When an atom absorbs a photon whose energy will make the outermost orbital electron jump farther out than the atom's largest orbit, the electron is separated from the atom and the atom is said to have undergone *ionization.* An electron-deficient atom is called a positive *ion.* Atoms lacking single electrons are said to be singly ionized, those lacking two electrons are doubly ionized, etc. Since an ionization cannot alter the atomic number of an atom's nucleus, an ionized atom retains its chemical identity but acquires a net positive electric charge. For example, un-ionized or neutral calcium is given the symbol Ca, singly ionized calcium is designated by Ca+, doubly ionized calcium by Ca++, etc. The most easily ionized atom is caesium; the most difficult to ionize is helium.

The outermost remaining electron of an ion is now the one which makes the transitions which result from an absorption or in an emission.

However, because the charge on the nucleus of the ion is not balanced by the collective charges of the remaining electrons, the electron orbits will

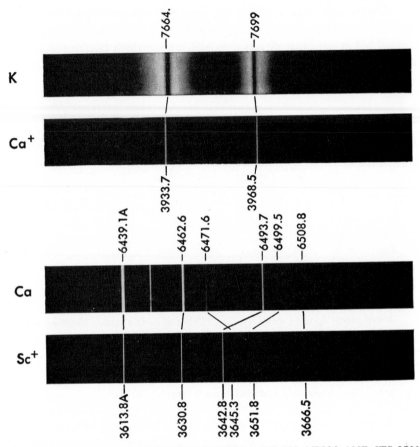

Figure 114. PORTIONS OF THE SPECTRA OF AN ATOM AND ITS ION. The spectrum of Ca+ is qualitatively similar to a corresponding part of that of K whereas the spectrum of Ca is qualitatively similar to a corresponding part of that of Sc+. There is no similarity whatever between the spectra of Ca+ and Ca; the spectrum of the neutral atom and its ion can be clearly distinguished. The two lines of Ca+ shown here are the H and K lines so prominent in most stellar spectra. (Courtesy National Bureau of Standards.)

be altogether different from those of the neutral atom, and consequently the spectra of the atom and its ions will be entirely distinct. The presence of an ion can thereby be identified by its spectrum lines in the same way as is a neutral atom. Including the neutral atom, there are usually not more than two ions present in a gas at the same time.

The reverse of ionization is *recombination*. In recombination an ion recaptures a free electron and simultaneously radiates a photon. The wavelength of the radiated photon will depend on the kinetic energy of the recaptured electron. Since there are no restrictions on the orbits which free electrons may have, the radiated energy may be any amount equal to or greater than that which would be radiated by an electron with no kinetic energy at the time of its recapture. Such recombinations thus form an emission continuum having an abrupt beginning at some minimum frequency

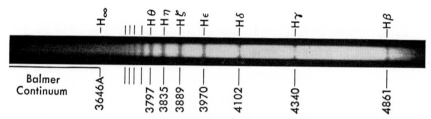

Figure 115. CONTINUOUS ABSORPTION AT THE BALMER LIMIT. The strongest lines in the spectrum of the star θ Crateris are the lines of hydrogen. They form a *series* which theoretically has infinitely many members which cluster ever closer together as they approach the limiting wavelength 3646 A (marked H_∞). Beyond this limit of one of the series of discrete lines of hydrogen is an absorption continuum in which the wavelengths that can be absorbed (or emitted) by excited hydrogen atoms are as close together as one pleases. The absorptive power of hydrogen atoms in this *Balmer continuum* falls off rapidly at shorter wavelengths. The Balmer continuum of normal hydrogen is, however, an analogue of the much more extensive absorption continuum of the negative hydrogen ion. (Courtesy Lick Observatory.)

(maximum wavelength) and fading off toward higher frequencies (lower wavelengths). Conversely, ionization will produce an absorption continuum.

Continuous absorption and emission are extremely important processes in astronomical bodies, for they provide one of the most effective modes of interaction between matter and radiation. By continuous absorption, electrons are released with energies which depend upon the character of the radiation flowing past. The electrons so freed interact with other electrons and nuclei by collision, a mechanical process which randomizes their velocities and energies. The subsequent continuous emission which results from recombination restores the absorbed energy to the stream of radiation but at frequencies which are determined by the randomized distribution of electron and ion velocities. The re-emitted radiation may therefore be of a different character from the absorbed radiation.

The re-emitted radiation will also almost as often as not be in the backward direction. We can say, therefore, that wherever there is a flow of radiation, as in the photosphere and atmosphere of the sun, continuous absorption will modify the nature of the radiation and reduce the amount of the flow.

Analysis of the Continuous Spectrum

Continuous emission and absorption in the photosphere of the sun are complementary. Without continuous absorption, we could see to unlimited depth into the sun; that is to say, the sun would have no photosphere. The level to which we give the name "photosphere" and the nature of the radiations from this level are therefore largely determined by the nature of the continuous absorption there. We can say in advance that the absorptive ability, or *opacity,* of the photospheric gases must be nearly uniform over the visual region of the spectrum, else the continuous spectrum of the sun would show corresponding distortions.

The opacity of the photosphere is remarkable for being so high. Indeed, the source of the high opacity was a major astrophysical mystery that was solved only as recently as 1938. Not until then was it suggested that the principal source of the opacity of the photosphere was a curious substance known as negative hydrogen. *Negative hydrogen* is an ion (symbol H^-) formed of an ordinary hydrogen atom and an additional electron. The extra electron gives the pair a net negative electric charge and thus makes of it a negative ion. It is surprising that such a combination of particles should exist; that they can was first predicted theoretically and their existence has since been demonstrated in laboratory arcs burning in a hydrogen atmosphere.

The negative hydrogen ion absorbs effectively from 16,000 Å to the ultraviolet region of the spectrum. The predicted opacity agrees well with the amount necessary to account for the intensity of the continuous spectrum of the sun. Much of the difference between the continuous spectrum of the sun and the energy curve of a perfect radiator may be laid to the specific absorptive properties of the negative hydrogen ion.

The amount of negative hydrogen in the atmosphere of the sun is really very small, about one ion for every million neutral hydrogen atoms. Even this amount would not be present but for the enormous abundance of neutral hydrogen and the presence of easily ionized metals. The latter supply about one electron for every 10,000 hydrogen atoms. It is remarkable that such a small impurity can change an otherwise transparent gas to a substantially opaque one.

The transition from transparency to opaqueness occurs in a layer of the sun about 20 miles in thickness. The comparative thinness of this transition layer accounts for the apparently sharp boundary of the sun in visible light. As a corollary to this observation, we may note that because the opacity is greater in some wavelengths than in others, the photosphere has a depth which is different in different wavelengths.

The Formation of Absorption Lines

We have seen that the existence of some opacity is essential to the formation of the continuous background of the solar spectrum. We now note that the existence of some transparency is necessary for the formation

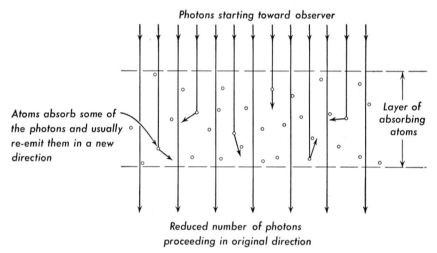

Figure 116. The individual atoms in a layer of cooler atmospheric gas will, by absorption and subsequent re-emission, divert some of the original number of photons from the beam which is directed toward any particular observer. When the absorptions are limited to discrete wavelengths, a dark-line spectrum is the result.

of dark lines, for if the photosphere were perfectly opaque to all wavelengths, there could be no contrast between adjacent wavelengths, i.e., no dark lines. The formation of the solar absorption spectrum is therefore a considerably more complex process than the formation of absorption lines in a laboratory demonstration. Let us compare the two.

A familiar demonstration of the production of a dark-line spectrum makes use of light from a glowing filament, which has a continuous spectrum. This light is passed through sodium vapor before it enters the spectroscope. The sodium atoms abstract two wavelengths in the yellow, known as the D lines. Most of the absorbed light is re-emitted in directions different from that of the original beam and is thereby lost to it; such a process of line formation has already been described.

In the photosphere of the sun, scattered photons might be expected to "ricochet" from sodium atom to sodium atom, so that every photon of the wavelength of the *D* lines could not fail to emerge from the photosphere eventually. The final intensity of the *D* lines would in this case be no less than the intensity of the initial beam, and no line would appear. However, because of continuous absorption, the life of a knockabout *D*-line photon is cut abruptly short. Though it is absorbed by negative hydrogen at the

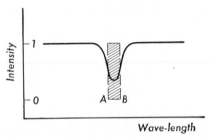

Figure 117. A graph of the dependence of monochromatic intensity on wavelength gives a *line profile*, as schematized by the solid curve. The width *AB* of the hatched section is defined to be the *equivalent width* of this line if the hatched section has the same area as the profile indentation. The profile of only a small section of spectrum is represented here.

wavelength of the *D* lines, there is almost no chance that it will be re-emitted in the same wavelength. In other words, much of the contribution made by the sodium atoms to the photospheric radiation is credited to general funds rather than to the specific account of sodium *D* lines. So it is with other kinds of atoms also. In this way, the radiation of the dark lines is taken from these wavelengths and added to the continuum; this transfer of funds is estimated to involve 10 per cent of the sun's radiation.

The study of both emission and absorption lines is best made with the aid of graphs called *line profiles*. Line profiles show how the intensity varies with wavelength over a section of spectrum which contains a line or lines; where there is an absorption line, the intensity is less and the graph will register a dip. Most profiles have the shape of a script "v." The area of the indentation corresponding to an absorption line is a measure of the intensity of the line. The strength of a line is therefore expressed in terms of its *equivalent width;* this is the number of angstrom units a profile of the same area would span in the graph if it were everywhere of a depth corresponding to complete absorption. Both the equivalent width of a line and the explicit contour of the profile are the result of a number of factors which must be taken account of in trying to make a quantitative analysis of the sun's atmosphere.

The first factor which we may note is the natural width of the line. The *natural width* of a line is the width the line would have if it were radiated by an atom at rest and in complete isolation. Even different lines of the same kind of atom have different natural widths because these are determined by probabilities characteristic of the atom; we may think of the atom as "preferring" some transitions more than others in a ratio proportional to the natural widths. Natural widths are calculable from the laws of atomic physics.

Next we recognize that the strength of an absorption line will depend also upon the number of atoms capable of making the necessary transition from the initial energy state to the final energy state. This number is called the *population* of the initial state. An energy state in which the outermost electron occupies the smallest available orbit is called the *ground state;* any other state is an *excited state.* The population of every excited state increases with temperature;

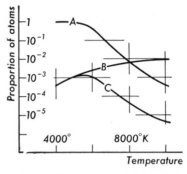

Figure 118. These curves show how the proportions of excited and ionized atoms depend upon the temperature, the pressure being constant. Curve *A* shows the proportion of *all* silicon atoms which are neutral. Curve *B* shows the proportion of *neutral* silicon atoms excited to the state from which they can absorb the line at wavelength 3905 Å. Curve *C* shows the proportion of *all* silicon atoms excited to the state from which they can absorb the line at 3905 Å. Note that their numbers initially increase, subsequently decrease, attain a maximum at slightly less than 6000° K.

the increase is at the expense of the population of the ground state, which therefore decreases with temperature. However, the population of the ground state always exceeds that of any other.

With increasing temperatures the increase of the populations of the excited states is countered by the fact that more and more atoms will be converted into ions by more intense radiation and more violent collisions. Though these two tendencies work at cross-purposes, it is easy to predict their joint effect. At sufficiently low temperatures the population of any excited state will be small but will increase with temperature as long as the number of atoms ionized is small. The growth of the population of this state will be checked, however, at a temperature where the rate of loss of atoms through ionization equals the percentage increase in the population of that state; thereafter an increase of temperature will bring about an actual decline in the population of that state. Hydrogen and helium are relatively difficult to excite and ionize, calcium and iron relatively easy. At the temperature of the photosphere, therefore, the populations of the excited states of hydrogen and helium are comparatively small, whereas those of iron are comparatively large. Calcium is to a large extent ionized.

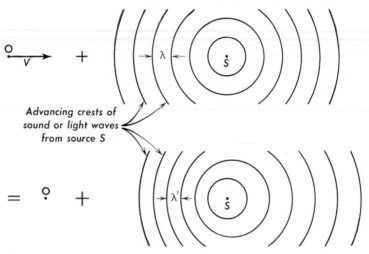

Figure 119. To an observer O approaching a wave source S with velocity V it will appear that waves of length λ are compressed to waves of length $\lambda' = \lambda - \lambda V/v$, where v is the true velocity of the wave. The apparent difference of wavelength between source and moving observer is called the Doppler effect.

The equivalent width of spectrum lines formed in a hot gas such as the sun's photosphere will be increased by an effect known as Doppler broadening. The *Doppler effect* is an apparent change of wavelength of any light or sound which originates in a moving source. Common experience includes no example of the Doppler effect in light, but instances of the effect in sound are numerous. Thus, for one, an apparent drop in pitch of the warning bell at a railroad crossing is heard by the passenger on a speeding train; to the motorist stopped at the crossing, the pitch seems constant. So, to an observer from whom a source of light is rapidly receding, the wavelength of each radiation will seem to be greater than normal, the frequency less than normal; an approaching source will produce the opposite effect.

Now, an absorbing or emitting atom will usually be in rapid thermal motion while it is absorbing or emitting; for example, the atoms of the solar atmosphere are flying about at an average rate of several miles per second because of the high temperature there. Let us suppose that the particular atom we fix our attention upon is momentarily rushing toward us and that before suffering a collision with another atom and rebounding in another direction, it radiates. Since the atom is an approaching source, the wavelength of its radiation will appear to us to be diminished because of the Doppler effect. On the other hand, if it radiates during one of its brief sallies away from us, the wavelength of its radiation will for the same reason appear to be increased. Among great numbers of atoms some will

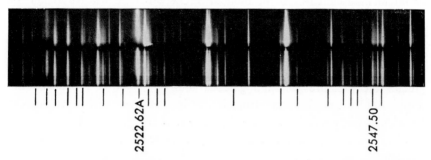

Figure 120. PRESSURE BROADENING. These two small portions of the ultra-violet spectrum of Cr+ show pressure broadening in a laboratory source. The upper was taken with the source in air at atmospheric pressure; the lower was taken with the source in air at one third atmospheric pressure. Even this relatively slight decrease of pressure has been sufficient to make a number of the lines more sharp in the lower than in the upper spectrogram. The markers indicate lines in which the effect is most pronounced. (Courtesy National Bureau of Standards.)

be doing the one and some the other, with all variety of speeds from one extreme to the other. The wavelengths of their radiations therefore appear to be distributed over a slight range of wavelengths to either side of the true wavelength, and the emission lines appear "broader" than they otherwise would. Plainly the converse process will cause absorption lines also to appear widened. Broadening of spectrum lines by this mechanism is appropriately called *Doppler broadening*. Since the pace of the thermal motions of atoms increases with temperature, the Doppler broadening will also.

We have tacitly assumed that radiating or absorbing atoms are mutually aloof and will perform with unconcern in the presence of neighbors. Such is not the case. To begin with, atoms perturb other nearby atoms merely by their presence, causing slight changes in the energy an electron will possess in any given permissible orbit; and, of course, a change in the energy associated with any electron orbit will result in a change of the frequency of radiation absorbed or emitted during a transition involving that orbit. This will result again in a broadening of spectrum lines. Since this broadening depends upon the proximity of the atoms, it will increase as the number of atoms per unit volume, i.e., as the density of the gas. Besides this interaction of atom upon atom, an effect which would occur even if all the atoms were placidly at rest, one atom may, as it darts by, interrupt a radiating neighbor, somewhat as a yawning man can be temporarily startled out of his yawn by an abrupt or threatening gesture. As before, the effect will be a broadening of the spectrum lines. Inasmuch as this type of broadening increases as the number of encounters, it will be greater for higher density and temperature than for low, and since the conditions for both this and the previous kind of broadening are met to an increasing degree with increasing pressure, these two mechanisms of broadening are frequently lumped together as *pressure broadening*. In other words, the greater the pressure within a gaseous source, the more broadened the absorption or emission lines from it will be; however, different lines are broadened unequally by increased pressure. If the pressure becomes sufficiently great, the lines will eventually become so broad as to form a continuous spectrum.

The Analysis of the Absorption Lines

The one factor to which no consideration has yet been given is the absolute abundance of each kind of atom. Plainly no lines of an element will appear if that element is not present in the sun. On the other hand, we might expect that two atoms would absorb twice as much as one atom, one hundred atoms one hundred times as much as one atom, and so on. If this were the case, one could conclude at once from the strengths of the absorption lines of the solar spectrum what number of atoms of each kind there are in the photosphere and atmosphere of the sun. Unfortunately a quantitative analysis of the sun is not quite so simple. To see why, let us consider an analogy.

Imagine that an upstream run of salmon or of smelt is in progress and that fishermen are catching them from a bridge that crosses the river. The location (wavelength) of the river (spectrum line) identifies the nationality of the fishermen (kind of atom). The wider the river, the longer the bridge, the more men that can fish from it, and the more fish that will be caught. The width of the river corresponds to the natural width of the spectrum line.

The first sportsmen to arrive at the bridge will take positions at its center, where the water is deepest; they will catch the most fish per hour.

about 15,000 times as strong as the magnetic field of the earth. It may change as much as 1 per cent of this in an hour. The magnetic force becomes more and more tangential toward the edges of the spot and at the same time weaker, vanishing at the edge of the penumbra.

The direction of the magnetic force determines its *polarity* or sense. The polarity is north if the direction of the force is such that the north pole of a magnet would be pointed in this direction by the force. The polarity of sunspot fields obeys a simple though surprising set of rules: Preceding and following spots are of opposite polarity; preceding spots of northern and southern hemispheres are of opposite polarity; and spots reverse polarities in succeeding 11-year cycles. In the cycle which began in 1954, preceding spots in the northern hemisphere had a north polarity. This is the fifth cycle for which polarity reversal has been observed.

The field of 38 per cent of all spots or groups has but a single polarity; 62 per cent show clearly two polarities; the remaining 1 per cent are multipolar. However, most unipolar spots are old bipolar spots whose following spots have dissolved; unipolar spots have bipolar faculae. During the development of a spot or spot group the magnetic forces grow rapidly until the spot reaches maximum size, remain constant in intensity the remainder of the life of the spot, then rapidly decline.

It was for a long time not clear whether the magnetic forces produced sunspots or vice versa. It now seems certain that the former is the case, for it is not easy to understand how a cool area of the sun's surface could generate a magnetic force, whereas it is possible to suggest how a magnetic force might create a cool area such as a sunspot. To this end we recall that the photospheric gas is highly ionized and therefore shows a number of properties usually associated with metals, such as being a good conductor of heat and electricity. Those properties which are of present concern to us may, in fact, be well simulated by a fluid (oil, for example) in which there is a suspension of a large number of small particles of iron. Such a mixture fills the cylinder of a magnetic clutch. When one end of the cylinder is spun about the axis of the cylinder, it will set the liquid of the cylinder into motion without disturbing the opposite end because the fluid cannot transmit a shearing force (as opposed to a compressive force). If, now, a magnetic force is applied so as to run the length of the cylinder, the metallic particles in the fluid "freeze," giving the mixture a rigidity which will transmit the torque of an axle as though the two ends were coupled by a solid shaft. What is important is this imperfect analogy is that magnetic forces can inhibit the motion of magnetically sensitive matter in any direction but that of the magnetic force. The magnetic force in a sunspot inhibits the normal convective circulation in the subphotospheric layers. The additional heat ordinarily transported by the convection is thereby denied to the affected area, and it lapses into a lower temperature just by losing its excess heat through radiation. A spot is thus thought to be a region of comparative tranquility in the photosphere. The spot is an indirect result of the magnetic field.

An observation which bears on the nature of a spot is the curious fact that there appear to be more spots visible in, more spots formed in, and more spots entering the eastern hemisphere of the sun than the western. Since this can hardly be the true state of affairs, it must be inferred that

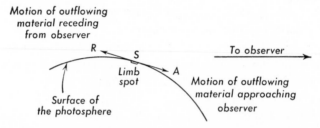

Figure 127. Solar gases flowing outward from a sunspot *S* will approach an observer on one side (*A*), recede from him on the other (*R*).

it is an illusion brought about by spots' being tilted in the direction of the sun's rotation. Further, since spots diminish in size and disappear altogether at the sun's limb, they must be depressions in the photosphere. Summing up, a sunspot is conceived of as a tilted, dish-shaped depression in the photosphere, cooler than the normal photosphere because magnetic forces inhibit the convective transport of subphotospheric energy within the spot area.

There is one last detail. Observations of the Doppler effect in the near and far edges of spots near the limb indicate a tangential flow of matter. At lower levels, the flow is radially outward with a maximum speed of about 2 miles per second at the boundary of the umbra. At higher levels, the flow is inward. The spots are thus cyclonic areas whose sense of rotation, like those on the earth, is determined by the rotation of the sun; the magnetic fields are, anticlimactically, not responsible for the whirlpool effect shown by the penumbra.

A phenomenon as complex as the cyclic formation of sunspots with polarity reversal is not to be accounted for easily. It is only recently, therefore, that a theory has been put forth which bids fair to explain most of the characteristic features of solar spot activity. To begin with, it is reasonable to suppose that since the spots are brought into being by magnetic forces, a theory which properly describes the behavior of the sun's magnetic field may at the same time elucidate the mystery of sunspots. To begin with, therefore, let us attempt to picture the magnetic field of the sun by means of lines of force; lines of force are imaginary curves which at each point of space have the same direction as the magnetic force at that point. The lines of force of the sun's magnetic field might be expected to have an arrangement such as would be possessed by an ordinary bar magnet which had been distorted from a cylindrical shape to the shape of a sphere by compressing it longitudinally. The lines of force would lie in planes at right angles to the solar equator. Each would be a complete loop, emerging near one pole of the sun, arching high over the sun's surface, re-entering the sun near the opposite pole, and completing its circuit along a shallow path parallel to and not far beneath the surface of the sun.

Such a line of magnetic force could not long remain undisturbed, however. For the same reason that a magnetic force can inhibit motion across itself, a magnetic line of force will be slowly transported by the flow of any medium in which it is embedded. Consequently, the sun's more rapid equatorial rotation will gradually wind the magnetic lines of force around the axis of rotation very much as a fishing line winds forward upon a reel when an inexperienced caster produces a backlash. In three years, approximately 5 turns about the equator would have been achieved. More lines of force, like more winds of wire in an electromagnet, are equivalent to a magnetic force of greater strength. In this way the magnetic forces may attain sufficient magnitude to contribute significantly to the expansiveness of the gas. The gas need therefore not have as great density as the gas nearby where magnetic forces are not so great. The regions of most intense magnetic force, local inhomogeneities in the field, will therefore rise like bubbles, bringing with them their lines of magnetic force.

Where a magnetically buoyed element of gas pops to the surface of the sun, a spot group will be formed. The lines of force above such an area form a loop like a missed stitch. At the points of a loop's emergence and return, the magnetic forces will be of opposite polarity even as they are found to be in a bipolar sunspot.

It should be noted that as the more rapid equatorial rotation of the sun winds the magnetic lines of force forward about the sun's axis, the sense of the force will be opposite in northern and southern hemispheres. Following a line of magnetic force continuously along its length requires that its direction in one hemisphere be the reverse of what it is in the other. This means that the loops of magnetic force which form the spots will have opposite senses in the sun's two hemispheres. Consequently, leading spots in the northern and southern hemispheres will be of opposite polarities.

The emergence of the lines of magnetic force and the consequent formation of sunspots arrest the winding process. The lines of force then re-form as before, but their gyrations have literally turned them inside out. This guarantees that the spots of the next cycle will be of reversed polarities. The distortion of the lines of force by the sun's differential rotation, their emergence and re-formation, is a process repeated over and over. A more detailed elaboration of the process will explain many more of the features of sunspots and their cycle—their tilt, the dominance of leading spots, spots' migration toward the equator, their absence in high latitudes, and much else. The successes of this theory argue strongly that it is substantially correct.

C. THE SUN'S ATMOSPHERE

"So may the outward shows be least themselves;
The world is still deceived with ornament."

—SHAKESPEARE

The Structure of the Chromosphere

The transparent chromosphere and corona are visible only under special conditions or by special means. One of these special conditions is a total solar eclipse, when direct photospheric radiation is blocked from view by the body of the moon. The projecting solar atmosphere may then be studied.

One method of study makes use of the flash spectrum of the sun. The *flash spectrum,* which appears suddenly and remains briefly, is a spectrum obtained with a slitless spectrograph during the short interval when the photosphere is entirely covered while the chromosphere is not. The crescent of exposed solar atmosphere provides a long and narrow source of light; the slit of a conventional spectrograph may therefore be dispensed with. The resultant spectrum shows bright spectrum crescents (lines) characteristic of a glowing transparent gas. An analysis of this spectrum tells much about the chromosphere.

For one thing, the flash spectrum is not a perfect bright-line complement of the solar dark-line spectrum. All elements having dark lines will show bright crescents, though not necessarily of proportionate intensity; in addition there are 30 lines of helium and a number of hydrogen which have no dark-line counterparts. Most of the lines of the flash spectrum arise from the bottommost 500 miles of the chromosphere and therefore are to be seen no longer than 2 seconds before totality. The strongest lines, on the other hand, may arise from the chromosphere's full 8500-mile depth and persist for about 40 seconds. The strength of a spectrum line and the height to which the corresponding atom or ion extends in the chromosphere may be readily gauged by the thickness or the length of the crescents in the flash spectrum. In this way one ascertains from the red line of hydrogen that hydrogen extends to a height of 7500 miles, from the H and K lines of Ca^+ that this ion may be found to 8700 miles.

To the emission lines known in the flash spectrum have been added approximately 30 emission lines in the far ultraviolet, as shown from rocket data. Of these, the strongest is the resonance line of hydrogen. A *resonance line* is one produced by a transition from the first excited state to the ground state. It will generally be by far the strongest of any line in the spectrum of an atom. Familiar examples include the D lines of sodium, which give the yellow color to a flame to which table salt has been added, and the H and K lines of Ca^+, which are the strongest absorption lines in the visible portion of the solar spectrum. Other lines in the ultraviolet spectrum of the chromosphere are due to neutral and five-times ionized oxygen, neutral and thrice-ionized silicon, quadruply ionized nitrogen, and others.

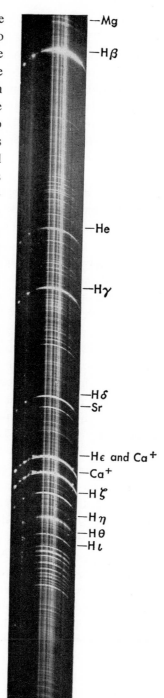

Figure 128. THE FLASH SPECTRUM. This flash spectrum was obtained at the eclipse of January 24, 1925. Both solar prominences and irregularities at the moon's eastern limb contribute to the uneven outline of the individual crescents. (Mt. Wilson-Palomar Observatories Photo.)

These emission lines are superposed upon a less intense continuous emission. This is due to the recombination of ionized hydrogen, to the formation of negative hydrogen, and to the scattering of photospheric continuous radiation by free electrons, much as sunlight is scattered in our own atmosphere by molecules of air.

Monochromatic images of the chromosphere may also be had outside eclipse by using a slitless spectrograph. We are prevented from seeing the chromosphere under ordinary circumstances only by the glare of light diffused by our own atmosphere in the vicinity of the sun in the sky. This diffused light will be widely dispersed into a dilute continuous spectrum by the slitless spectrograph, whereas the light from the chromosphere is divided into only a few lines. The contrast between continuous and bright-line spectrum is thereby reversed, and the chromosphere becomes visible when the photosphere is screened from view.

Though the chromosphere appears to be stratified, it is not. The chemical composition of the chromosphere is not distinguishable from that of the photosphere. Some spectrum lines owe their greater strength in the chromosphere simply to the fact that the pressure there is lower. The higher pressure of the photosphere is more favorable to the recombination of ions with electrons and therefore limits the production of strong lines by many ions. Other lines of the flash spectrum are limited in height by the altogether unexpected increase of temperature with height in the chromosphere. For example, hydrogen is mostly neutral below 2500 miles, becomes predominantly ionized above 3700 miles. Similarly, lines of neutral calcium are limited to the lower 3000 miles because calcium becomes completely ionized at greater heights; strontium and barium, which ionize easily, are found only in the lower chromosphere; magnesium, which is more difficult to ionize, reaches a height of 4500 miles. Above a height of 2400 miles, the temperature of the chromosphere rises steadily toward the extremely high values which we shall find for the corona.

The actual temperature of the chromosphere has been the subject of widespread disagreement. A temperature of 30,000° K or more seemed to be required to explain the very height of the chromosphere in the face of the sun's strong surface gravity; only a hot gas was thought to be able to resist the sun's gravitational compression. High temperature seemed to be necessary also to account for the excessive width of the hydrogen and helium lines.

Opposed to this evidence was the fact that radio wavelength radiation, which might be expected from so hot a chromosphere, was absent. The observed ionization and excitation of atoms and ions of metals likewise do not square with a high chromospheric temperature. Neither do the effects of solar radiation upon the earth's upper atmosphere.

The discrepancy seems to be caused by the presence of a very great amount of turbulence in the chromosphere. In fact the chromosphere is so roiled that the velocity of 7 to 10 miles per second of the churning elements and eddies exceeds the thermal velocity of the atoms and ions. This has the effect of stiffening the gas, making it less compressible. By the Doppler effect, it also widens the spectrum lines; this is called *turbulent broadening*. The effects of turbulence thus simulate some of the effects of high temperature. It therefore seems most likely that the temperature of the lower chromosphere is only about 4600° K, rising to 6100° K at 2500 miles, and increasing rapidly beyond this point. Actually, the chromosphere is probably a mixture of hot and cold elements in violent commotion, something like the water being run into a basin from wide-open hot and cold water faucets.

The pressure at the base of the chromosphere is about a hundred-fiftieth of an atmosphere, the density about a hundred-millionth the density of water. Both have fallen off about a million times at a height of 3700 miles. The total mass of the solar atmosphere is about a ten-billionth the mass of the entire sun.

Chromospheric Phenomena

The phenomena of the chromosphere are studied, as is its structure, with slitless spectrograph and radio telescope. Of great supplemental value is another instrument known as the *spectroheliograph*. A spectroheliograph is an instrument with which a photograph of the entire sun may be taken in the light of a single wavelength, such as an emission line. The newest forms of spectroheliographs amount simply to light filters admitting only a few angstroms or less.

A spectroheliograph may be used to observe the radiation of one element at a time. It is tuned to a wavelength in the spectrum of the element in question. Other atoms' radiations will be strained out, much as a radio set strains out all but one station's broadcasts. Spectroheliograms are most often made in the light of the red line of hydrogen or the violet line of ionized calcium but sometimes in the light of iron, magnesium, sodium, or ionized strontium as well.

Preference for spectroheliograms in the light of hydrogen or ionized calcium is due to the fact that these species of atom are distributed through the full depth of the chromosphere, whereas most of the rest are to be seen

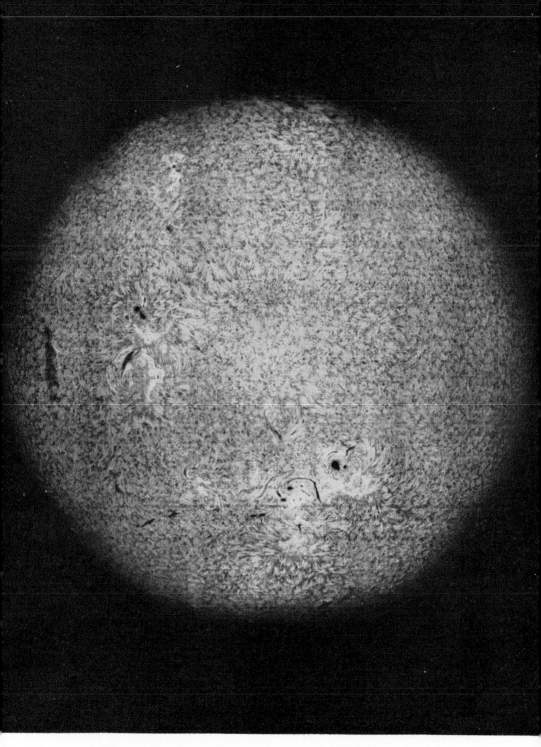

Figure 129. SPECTROHELIOGRAM. This photograph was taken in the light of the red line of hydrogen. It vividly suggests the turbulent conditions at the surface of the sun. (Mt. Wilson-Palomar Observatories Photo.)

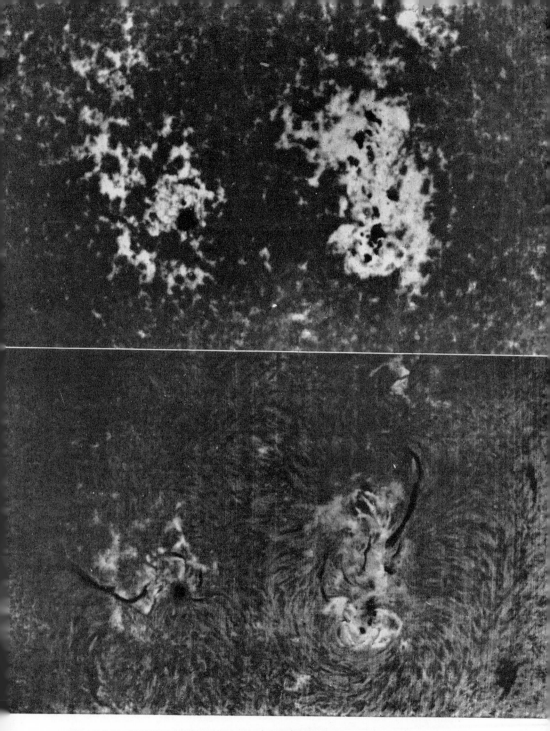

Figure 130. SPECTROHELIOGRAMS OF SUNSPOTS. These spectroheliograms of the same two spot groups have been taken in the light of hydrogen (below) and calcium (above). The spot groups are in opposite hemispheres, as may be judged from their opposed senses of whorling in the lower spectroheliogram. (Courtesy Yerkes Observatory.)

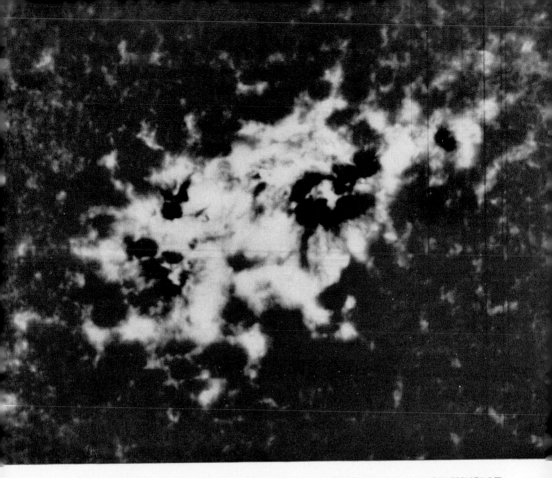

Figure 131. HIGH LEVEL SPECTROHELIOGRAM OF A LARGE SUNSPOT.
This calcium spectroheliogram was taken of a large spot group on October 10, 1903.
The bright areas are *flocculi.* (Courtesy Yerkes Observatory.)

only in the lower levels, as the flash spectrum shows. What is more, the
spectroheliograph can discriminate to a considerable extent between high
and low levels of the chromosphere, for the center of a strong line of the
solar spectrum is formed at high levels and is not perfectly dark (some of
the "fish" got away); a spectroheliogram in this central wavelength therefore shows a high level of the chromosphere. On the other hand, the wings
of a line are formed by pressure broadening at low levels where the pressure
is greater. A spectroheliogram in an off-center wavelength will therefore
show a low level of the solar atmosphere; it looks much like an ordinary
photograph inasmuch as most sunlight comes from the bottom of the solar
atmosphere. The most detailed spectroheliograms are those of the upper
levels in the red line of hydrogen.

Spectroheliograms are able to show particularly well the vortical pattern of gases about a sunspot. In hydrogen, they show that the whorls
have the normal cyclonic sense in more than four-fifths of all spots and

do not reverse themselves when the magnetic polarity changes. However, large bipolar spots show a pattern which is certainly affected by the magnetic forces of the spot. Spectroheliograms also show that in the light of hydrogen, the vortices are opposite those in the light of the metals. This is assuredly an effect due to the difference of the sense of flow at different heights above a spot—outflow below, inflow above.

Spectroheliograms make it evident that faculae extend upward from the photosphere into the chromosphere, increasing in temperature upward. Such bright chromospheric faculae are sometimes called *flocculi*. They are to be found over all parts of the disk of the sun. They migrate toward the poles about 2° per solar rotation.

The chromosphere appears to vary in depth around the limb and probably varies in depth during a sunspot cycle as well. The top of the chromosphere is given a stubbly appearance at the limb by the presence of a great number of small tongues of bright chromospheric gas called *spicules*. The spicules have diameters of 300 to 350 miles, individual lifetimes of about 2 minutes. They rise with uniform velocity of 12 to 15 miles per second, stop abruptly, and fade. Though they may rise to 6000 miles, their average height at the equator is 4500 miles, at the pole 4700 miles. They are most numerous at the poles, least numerous in latitude 35°. They stand almost vertically at the poles but incline as much as 30° to the vertical elsewhere. The spicules emit strongly in the far ultraviolet resonance line of hydrogen; to do so, they must be at a considerably lower temperature than the adjacent corona. It is thought that the buffetings of the chromosphere by the photospheric granules produce the spicules which in turn are visibly conveying their kinetic energy to the lower corona.

Spectroheliograms show on the solar disk long, dark, threadlike markings called *filaments*. When rotation carries a filament to the limb, it becomes clear that the filament has been simply the projection against the disk of a long ribbon of chromospheric gas. The ribbon lies on edge, so that when seen at the limb, it appears to project out from the edge of the sun as a *prominence*.

Though prominences are usually visible at total eclipses of the sun, it was not until an eclipse in 1860 that they were shown to be a part of the sun rather than an appendage of the moon. A typical prominence is 18,000 to 60,000 miles high, more than 100,000 miles long, but only 3000 miles thick; the volume of the average prominence is 90 times that of the earth. These dimensions make it evident that prominences project well into the corona. Prominences are, in fact, condensations within the corona. They are surrounded by a dark coronal space where the density of matter is only

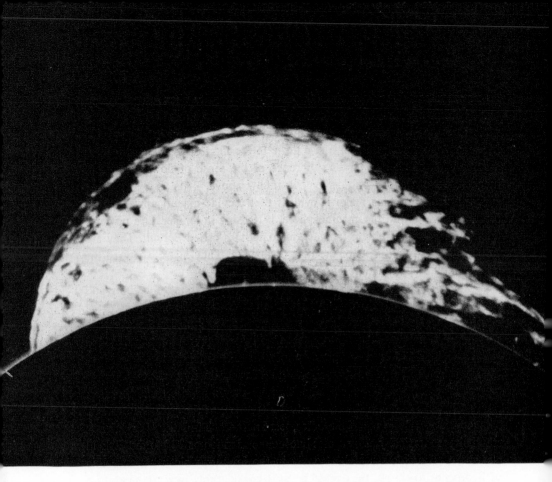

Figure 132. SOLAR PROMINENCE. This rapidly rising eruptive prominence of June 4, 1946, is one of the largest ever seen. Its height as shown here is more than 200,000 miles above the sun's surface. Within 80 minutes this huge prominence had risen to such heights as to have vanished from the field of view except where the arch meets the sun's surface at left and right. (Courtesy High-Altitude Observatory of Harvard University and the University of Colorado.)

about 1 per cent of that in the cooler prominence. As coronal material condenses on the "cold" prominence, the prominence grows until it falls into the chromosphere. Every second, an estimated millionth of the coronal mass condenses into prominences. Individual prominences last as long as six or eight months.

The spectra of prominences show as many as 40 of the Balmer series lines of hydrogen in the visible region, 26 of the Paschen series in the infrared, and numerous neutral and ionized atoms of other kinds. The prominences show the same form in all lines and are therefore of uniform chemical composition. The outer parts of prominences are subject to intense ultraviolet and x-ray radiation from the corona, whereas the inner parts are shielded.

Figure 133. QUIESCENT PROMINENCE. This photograph shows a promi-
nence hovering in a comparatively immobile state at the sun's limb. (Sacramento
Peak Observatory, Geophysics Research Directorate, AFCRC, courtesy Dr. D. H.
Menzel.)

Prominences are to be found everywhere on the sun, though concentrated in each hemisphere into a polar crown and a belt about 10° poleward of the spot zone. The latter migrates with the spots during a cycle.
The number of low prominences, like the number of spicules, does not vary
greatly during the sunspot cycle; the number of high prominences shows
an 11-year periodicity. Polar prominences are most numerous between
minimum and maximum of the spot cycle.

Though no prominences are static, the polar prominences and a
majority of those in the spot belt are quiescent. However, rapid motion
characterizes certain kinds of prominences known as surges, spot prominences, active prominences, and eruptive prominences. Spot prominences
form loops and arches and move mostly down toward an adjacent spot,
seemingly along lines of magnetic force. Active prominences are hotter and
more turbulent than average. Eruptive prominences are less a special class
than a phase in the development of other types. Eruptive prominences rush
out from the surface of the sun at speeds occasionally as high as 700 miles
per second, well above the velocity of escape and great enough to observe
visually. They attain heights of a million or more miles before they dissipate
or fall back into the sun. For periods of a few minutes they may be ac-

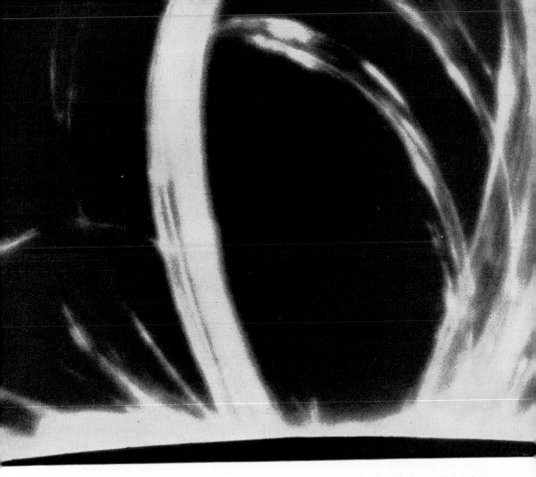

Figure 134. LOOP PROMINENCE. A loop of chromospheric material has formed a prominence in the vicinity of a sunspot. Its shape and motion are probably governed by local magnetic forces. (Sacramento Peak Observatory, Geophysics Research Directorate, AFCRC, courtesy Dr. D. H. Menzel.)

celerated discontinuously by as much as 50 times the surface gravity of the sun. A flash of light accompanies such sudden accelerations. The accelerations and the light flashes may be the result of outward-moving shock waves in the solar atmosphere, waves that travel with a velocity greater than the thermal velocity. Prominences which disappear eruptively may reappear in almost the same form and place within a few days to two weeks. Nearly half of all equatorial filaments disappear suddenly but temporarily, some by eruption, some by shrinking, others by flowing into a spot.

Most equatorial prominences initially align themselves approximately along a solar meridian. As they age, they are stretched out parallel to the equator by the differential rotation of the sun, moving slowly toward the pole. The poleward migration results from a gradual disintegration of the

Figure 137. THE CORONA. This remarkable photograph shows the corona of the sun at total solar eclipse much as the eye would see it. Only by the use of a special rotating shutter was it possible to record the detail of the outer portions of the corona along with the structure of the inner parts. (Courtesy M. Laffineur, Observatoire de Haute Provence.)

1941. In the interim they were half-seriously attributed to a hypothetical element "coronium." They are now known to be produced by an array of highly ionized atoms: iron ionized 9 to 14 times; nickel ionized 11 to 15 times; manganese 11 and 12 times ionized; calcium 11 to 14 times ionized; argon 9 and 13 times ionized; vanadium ionized 9 times; cobalt ionized

269 . . . .

14 times; and potassium and chromium 10 times ionized. The strongest coronal emission line is one in the green at 5303 Å due to 13-tuply ionized iron. The outer corona shows a weak solar dark-line spectrum attributable to diffraction of sunlight by interplanetary dust particles.

It has also been found that the chromosphere and corona emit radio waves. In the long wavelengths, radio telescopes "see" the sun to be at least twice as large as it appears in visible light, fading gradually toward the edges, with no apparently sharp boundary such as we see with eye or camera. The chromosphere is visible only in short wavelengths, which can penetrate the highly ionized corona.

The coronal radiations are remarkable in that the emission lines come from ions of such a high order and the long wavelength radio radiations are of such unexpectedly high intensity. There can be only one explanation: the temperature of the corona is approximately $1,000,000°$ K. Though this is only a round figure, possibly uncertain by a factor of two, the corona is nonetheless the hottest visible matter in the universe. Its high temperature is the cause of the obliteration of the dark lines in the light scattered by the free electrons of the inner corona moving with velocities of 3000 to 6000 miles per second.

The temperature is uniformly high throughout the corona, varying little over large distances. Yet there are differences. The strong green line, one of the most easily excited, is found entirely around the limb; in contrast, the yellow line at 5694 Å due to 14-times ionized calcium is found only over the hottest spots.

Coupled with the small temperature gradient is the gradualness of the decrease in density. Using the density of electrons as an index of the density of coronal matter in general, we note that the density of electrons is about 100 million per cubic centimeter at a height of 300 miles above the photosphere, about 1 per cent of this at one solar radius, but only 1 per cent of this another eight solar radii farther out. The density in streamers is about five times that between streamers.

Some appreciation of how very tenuous the corona is may be had by noting the behavior of the few comets which have passed through it. The great comet of 1882 passed close to the surface of the sun and was enough brighter to be visible even in daylight. The great comet of 1843 traversed the corona within 300,000 miles of the surface of the sun without visible deceleration. Its speed was 350 miles a second. Contrast the fate of a meteor having this velocity even in so rare a gas as the earth's atmosphere at a height of 100 miles. Such considerations lead to estimates that a column of corona 1 square centimeter in cross-section would have a total mass of no more than a ten-millionth of an ounce.

The high temperature and low density account for many of the features of the corona and chromosphere. In the first place, both favor high ionization. Consequently only one hydrogen atom in a million will be

Figure 138. THE ZODIACAL LIGHT. The conical glow extending up from the horizon at the bottom is the zodiacal light in the pre-dawn autumn sky. The brighter glow to the right of it is produced by the lights of the city of Chicago, about 75 miles away. The large dark projection next to this is one of the smaller domes of the Yerkes Observatory (Fig. 262). This unusual photograph, covering a field 140° in diameter, shows a large section of the winter Milky Way, from Perseus (upper left) through Auriga, Taurus, Gemini, Orion, and Canis Major. Sirius is the very bright star nearest the dome. The Sickle of Leo may be seen rising in the east (at the bottom) while the bowl of the Big Dipper is intersected by the shadow of one of the struts which support the camera and plate holder above the mirror. (Courtesy Yerkes Observatory.)

neutral and almost as small a proportion of helium; the absence of their emission lines is therefore to be expected. In the second place, the high state of ionization implies that highly mobile electrons will outnumber ions. The coronal gas is therefore an excellent conductor of heat and electricity, like copper or silver. This means that large differences of temperature would be difficult to establish in the corona. The temperature of the corona is high, therefore, because free electrons conduct heat so efficiently from the zone where the energy of hydromagnetic waves is dissipated.

The low density and small mass of the corona set a bound to the amount of thermal energy and radiation which the corona can contribute to the chromosphere and photosphere. The simple fact that its luminosity is but a millionth of the whole shows that the corona will have little influence in determining the effective temperature of the sun.

The slow decrease of the density and temperature of the corona makes it difficult to set a definite limit to it. The corona appears to merge into the *zodiacal light,* a faint cone-shaped glow which precedes and follows the sun. It is best seen in the tropical regions where twilight is short and the cone stands most nearly vertical to the horizon. It is thought to be the reflection of sunlight from particles of interplanetary dust. They are distributed symmetrically about a plane inclined $1°$ to the ecliptic; this is the invariant plane of the solar system, a sort of weighted average of the orbital planes of the planets. Their symmetry to the invariant plane rather than the equator of the sun makes it almost certain that the zodiacal light is from small electrically neutral particles rather than from electrons or ions, for the former would be governed by gravitational forces whose average is symmetric to the invariant plane, whereas the latter would be governed by solar magnetic forces which are more nearly symmetric to the sun's equator.

These particles whose reflections create the zodiacal light are most likely the same particles whose diffraction adds the faint dark lines to the light of the inner corona. Though nearly in the line from earth to sun, they must actually be closer to the earth than sun, for solid particles close to the sun would be evaporated. What is more, very small particles would be expelled by radiation pressure and solar corpuscular wind just as are small particles in comets. There are an estimated four particles per cubic mile in interplanetary space. It is probable that they are cometary debris.

Coronal Phenomena

The corona shows variations correlated with the sunspot cycle. The intensity of the coronal lines is greatest about spot maximum and the corona about a facula is a few thousand degrees hotter than elsewhere. There is also a close relation between the form of the corona and the distribution of prominences. Prominences and coronal changes develop simultaneously but show the best correlation with the spot numbers of about three months previous. Streamers of the polar corona are most disorderly when the majority of prominences are in the higher latitudes, shortly after spot maximum. The equatorial corona shows a strong concentration of main streamers toward the equator when the main prominence zone is in latitude 45°. The effect of this is that the corona will appear relatively flattened at spot minimum, irregular but less flattened at maximum. Photographs of the corona just 2 hours apart show changes in the coronal streamers or "petals."

The high temperature of the corona gives its radiations a somewhat different character from those of the photosphere or even the chromosphere. Faint though it is over-all, the corona's radiations exceed those of the rest of the sun for all wavelengths less than 800 Å. Rocket photographs show that the sun's x-radiation comes almost entirely from the corona. This and the rest of the corona's ionizing radiation of very short wavelength fluctuate in amount by about 50 per cent during the spot cycle, though the sun's visible radiation is almost constant.

The high coronal temperature is also responsible, as we have seen, for radio radiation of far greater amount than that of the photosphere, though only a small part of the sun's total energy output. It is received on wavelengths from 1 centimeter to 15 meters. Although first observed about 1937, its solar source was not appreciated until 1943. It is produced by free electrons which make a transition from one hyperbolic orbit to another of different energy while in the presence of an ion, most likely an ionized hydrogen atom. No atomic spectral lines have yet been found in the radio spectrum of the sun. It is clear that, because of the different emission and propagation characteristics of radio waves, radio observations of the sun give information about the sun not obtainable from observations in visible light.

The high temperature of the corona implies a continuous evaporation of particles from it. An estimated 10^{33} particles, chiefly hydrogen ions, escape from the sun each second even when solar activity is at a minimum. It is presumably these corpuscles which so affect the behavior of comets' tails.

A number of transient phenomena in the corona are also associated with solar radio and corpuscular radiation. These are characteristic of the *active sun,* as distinguished from the normal or *quiet sun.* One of these is enhanced radiation, a general increase of the intensity of radio radiation. There are also *noise storms* in radio radiation of meter wavelength, consisting of numerous bursts of less than a second duration; such storms may last for days. The radio noise storms arise in the neighborhood of large spot groups. The source of them is at a height of 0.3 to 1.0 solar radii above the photosphere. Sudden *bursts* in single wavelengths represent intensity increases of ten times and last only a few seconds. They have no optical counterparts.

Outbursts on all frequencies have durations up to 10 minutes. The wavelengths are restricted to certain emission bands and are due to macroscopic features of the sun, not to atomic processes. Outbursts are the most spectacular solar radio emission and are associated with the similarly spectacular flares in visible light. During an outburst, a million-fold increase in intensity is sometimes observed in radio emission bands within seconds. These radiations are probably emitted by oscillations of the coronal plasma, the oscillating masses being of the dimensions of 50 to 500 miles. At the same time the radiation source rises rapidly through the corona with a velocity of about 600 miles per second. There is a delay of several minutes between the "flash" of the visible flare and the onset of the radio outburst. The interval of delay increases with wavelength, since the long wavelengths can penetrate the corona only when the source reaches great heights. If the outburst radiation were of thermal origin, it would require temperatures of 10^{10} degrees absolute or more. It appears necessary to invoke strong magnetic forces for the production of outburst radiation.

The radio outburst source appears to be a corpuscular cloud blown bodily out of the corona when a flare occurs. Because of this, the sun loses particles about a thousand times as fast when in an active state than when quiescent.

Solar-Terrestrial Relationships

A solar facula, with its associated spot group and possible prominences, flares, and coronal disturbances, is called a *center of activity*. Centers of activity are the source of variable solar electromagnetic and corpuscular radiation which produce effects upon the earth. Most of these effects are subtle, not to be perceived except with the aid of some special sensing device. For example, though solar activity is not the direct cause of variations in the weather, there is a strong suggestion of a relation between the two. The rate of growth of trees, as measured by the thickness of the annual rings, shows an 11-year cycle. There is also a temperature fluctuation of about 2° F synchronous with the spot cycle. Contrary to many suggestions, however, there is no established correlation between the spot cycle and business cycles, birth rates, etc.

The effects of the solar activity upon the earth may be classed as of two kinds—those produced by corpuscular radiation from flares and those produced by electromagnetic radiation, chiefly ionizing radiation in the ultraviolet region. The ultraviolet radiation is propagated in straight lines and therefore affects only the daylight hemisphere of the earth; charged corpuscles are deflected by the earth's magnetic field and may therefore reach the nighttime hemisphere. This difference of behavior is well illustrated at time of total solar eclipse when all electromagnetic radiations are cut off simultaneously, though the corpuscular radiation is not. Furthermore, because ultraviolet is radiated in all directions, it matters not where on the surface of the sun a center of activity may be, whereas corpuscular radiation can be received only for the short time during which a center of activity occupies a central position on the solar disk.

One effect of corpuscular radiation is the production of magnetic storms. These are rapid, large changes in the strength of the earth's magnetic field; they have no relation to "electrical storms" or any other meteorological phenomena. However, they may cause induced electrical currents in the earth and thereby disrupt telegraphic and cable communication. Both positive and negative ions reach the earth about a day after the central meridian passage of a large spot, especially if the spot is flare-active. Their average velocity must therefore be about 1000 to 1500 miles per second. The flares themselves are probably not the cause of the corpuscular radiation and magnetic storm; large spots, flares, and magnetic storms have a common cause, for magnetic storms occur for which no related event can be blamed. Terrestrial magnetic activity shows an almost perfect correlation with spot numbers.

There are also moderate magnetic storms whose onset is gradual. These recur every 27 days, the synodic period of the sun's rotation. They are presumed to be caused by centers of activity carried around by the solar rotation like an ambulance flasher, spraying the earth lightly at each passage. These 27-day magnetic storms are most numerous when the coronal rays are longest at the solar equator, suggesting that the coronal streamers are corpuscular streamers. This has led to the description of the earth as a cold spot in the sun's corona.

Magnetic storms are often accompanied by displays of *aurora*, mostly in high or middle latitudes on the earth. They are probably the direct effect of the corpuscular radiation, as the magnetic storms are the indirect effect, for the auroral spectrum shows hydrogen emission lines with Doppler shifts of several hundred miles per second; these cannot have been produced by

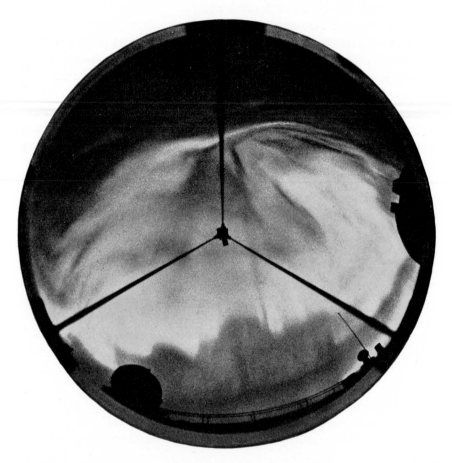

Figure 139. AURORA BOREALIS. This photograph of the great aurora of August 19–20, 1950, was taken in a 10-second exposure by the same wide-angle camera used to photograph the zodiacal light. At the right is the dome of the Yerkes 40-inch refractor. (Courtesy Yerkes Observatory.)

atoms of the atmosphere. The auroral radiation proper, however, is due to lines of atmospheric oxygen in the green and red and lines of atmospheric nitrogen in the blue and violet. Auroral arches and streamers emit their ghostly light at heights of 60 to 300 miles above the earth, sometimes even higher. The excitation is provided by colliding corpuscles.

The ionosphere of the earth, that layer of the earth's upper atmosphere which is strongly ionized by the ultraviolet radiation of the sun, is created and maintained by the sun's normal short wavelength radiation. At sunspot maximum, the amount of such radiation is about doubled. The increase is contributed by centers of activity. Sudden large bursts of ultraviolet radiation in a few emission lines come from flares. The flares thus may alter the condition of the ionosphere abruptly. This is registered as a magnetic crochet, or sharp change in the earth's magnetic field, as soon as the flare becomes visible, with no delay for particle transmission. It may also produce a sudden short-wave radio fade-out lasting for hours or days. Other effects include a sudden increase of static on long-wavelength radio, freakish multiple and long-distance radio reception, and a sudden fading of short-wave cosmic radio sources.

D. THE SUN'S INTERIOR

"If we add observation to observation, without attempting to draw not only certain conclusions, but also conjectural views from them, we offend against the very end for which only observations ought to be made."
—SIR WILLIAM HERSCHEL

It may seem that of all parts of the sun, its deep interior might well be a part about which the astrophysicist could discourse with the least likelihood of being contradicted. On the other hand, his statements about this part of the sun would be the most liable to skepticism, for it is difficult to imagine anything more inaccessible to observation than the vitals of a star. And yet we presume to say something about the inside of the sun. Naturally the results are not based on direct inspection but rather on many related observations and on inference. A much less extreme but common example of this is offered by wind, which we never see but whose existence is made known to us by a variety of effects; likewise, conditions of life and climate on the earth many millions of years ago are forever gone, but geologists have nonetheless reconstructed a very credible account of the earth's history during the past few billion years. The chain of inferences which leads to the center of the sun may be somewhat longer and its links less familiar than that which extends to a remote geological age, but unless a flaw of fact or logic can be exposed, it would be prejudice rather than skepticism to deny the conclusions. In short, rather than investigate the interior of the sun with telescope and spectroscope, we use what has been called a "mathematical boring machine." Our safeguards are a thoroughgoing scrutiny of each step of the argument and a general consistency of the results.

The Structure of the Interior

The interior of the sun does communicate indirectly with the rest of the universe. The radiation which flows across its surface has streamed up from the interior, and the material beneath its surface exerts a gravitational attraction in accord with Newton's law. Our problem is to interpret these communications. In doing so, we think of the sun as a stable physical system. Though it is actually in a process of evolution, its evolutionary life is so extremely long that any changes that may have taken place are inappreciable in the period available to observation. For example, geologists are convinced that the sun must have been radiating at almost exactly its present rate for all of geological time, for fluctuations of even a few per cent would have created significantly different conditions over the entire earth. We assume, therefore, that the interior of the sun is in a state of equilibrium and that all forces are internal.

The problem of investigating the interior of the sun may be naïvely outlined in the answers to two questions. The first is: What holds the sun together? The answer is that the mutual gravitational attractions of its particles prevent its indefinite dispersal. Their attractions upon each other draw them into a spherical mass. In the light of this answer, the second question is: What prevents the sun's collapse upon itself? The answer is that at any interior point the solar gases exert a pressure which forestalls its indefinite compression. In similar fashion, the air in an automobile tire prevents the collapse of the tire. The forces in balance inside the sun are therefore the compressive force of the sun's gravity and the expansive force of gas pressure.

We may now frame the problem of determining the structure of the sun somewhat more explicitly: How is the matter of the sun distributed throughout it so that equilibrium will prevail everywhere? The answer might be given in the form of a table stating what proportion of the solar mass is contained within a sphere of any specified fractional solar radius. Table 8 is such a table. The problem is to construct it. This requires a very great amount of tedious calculation, much of it carried out on a high-speed electronic computer. Let us follow a reverse procedure whose own reverse, it is clear, would be the direct procedure; this is far simpler than tracing the direct procedure itself.

Imagine, then, that Table 8 has been supplied us in some painless way, such as divination. We can readily test its merits. It has in effect sectioned the sun into layers, like an onion, each layer having a thickness of one-tenth of the sun's radius; a more refined calculation would use

table 8

FRACTIONAL RADIUS	FRACTIONAL MASS	DENSITY	PRESSURE	TEMPER-ATURE	FRACTIONAL LUMINOSITY
0.0	0.0	134.3	3,250.	14.6	0.0
0.1	0.073	85.5	1,980.	12.6	0.396
0.2	0.337	36.4	674.	9.35	0.909
0.3	0.626	12.86	171.	6.65	0.994
0.4	0.818	4.13	39.2	4.74	1.000
0.5	0.919	1.297	8.90	3.43	1.000
0.6	0.967	0.405	2.02	2.49	1.000
0.7	0.988	0.124	0.447	1.80	1.000
0.8	0.996	0.0354	0.0898	1.27	1.000
0.9	0.999	0.00946	0.0115	0.605	1.000
1.0	1.000	0.0	0.0	0.006	1.000

The density is times that of water, the pressure in billions of pounds per square inch, and the temperature in millions of degrees.

thinner layers which are more truly homogeneous. From the table we can at once determine the density in each layer. For example, the layer between 0.3 and 0.4 radii contains $0.818 - 0.626 = 0.192$ solar masses. At the same time, it comprises $(0.4)^3 - (0.3)^3 = 0.064 - 0.027 = 0.037$ solar volumes. Hence the density is $0.192/0.037 = 5.19$ solar densities, or 7.32 times the density of water. This is, of course, an average for the whole layer, the actual value being somewhat more at the bottom of the layer, somewhat less at the top, as the table shows. Using thinner layers, the values given in the third column of the table would be gotten. The densities run up to 134 at the sun's center.

Since the weight of the outer layers is to be balanced by the pressure in the inner layers, the pressure at each depth is calculated by finding the weight per unit area of the layers above it. The weight of each layer is the product of the mass and the strength of solar gravity at the point. The latter is found, as it is at the surface, by dividing the mass interior to the point by the square of the radius to the point. For example, at 0.4 radius, the local gravity is $0.818/0.16 = 5.11$ times its value at the surface. In this way, the fourth column can be had. The central pressure of the sun is seen to be 3 trillion pounds per square inch.

At this point it is necessary to reckon with the chemical composition of the material. This is necessary because gases of different compositions require to be at different temperatures to exert a given pressure. For example, the absolute temperature of atomic oxygen would have to be 16 times that of atomic hydrogen of the same density in order to exert the same pressure. One therefore makes an assumption about the chemical composition of the material; the most obvious and defensible one is that the material is the same mixture of elements as has been determined for the solar atmosphere, namely, 74 per cent hydrogen by weight, 24 per cent helium, and 2 per cent heavier elements. With this, it is possible to infer the temperature of each layer of the sun, since the pressure is proportional to the product of the density and temperature. This latter is a familiar fact, for we know that by putting more air into a tire—increasing its density—we raise the pressure, and that on a hot day's drive, the increased temperature will increase the pressure in the tire so that some air must be released for safety. We see, therefore, that there is but one temperature at which a gas of given chemical composition and known density will exert the pressure required at each level of the sun. We have in this way found the distribution of temperature in the sun, given in the fifth column of Table 8. The sun's central temperature is computed to be 14,600,000° K.

One is now in possession of all the information necessary to confirm or dispel any doubts about the state of the material. Conditions at the sun's surface are such that the state of the matter is gaseous beyond the shadow of a doubt. Do they remain so even at enormous pressure and high density of matter in the sun's deep interior? It is possible to establish that in fact the material of the sun is gaseous throughout, though this is not the case in all stars. It is even possible to be reassured that the solar gases retain their compressibility to the very center of the sun, at densities far in excess of the laboratory limits for the compressibility of terrestrial gases. This is due to the fact that in the sun the gases are composed of ions, not of complete atoms or molecules. Since an ion has one or more fewer occupied electron orbits, its diameter and volume are much less than that of a complete atom of the same element. Therefore there will be much more space between a given number of ions than between the same number of complete atoms; for this reason the gases of the sun retain a normal compressibility at densities far exceeding that of platinum.

At the same time, one may test the distribution of temperature to see whether a bubble of hot gas would cool faster than its surroundings as it rose toward the surface. If so, it would be soon brought to rest, and internal convection would be brought to a halt; if not, the gas would begin to be stirred by currents of rising hot gas and descending cool gas. Where this occurs, slightly different equations are called for, since some of the pressure may be due to the currents themselves and the heat transported by the currents will affect the pressure of the circulating layers. Such is the case in the outer 15 per cent of the sun; this is the hydrogen and helium convection zone already mentioned. In other stars the convection zone may occur in a different part of the star.

The next step is to determine the opacity of the solar material at every depth. It depends on the density, temperature, and chemical composition. The opacity is important because it determines how efficiently the solar matter dams back the radiation inside the sun. Were it not for this retardation, the radiation within the body of the sun would surge forth with the speed of light and leave a cool, dark, unstable, material, skeleton sun. As it is, the opacity must be just such that each layer blankets the one beneath it sufficiently to keep it hotter by the amount specified in Table 8. Were this not so, a star of this structure could not persist.

Finally, because each layer is cooler than the one beneath it, it cannot return to it the amount of radiation it receives from it; Stefan's law implies such a consequence. Hence there is an outward flow of radiation at a rate depending upon the rapidity of the decrease of temperature outward. The amount of the flow is given in the sixth column of Table 8. Beyond 0.4 radii, the same energy flows through each layer as makes its exit at the surface of the sun. But in the preceding layers, each makes a contribution. The first layer contributes nearly 40 per cent, the second almost 50 per cent, and the third about 10 per cent. The core of the sun is evidently a continuing source of radiant energy, replacing what is radiated at the sun's surface at the same rate that it is lost. The last step, therefore, is to calculate the rate of energy generation in a gas having the density, temperature, and chemical composition of the sun. Making the charitable assumption that this can be done, we compare the calculated amounts with those required by Table 8. If they are the same, the model of the sun in the table has been vindicated. If they are different, we have at least the cold comfort of having eliminated one unsatisfactory model.

Our analysis of the interior of the sun has attempted to show in principle how the interior of the sun can be studied. To use it, however, required that we enjoy an advantage which the practical astrophysicist can do no more than envy: We began with a postulated table of the mass distribution in the sun. The table must in fact be constructed by starting at the other end of the analysis and retracing one's way step by step. One need not be able to do this to see that it can be done.

The Process of Solar Energy Generation

The conviction of our preceding analysis hangs upon the prospect of determining a suitable source of energy generation at the heart of the sun.

This is of more than academic interest, for nearly every terrestrial source of energy is ultimately traceable to power from the sun.

How has the sun been able to radiate at virtually its present enormous rate for some 5 billion (5×10^9) years? Any ordinary source of energy would have been exhausted in but a fraction of this time. For example, though of course the sun is in fact too hot to burn, if the sun were only oxygen and high-grade coal in the optimum proportions, its complete burning could supply sunlight at its present rate for only a mere 2500 years. In fact, the sun's rate of radiation of energy is so enormous that if the entire solar energy could be purchased at the very low rate of one cent per kilowatt-hour, it would cost a billion billion dollars every second. We must evidently look to a process of a sort radically different from any of the familiar ones if we would account for the sun's radiation.

Only in the present century have physicists become acquainted with energy sources of the vastness required and with some of the processes by which this energy is released. The energy resources of the sun are contained in the nuclei of its atoms. To understand how the sun is able to tap these resources, we shall need a little more information about nuclei.

The nuclei are themselves composed of two smaller units. One kind of subunit is called the *proton,* the other the *neutron.* The proton is a positively charged particle and forms, by itself, the nucleus of the hydrogen atom; its positive charge is therefore equal in amount to the negative charge of the electron, but its mass is nearly 1840 times greater. The neutron, as its name implies, is electrically neutral; the mass of the neutron is a bare trifle more than the proton's. From these two fundamental particles the nucleus of every atom may be constructed. To obtain the proper number of nuclear charges, one need only include a number of protons equal to the atomic number of the desired atom; to these must be added enough neutrons to obtain the mass of the nucleus. For example, an iron nucleus has an atomic number of 26 and a mass approximately 56 times the mass of the hydrogen nucleus; therefore it must contain 26 protons and $56 - 26 = 30$ neutrons. The nitrogen nucleus, with atomic number 7 and approximately the mass of 14 protons, must be made of 7 protons and 7 neutrons.

Perhaps this description of the contents of nuclei suggests that nuclei may be assembled or disassembled to suit the experimenter's fancy. Actually it is extraordinarily difficult to do either. Neither the most violent chemical reaction nor the most extreme laboratory temperatures or pressures can produce any trace of an effect upon the nuclei of any atoms. However, the physicist has devised means of bombarding the nuclei of any "target" substance with any of a variety of missile particles (protons, electrons, neutrons, helium nuclei, etc.); this is the process popularly (but incorrectly) known as "atom smashing." With the inefficiency characteristic of bombardment, most of the missile particles will spend their kinetic energies colliding with and rebounding from the nuclei of the target. A few, however, will chance to hit squarely; the result of the encounter depends upon the nature of the missile, its speed, and the kind of target nucleus. Whatever the result, the process is known as a *nuclear reaction*. A *nuclear* reaction is not in any way similar to a *chemical* reaction.

In one type of nuclear reaction the bombarding particle is simply swallowed up. For example, practically any nucleus will swallow a neutron

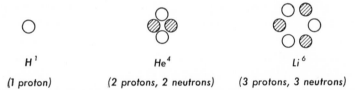

H^1 He^4 Li^6

(1 proton)   *(2 protons, 2 neutrons)*   *(3 protons, 3 neutrons)*

Figure 140. The nuclei of the common isotopes of these three simplest atoms are represented purely schematically. The isotopes of these elements would contain more or fewer neutrons. The nuclei of other elements would have more protons.

and convert its kinetic energy into very high-frequency radiation called a γ-ray (gamma ray). A specific example is offered by hydrogen; a proton (hydrogen nucleus) and neutron will combine to form "heavy hydrogen" (deuterium) and liberate a γ-ray.

A captured neutron does not increase the charge of the resulting nucleus but does add one unit to its mass; therefore the nucleus will have its original atomic number but a larger atomic weight. Nuclei so related are called *isotopes*. For example, hydrogen has isotopes of mass equal to, double, and triple the mass of the proton. Isotopes of any particular element thus have the same atomic number, the same number of orbital electrons, and therefore the identically same chemical properties. All but 20 of the elements have natural isotopes, and the number of isotopes known has been increased many fold by the products of various artificial nuclear reactions.

A different type of capture reaction will occur if the bombarding particle is a proton. The single positive charge of a captured proton increases the net charge of the capturing nucleus by one; in other words, both the atomic weight *and* the atomic number of the resultant nucleus is greater by one than that of the original, since the proton adds one unit of each. The product of the reaction is therefore a nucleus of the element of the next greater atomic number, and a transmutation has been effected. For example, if a carbon nucleus of atomic weight 12 captures a proton, the result is a nitrogen nucleus of atomic weight 13 (plus a γ-ray).

In a considerable number of nuclear reactions the product nuclei spontaneously disintegrate. Spontaneous disintegration normally occurs only among the naturally radioactive elements such as radium, and in fact it is this process which makes radium of therapeutic value. In disintegrating, a malcontent nucleus ejects a charged particle of some particular kind and thereby transforms itself into the nucleus of a different element. If the ejected particle is a proton, the nucleus loses one unit of charge and one of mass so that atomic number and atomic weight are both diminished by one unit. If the ejected particle is an electron, the remaining positive nuclear charge and atomic number must be greater by one, while the net loss of mass to the nucleus is negligible. (An electron does not exist as such within a nucleus but is produced by the transformation of a nuclear neutron into a proton.) In some cases the ejected particle may be like the electron except that it is positive rather than negative; this kind of particle is called a *positron*. (Like the electron, it does not exist as such in the nucleus but results from the conversion of a proton into a neutron during the disintegration.) Emission of a positron will obviously produce an effect opposite to the emission of an electron; the net charge of the nucleus and the atomic number will be one less, but as with electron emission, the mass is reduced inappreciably. Spontaneous disintegration may also result in the emission of types of particles other than proton, electron, or positron; in the disintegration of radium, for instance, helium nuclei are emitted.

Needless to say, not all kinds of nuclei spontaneously disintegrate; aside from the naturally radioactive elements like radium and uranium, none of the common nuclei does so. However, among artificially created isotopes, spontaneous disintegration is practically universal; they are said to be *unstable* nuclei. The nitrogen isotope of atomic weight 13, for example, disintegrates into the carbon isotope of atomic weight 13, simultaneously emitting a positron.

The importance of nuclear reactions in the problem of accounting for the sun's source of energy lies in the facts that (1) simple particle capture is always followed by the radiation of much energy in the form of a γ-ray, (2) the disintegration of unstable nuclei releases from these nuclei the energy which appears as the kinetic energy of the disintegration products, and (3) emitted positrons quickly combine with free electrons to become γ-ray pairs of high energy. The total energy released in these ways may be very large, considering the smallness of the nuclei.

In considering the possibility of nuclear reactions occurring in the sun, it is instructive to note the dissimilarity between laboratory conditions and those in the solar deeps. The nuclear physicist achieves most nuclear reactions in his laboratory by projecting a comparatively small number of particles at extremely high speed against target particles. High speed must be given to charged particles like protons so that they will be able to override that electrical repulsion which positively charged particles feel for each other, until they reach the point at which the still mysterious attractive forces within the nucleus can exercise their close-range dominance.

Circumstances in the sun must be rather different. Nuclei, stripped of all or most of their electrons, charge about wildly at high speeds. But even the average thermal velocities of nuclei near the sun's center are not nearly as great as those of the laboratory particles; only a fraction will have speeds abnormally high enough to bring off a nuclear reaction. While particles with these velocities are *relatively* infrequent, their *absolute* number must be enormous on account of the enormous number of nuclei per cubic centimeter of gas near the sun's center. Therefore, whereas in the laboratory nuclear reactions are accomplished by a few very high-speed particles, nuclear reactions in the sun will occur between many particles of above-average thermal velocities. For this reason the reactions are known as *thermonuclear reactions*.

To be of importance as a source of energy in the sun, a nuclear process must take place sufficiently often and must liberate a sufficiently large amount of energy per occurrence. At the same time the process must not occur so often as to exhaust the sun's supply of these nuclei in a short time. In the sun, the most important reactions satisfying all the conditions appears to be a series of syntheses beginning with the formation of H^2 (heavy hydrogen) by the collision of two protons and the release of a positron and neutrino (see below). By capturing a further proton, the H^2 becomes a helium isotope, He^3. Symbolically these reactions are written

$$H^1 + H^1 \rightarrow H^2 + e^+ + \nu, \quad e^+ + e^- \rightarrow 2\gamma,$$

$$H^2 + H^1 \rightarrow He^3 + \gamma.$$

In the first equation the ν stands for the neutrino, an electrically neutral, massless particle which carries a portion of the energy; the neutrino, together with the proton, neutron, electron, and photon are the only stable fundamental particles of physics. Because the neutrino is without electrical charge and virtually without mass, it slips through matter with the greatest of ease. On this account, about 2 per cent of the energy of these nuclear reactions leaks out of the sun as neutrinos. Neutrinos direct from the core of the sun flow outward in vast numbers, unobstructed by anything in their paths. Through each square inch of our bodies hundreds of billions of them pass each second; they come from above during the day, from below through the body of the earth during the night.

The reaction series is completed by the formation of He^4 and the release of two protons as a result of the interaction of two He^3 nuclei. The reaction equation is

$$He^3 + He^3 \rightarrow He^4 + 2H^1.$$

Evidently the first pair of reactions takes place twice as often as the third. With this in mind, we see that from six protons a helium nucleus and two protons have been formed. The net effect has been the synthesis of a helium nucleus from four hydrogen nuclei and the release of considerable energy. Each of the two first reactions contributes 5 per cent, each of the two second reactions contributes 21 per cent, and the final reaction makes up the remaining 48 per cent. Approximately 10^{38} syntheses take place in the sun each second.

Where does the liberated energy come from? It comes from the mass of the four captured protons and the two annihilated electrons and positrons. Einstein, in his now celebrated equation $E = mc^2$, showed that mass and energy are interconvertible; in other words, if by any means an amount of mass m could be wholly converted to energy, the amount of energy E would be m times the square of the velocity of light, c. In the helium synthesis we find that the mass of the four captured protons is 0.027 of a proton mass more than the mass of the synthesized helium nucleus. This difference of mass plus the mass of two electrons has been converted to the energy of the liberated γ-rays and the kinetic energy of the product particles. We therefore conclude that if the sun is losing energy, its mass must be decreasing at a corresponding rate. It must, in fact, be losing 4,700,000 tons of mass every second!

Impressive as this rate is, the decrease in the sun's mass has no effect on the sun's behavior. In a year's time the sun loses by radiation less than a hundred-billionth (6.8×10^{-12}) of its total mass. Of much more consequence in the long run is the fact that it is using up its hydrogen reserves. The result is that the sun is beginning to show its years (about 5 billion of them), at least near the center. Only there, where the temperature is highest and the density is greatest, does the proton-proton process proceed at all. That is why only the core of the sun contributed to the luminosity. In consequence, though the outer layers still contain 74 per cent hydrogen by weight, at the center the hydrogen content is down to 49 per cent, at a tenth of a radius it is 61 per cent, and at a fifth of a radius 72 per cent.

The gradual burning of the sun's hydrogen supply implies the eventual demise of the sun; this is a fate 5 billions of years in the future. There will at the same time be changes in the sun's luminosity, radius, and effective temperature. It seems probable that the sun's present luminosity is about 60 per cent greater than it was 5 billion years ago at the approximate time of the sun's birth. There is also reason to believe that in the same time the sun's radius has increased by 4 per cent and its effective temperature by 10 per cent.

QUESTIONS

1. Describe two methods by which the earth's distance from the sun may be measured.
2. Using the formula for diameter, calculate the diameter of the sun from its distance (92,913,000 miles) and angular diameter (31′50″.3).
3. If the earth were diverted less than $\frac{1}{9}$ inch toward the sun each second, what would eventully happen to it? Would a smaller planet be diverted differently than the earth? What causes the earth to be diverted this amount? How can this effect of the sun be used to measure the sun's mass?
4. By applying Kepler's harmonic law to the motion of the moon about the earth, find the mass of the sun compared to the earth.
5. What is the solar constant? What is its numerical value? How does it determine the sun's luminosity? How great is the sun's luminosity?
6. What is a perfect radiator? Why is it also known as a "black body"? How may the radiations of a perfect radiator be studied? Why is a perfect radiator the most suitable standard for comparison? (*Hint:* Consider how the radiations of a black body depend upon its chemical composition, pressure, temperature, etc., as compared with other possible standards.)
7. By what means do we minimize both ambiguity and arbitrariness in determining the sun's temperature? Why are we unaccustomed to ambiguity in temperature determinations in familiar circumstances? (*Hint:* Suggest at least two ways in which temperature may be defined. Under what conditions are these definitions equivalent?)
8. What is the rate of radiation per square centimeter per second from the surface of a perfect radiator whose absolute temperature is 3500° K? 5500° K? 20,000° K?
9. What is the absolute temperature of a perfect radiator whose rate of radiation is 46.332×10^{12} ergs per square centimeter per second?
10. Compare the rates of radiation from unit areas of perfect radiators at temperatures of 500° K, 1000° K, 5000° K, 10,000° K, and 50,000° K.
11. What is the effective temperature of the sun? Why is this called "effective"? What does the temperature of the sun imply concerning the state of matter at the sun's surface?

12. What is light? What observations indicate that it possesses a wave nature? A corpuscular nature? How may the two sets of observations be reconciled?

13. If the wavelength of a certain kind of light is 4500 Å, determine the wavelength in centimeters; in inches. What is the frequency of this light? What is its approximate color?

14. List the essential parts of a spectroscope. Explain the function of each. What is a spectrum line? What is a spectrum?

15. Describe the three types of spectra. What determines the type of spectrum that will be produced by any source? Give examples of a source of each type. Why are line spectra *usually* from gases?

16. Explain how line spectra permit relatively simple qualitative chemical analyses of their sources. Explain how a qualitative analysis may be made of the sun. Summarize the results. How do we account for the failure to detect certain elements? What is the possibility of their future discovery?

17. What is the usefulness of Planck's law? What does application of it to the sun show? On what grounds might this result be expected a priori?

18. What is an element? What is an atom? How many kinds of atoms are there? How large are atoms?

19. Of what does an atom consist? What holds it together? Point out the similarities and the differences between an atom and the solar system. Which preponderate?

20. Describe what we picture as taking place during the absorption or emission of radiation by an atom. Why do atoms absorb and emit light only of certain frequencies? How are absorption lines produced by the solar atmosphere? How does the same atmosphere produce emission lines at times of total solar eclipse?

21. What is ionization? How does it affect the spectrum of an atom? What is recombination? How does it produce continuous absorption? What function does continuous absorption and emission have in the process of radiative transfer?

22. What would the sun look like if there were no continuous absorption? What provides the continuous absorption in the photosphere? How much is present?

23. What would the spectrum of the sun look like if the solar atmosphere were perfectly opaque? How are the dark lines of the solar spectrum formed in the photosphere? What fraction of the sun's radiant energy do they represent?

24. What is it possible to tell from a line profile? In what terms is the strength of a spectrum line stated? On what factors does it depend?

25. What is the relation between the temperature and the population of an atomic state?

26. What is the Doppler effect? Cite familiar instances of the Doppler effect in sound. Why are there no familiar instances of Doppler effect in light? How does the Doppler effect produce Doppler broadening of a spectrum line?

27. What factors affect the strength of a spectrum line? How may the abundances of the elements in the sun be calculated from measures of the

solar spectrum lines? If any of the factors were omitted, how would the omission affect the calculated abundances of the elements?

28. What are the solar granules?

29. Describe a complete sunspot and its parts. Why is it dark? How do spots vary in numbers and in distribution over the sun's surface?

30. What is the Zeeman effect? What causes it? What does its presence in the spectrum lines of sunspots indicate? What is spot polarity? What is the rule for polarities? How may magnetic forces be responsible for creating the lower temperature of a sunspot?

31. What is the flash spectrum? Why is it not a perfect bright-line counterpart of the normal solar spectrum?

32. What are the physical conditions in the chromosphere? Why was there disagreement as to the temperature of the chromosphere? What is the probable temperature?

33. By what means may the upper and lower levels of the chromosphere be studied separately? What do such studies show?

34. What is a filament? A prominence? What is their general behavior? What differences of behavior do they exhibit?

35. What is a solar flare? By what means is it generally observed? Why are such means necessary? What appearance does a flare give when seen at the solar limb? What means have been postulated for the production of flares?

36. Why is the corona difficult to study? What structure does it show? What is the nature of its light? By what are these radiations produced?

37. What is the physical condition of the corona? Its temperature? Why is its temperature approximately uniform?

38. What is the zodiacal light? What relation does it bear to the corona? How is it known that the particles responsible for the zodiacal light are electrically neutral?

39. How does the form of the corona vary with the spot cycle? How does the corona radiate so strongly at radio wavelengths? How do noise storms, bursts, and outbursts differ? What is the probable mechanism which produces them?

40. Describe the various effects which solar activity has upon the earth.

41. Describe the method by which the interior of the sun is investigated. What are the calculated conditions at the center of the sun? What requirements determine the conditions at each point within the sun? What changes would be entailed by a change in the sun's mass, radius, or luminosity? What is the condition of the solar material generally? How can the solar gas remain compressible at relatively high density?

42. Trace a number of familiar terrestrial energy sources to their ultimate origin. How many, if any, are independent of the sun?

43. Point to at least two reasons why combustion cannot be the source of the sun's energy. What condition rules out all but one possible source of solar energy?

44. Of what are nuclei composed? In what two ways are nuclei differentiated from each other?

45. How may the identity of a nucleus be changed? How easily can nuclear reactions be brought about? How does a nuclear reaction differ from a chemical reaction?

46. What types of nuclear reactions may occur? What determines the type of a nuclear reaction in any instance?

47. What is a spontaneous disintegration? In what elements do spontaneous disintegrations occur naturally? In what elements can they be induced?

48. In what forms are the energies released by nuclear reactions? State the reactions of the proton-proton process and point out how energy is released.

49. What is consumed in the course of the nuclear reactions in the sun? What is produced? Will this have any long-range effect on the chemical composition of the sun?

50. Are nuclear reactions an adequate source of energy for the sun? Are there any other possibilities?

51. What is the ultimate source of energy released by the nuclear reactions? What does this imply for the structure of the sun?

Figure 141. STAR CLOUDS IN SCUTUM, SERPENS, AND SAGITTARIUS.
The clouds of stars shown here appear in the densest parts of the Milky Way near
the direction of the galactic center. (Courtesy Yerkes Observatory.)

part II
The Stellar Population

●●●

chapter 7
How Do We Know?

•••

Thus far we have fixed our attention almost exclusively on the bodies in our immediate astronomical neighborhood, i.e., on the solar system. Our initial preoccupation with the solar system is understandable and the extent of our consideration of it is a reflection of the fact that we have a much more detailed knowledge of near bodies than of far ones. So that a handicap of distance may not become a prejudice, however, let us see what is known of the successively more distant regions of the universe—of their respective contents and organizations; we hope thereby to gain a more balanced perspective of the cosmos.

If we exclude all the astronomical bodies which we know to be in the solar system, we are most aware of the stars among the objects that remain. What are stars? We shall find presently that they are suns, some larger, some smaller, some hotter, some cooler than others, but all of them huge spheres of glowing gases. Their number is very great and in the aggregate they constitute what may be metaphorically termed the *stellar population*. Its members pose for us two problems: (1) what can we know of an individual star, and (2) from what we know of individual stars, how can we characterize the entire stellar population? These problems are exactly analogous to ones which would arise if we were to study any sizable segment of human society. In the latter instance we could collect such data as age, height, color of eyes, and marital status. We could then condense the results of our census into statistics which would characterize the part of the population we had canvassed. For example, it would be possible to state what per cent of this population is between any specified age limits or what per cent possesses blue eyes. As a first result, a comparison of the statistics of different quantities could be expected to establish correlations among some of them; for instance, color of eyes would undoubtedly be correlated with nationality; marital status would be correlated with age, and so on. As a second result, the statistics would serve to establish norms by which to judge what is unusual and what is not; thus an age of 25 years is not remarkable, whereas one of

125 years is very exceptional; or a height of 5 feet 9 inches for a full-grown man is common, whereas a height of 7 feet is quite rare.

We propose to survey the stellar population in a manner similar to the one we might use on human society. The undertaking is executed in three steps: first, the data must be secured; second, the statistics must be analyzed; and third, separate consideration must be given to out-of-the-ordinary stars, which are of interest because of their differences. Let us consider the first step—securing the data.

The data we can secure about any particular star are just those quantities for which there exists a method of measurement. This is not as trivial an observation as it may at first seem; for example, we cannot yet obtain the masses of most single (rather than double) stars, simply because there is at present no method of doing so. In fact, our knowledge of the stars is so entirely dependent upon our means of coming by it that the primary emphasis in this part of the problem will necessarily be on method.

In considering the methods whereby the various quantities pertaining to a star may be determined, we note that many of the quantities may be determined in more than one way when special circumstances permit the application of more than one method; for instance, the distance to a certain type of double star may be determined in at least two ways. We are thus able to check enough of our results to gauge the reliability of most methods. The sundry methods will vary in their degree of elaborateness. We shall begin with the most direct and most general ones, seeing later how they may be checked and supplemented by more specialized methods.

A. DIRECT METHODS

"I could never see any profit in being mistaken about anything important enough to excite my curiosity."

—DANIEL FISH

How Far?

We have several times made use of the fact that all stars are very far away—enormously farther even than Pluto. The principle made use of in finding a star's distance is at bottom identical with the one we made use of in finding the moon's distance. In brief, we note the star's direction from two widely separate positions; the angular difference between the two directions is the star's parallax, and the line between the two positions of observation is the base line. These two quantities determine the star's distance by use of the same simple formula used in the case of the moon, namely,

$$d = 206,265\ \frac{b}{p}$$

where b is the base line, d is the distance in the same units as b, and p is the parallax in seconds.

The actual base line for measurements of the stars' distances is the largest one available, but even so is much less than we could wish; it is the

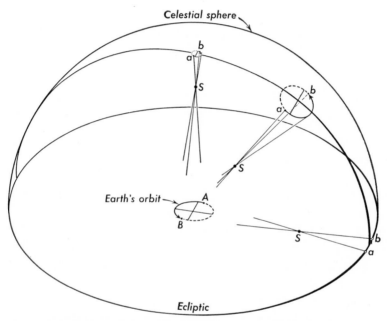

Figure 142. The parallactic ellipse of any star is simply the projection of the earth's orbital ellipse through the star's position, *S*. Points such as *A* and *B*, for example, project into points such as *a* and *b* on the celestial sphere. Except at the pole of the ecliptic every parallactic ellipse will suffer foreshortening. Its size will be in inverse proportion to the star's distance from the earth.

diameter of the earth's orbit. Of course observation of any star from the ends of a diameter of the earth's orbit cannot be made simultaneously but rather at intervals of six months, during which time the earth will have moved half a revolution in its orbit, carrying the observer from one end of a diameter around to the other.

The parallax is measured by using the more remote background stars as reference points with which to compare the position of a nearer star.

As the earth revolves about the sun, its change of position will little affect the direction of the remotest stars while effecting an apparent relative displacement of the nearer ones. The apparent parallactic displacement varies continuously, and hence a star appears to describe a path called its *parallactic orbit*. The parallactic orbit of a star directly "above" or "below" the earth's orbit, i.e., at the poles of the ecliptic, would evidently have the same shape as the earth's orbit; the parallactic orbit of all the rest would be foreshortened into ellipses, the *parallactic ellipses*. Parallactic orbits of stars exactly in the plane of the earth's orbit, i.e., on the ecliptic, will be completely foreshortened into small line segments along the ecliptic (Fig. 142).

The major axes of the parallactic ellipses are the only diameters of the parallactic orbit that are unaffected by foreshortening, and therefore the angular separation of the ends of the major axis of any star's parallactic ellipse constitutes the parallax of that star if we take the diameter of the earth's orbit as base line.

Because the earth goes once around its orbit in a year, a star will traverse its parallactic ellipse once in a year. At intervals of six months, therefore, it will appear at the ends of the major axis of its parallactic ellipse; the dates upon which this happens depend only on the star's position in the sky. Because of this fact, one need only observe the star's relative position on or near these two dates; the angle by which its positions differ is by definition its parallax. The modern technique of measuring stellar parallaxes consists in photographing a star of interest together with faint background stars on these two particular dates. By careful measurement of the apparent positions of the star relative to the background stars, the parallax is obtained.

In practice it is customary to use as a base line the *radius* of the earth's orbit rather than the diameter. A star's parallax is then the major semi-axis (rather than the full major axis) of its parallactic ellipse. Observing this convention, what values do we find for stars' parallaxes? All are extremely small. It is hardly to be wondered that the first successful parallax measurement was not made until 1838 when Bessel measured the parallax of 61 Cygni; the largest parallax, that for Proxima Centauri, is only 0.785 seconds of arc. Since our base line is 1 astronomical unit, we find by the formula that this corresponds to a distance of $206{,}265 \times 1/0.785 = 262{,}760$ astronomical units. This is 6650 times farther than Pluto is from the sun, and Proxima (as its name suggests) is the nearest star.

Evidently all stellar distances are enormously greater than any we have encountered heretofore. We should before long find it awkward (to put it mildly) to continue to use such unsuitably small units of length as astronomical units. A more convenient unit is the *parsec*. One parsec is 206,265 astronomical units, or 19.2 trillion (19.2×10^{12}) miles; using our formula in reverse, we see that the parallax of a star at 1-parsec is 1 second of arc, hence the term "parsec" by contraction of "parallax second." If we substitute an equivalent number of parsecs for the astronomical units in our formula for distance, we have the still simpler relation that

$$d = \frac{1}{p},$$

if d is in parsecs and p is in seconds of arc. For example, Proxima Centauri's distance in parsecs is $1/0.785 = 1.27$.

Another convenient unit of distance for astronomical purposes is the *light year*. The light year is the distance traveled in 1 year's time by a beam of light (whose velocity through space is 186,000 miles per second); it amounts to 5.88 trillion (5.88×10^{12}) miles. By simple comparison we see that a parsec is 3.258 times larger than a light year. Proxima Centauri must therefore be $1.27 \times 3.258 = 4.15$ light years away, since 3.258 light years are required to span each parsec.

It is probably impossible to attain any adequate appreciation of how enormous stellar distances are. Nonetheless, comparisons are not necessarily idle. We note, for example, that the distance to Proxima Centauri is such that if a sound could reach it (which of course it could not, since sound will not travel through the near-perfect vacuum between the stars), a terrestrial thunderclap could not be heard on Proxima until some 3,860,000 years later; a streamliner traveling nonstop at 60 miles per hour would need almost a half-billion years to make the trip.

Determining stars' distances from their parallaxes is simple and straightforward—in principle. It is, however, a method of very limited usefulness. Even by repeated measurements with the aid of the largest telescopes, it is not possible to reduce the observational uncertainty of a parallax measurement to less than approximately three-thousandths of a second of arc. While this is about the angular size of a dime in New York viewed from Chicago—really a remarkably small angle—it is a sufficient uncertainty in a parallax of 0.010 second that the corresponding distance would be doubtful to the extent of over 40 per cent. This is a practical limitation which prevents direct determinations of stellar distances beyond approximately 35 parsecs, or roughly 100 light years. Thus far, direct parallaxes have been measured for only a couple of thousand stars while billions lie beyond the reach of this method.

The few thousand stars whose parallaxes are measured with at least fair accuracy are disproportionately important to our further needs, however. For future reference we therefore note that the distances of these stars are known with an accuracy which varies from about 1 per cent for the nearest to about 10 per cent for those at the extreme limit of usefulness.

It is an interesting sidelight to parallax measurement that occasionally a negative parallax is obtained. The only literal interpretation of this result is the absurd one that the star is farther away than infinity. It is, of course, either a result of unavoidable errors of measurement or a consequence of choosing one or more comparison stars that are less distant than the star being measured. This latter possibility emphasizes the fact that actually we have considered only *relative parallaxes,* since in strictness the comparison stars would have to be infinitely far away in order not to show a small parallactic displacement of their own; a slight allowance is generally made for this fact (see p. 383).

How Bright?

A star's distance, although a statistic concerning that star, does not specify any intrinsic datum of the star. A knowledge of it is quite essential, however, in determining a star's true brightness, or *luminosity,* for example. For, apparent brightness diminishes inversely as the square of the distance from the source, as we have seen. Thus, at double our distance from the sun, sunlight would be only a quarter as strong; at treble our distance it would be one-ninth as strong, etc.; conversely, at half our present distance from the sun it would appear four times as bright, and at a third of an astronomical unit it would be nine times as bright, etc. Evidently we cannot gauge a star's true brightness until we know its distance.

Luminosity is measured in multiples or submultiples of the sun's absolute brightness. The luminosity is found for any star by simply comparing the apparent brightnesses which that star and the sun would have if placed side by side at some convenient distance from us. Let us adopt a distance of 1 parsec as a convenient standard distance at which to compare the brightnesses of the two. At this distance the sun's brightness would be reduced slightly more than 42½ billion times; painstaking measurements of the sun's brightness show that the sun would then appear as a moderately bright star, just 290 times brighter than the faintest star visible with the naked eye, some 3.6 times less luminous than the brightest (Sirius) presently appears in the sky.[1]

An actual determination of the luminosity of any star requires that we first measure its apparent brightness. This is done by visual estimate or by some form of a light-measuring instrument known as a photometer. The measured apparent brightness b can be expressed in any convenient units; hence, for our own convenience, let us take unit brightness to be that which the sun would appear to have at the standard distance of 1 parsec. In these units Sirius, for example, would have an apparent brightness of 3.6.[2]

Having determined a star's apparent brightness, we need also know its distance (or equivalently, its parallax). Unless the star is at the standard distance, its apparent brightness will not indicate its luminosity. Let us suppose that the star is d parsecs away. If we *decrease* its distance to 1 parsec, the standard distance, we *increase* its apparent brightness d^2 times, according to the inverse square law. Hence it would then have an apparent brightness of $b \times d^2$, i.e., its luminosity L must be equal to

$$L = b \times d^2,$$

where L is in solar luminosities, b is in brightness units, and d is in parsecs. Alternatively, it is sometimes more convenient to make use of the equivalent formula

$$L = \frac{b}{p^2}$$

involving the parallax, p; the second equation follows from the first by substituting $1/p^2$ for d^2, to which it is equal.

To see how these formulas are used, we may apply them to Sirius, whose parallax p is 0″371 and whose apparent brightness b is 3.6 units. By the second formula we have that L is $3.6/(0.371)^2 = 26.2$; or since a parallax of 0″371 corresponds to a distance d of $1/0.371 = 2.695$ parsecs, we find by the first formula that L is $3.6 \times (2.695)^2 = 26.2$. In other words, Sirius is actually sending out 26.2 times as much radiation per second as is the sun.

[1] Sirius and a star that can just barely be seen with the unaided eye differ in apparent brightness by slightly more than a thousand times.

[2] By the misfortune of historical inheritance and a quirk of the nature of the human eye's response to the stimuli of light of differing intensities, astronomers have been saddled with a less simple system (see Appendix 2, p. 534). Although from constant usage and long familiarity astronomers find their system quite satisfactory, an explanation of its intricacies would here contribute little to our understanding of the method of determining stellar luminosities.

It is found that the stars differ enormously in luminosity. The most luminous known at present (the star S Doradus, invisible in the middle northern latitudes) is about 1,000,000 times as luminous as the sun. The intrinsically faintest star thus far recognized (an unnamed star) has a luminosity of only about 1/2,000,000; if it were in the sun's place, it would appear to have about the same brilliance as the full moon. Thus the range in luminosity between greatest and least is a factor of approximately 1 trillion (33×10^{12}).

How Big?

Another statistic which pertains immediately to a star and whose direct determination depends on a knowledge of the star's distance is its diameter. We already know that the sun's diameter is nearly a million miles; now we hope to find out the sizes of the stars. In doing so we must in some way overcome the fact that even in the largest existing telescope, no stars can be made to show true disks but will appear simply as points of light; the telescope's function for single stars is primarily that of making each star appear brighter by collecting more of its light than does the unaided eye, incidentally making visible thousands and millions of stars beyond the 6000 within the reach of the eye alone.

That is not to say that the stars do not have apparent disks; they are just so small as to be beyond the capabilities of most present telescopes.[3] The limitation inherent in a telescope is due to an effect of the phenomenon of diffraction of light (p. 218). Because of diffraction, a telescope is unable to form a perfectly sharp point image of a point source; the image will instead be a small spot. Hence adjacent *points* in a source will be represented by adjacent small *spots* in the image formed by the telescope. If the spots overlap to too great an extent, the points of which they are the images will be effectively indistinguishable no matter how greatly the images are magnified or enlarged. Thus there is a definite limit to the ability of any telescope to distinguish between nearby points of a source object; this limit measures the telescope's *resolving power*. A telescope's resolving power is in proportion to its aperture. To separate distinctly the points on the opposite limbs of any star requires a greater resolving power than that of any telescope now available (except, of course, the 200-inch).

Our purpose would be served, however, if we could somehow measure

[3] Theoretically, the 200-inch telescope of the Hale Observatory at Mount Palomar will show the true disks of a few stars.

the *angular* diameter of a star even though we fail to see its true disk. If we knew the angular diameter, we could use the very same formula that has been so successfully applied to the sun, moon, and planets, namely

$$D = \frac{d \times \beta}{206,265} ;$$

here D is linear diameter in the same units as d, d distance, and β the angular diameter in seconds of arc. For our greater conveniences we shall

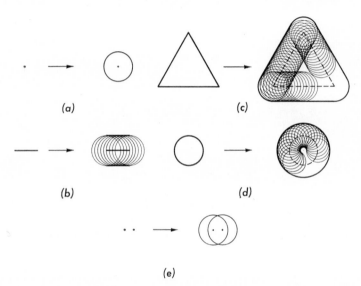

(a)

(c)

(b)

(d)

(e)

Figure 143. Each object on the left becomes the image on the right because each object *point* has its diffraction *disk* in the image. Thus a point becomes a circle (a), a circle becomes a larger circle (d), etc. The result is that detail of greater fineness than the diffraction disk remains unresolved in the image.

modify this formula slightly so as to obtain D in astronomical units rather than parsecs. This we do by replacing d parsecs with $206,265 \times d$ astronomical units, getting

$$D = d \times \beta \quad \text{astronomical units};$$

here D is linear diameter, d the distance in parsecs, and β the angular diameter in seconds of arc. It may sometimes also be desirable to have D in comparison with the sun. This is easily had, since 1 astronomical unit is equal to 107 solar diameters, and therefore

$$D = 107d \times \beta \quad \text{solar diameters};$$

Figure 144. BEAM INTERFEROMETER. The 20-foot beam interferometer is shown attached to the 100-inch Hooker reflector of the Mt. Wilson Observatory. The outer mirrors are at a separation of 12 feet. (Mt. Wilson-Palomar Observatories Photo.)

here again D is linear diameter, d the distance in parsecs, and β the angular diameter in seconds of arc. We now have brief and simple formulas for stars' diameters, but as yet cannot use them for lack of knowing the angular diameter of any star.

The angular diameter could be measured if a large enough telescope were available. For example, an angular diameter of 0.01 seconds of arc could be just resolved with a telescope of some 450-inches diameter. The prospect of such a telescope is remote indeed. But let us perform an imaginary experiment with such a hypothetical telescope. Let us place before the objective lens or mirror a diaphragm whose size and shape may be varied to suit our purpose. Let it first be a central circular diaphragm concentric with the telescope objective. It will obstruct some of the light which would have been collected by the center of the objective, but it will not alter the resolving power of the telescope. Images will be fainter but equally well resolved. Let us enlarge the diaphragm until it obscures all but a small ring about the perimeter of the objective. The light-gathering power will be reduced to that of a small telescope, but the resolving power will remain that of a large one. Now let us augment the diaphragm by obscuring even the perimeter annulus except for two small areas at the ends of a diameter. This will distort the images but still not reduce the resolving power. Such an instrument would in principle be as potent as the original telescope in resolving details in a direction parallel to the diameter connecting the two undiaphragmed portions of the objective.

Of course no telescope of such size would be used in such a way if one were to be built. However, two small mirrors simulating the unobscured areas in our imaginary experiment may be mounted at the ends of a rigid beam. In conjunction with a telescope to focus the light from these two small mirrors, a working approximation to the final apparatus of our experiment could be achieved. This is the essence of a very special angle-measuring device known as a *beam interferometer*. It may be used to measure the angular diameters of a few of the stars.

In this way it is found that the star Antares, for instance, has an apparent angular diameter of 0".040. Since its distance has been found to be 67 parsecs, our formulas show that its diameter must be $67 \times 0.040 = 2.7$ astronomical units, or $107 \times 67 \times 0.040 = 285$ times the sun's.

table 9

STAR	ANGULAR DIAMETER	PARALLAX	LINEAR DIAMETER
Betelgeuse (α Orionis)	0".047	0".021	$420D\odot$
Arcturus (α Bootis)	0 .020	0 .092	23
Antares (α Scorpii)	0 .040	0 .015	285
Mira (o Ceti)	0 .056	0 .013	460
Ras Algethi (α Herculis)	0 .030	0 .004	800
Aldebaran (α Tauri)	0 .020	0 .059	36
Scheat (β Pegasi)	0 .021	0 .020	110

Antares is obviously of an extraordinary size as compared even with the sun. In fact, only a few of the very large and not too distant stars like Antares have angular diameters which can be measured by the interferometer, for the separation of the interferometer mirrors is usually at least 20 feet. Smaller angular diameters require larger mirror separation; clearly, a very much larger beam interferometer would be quite unmanageable. Consequently the angular diameters of not more than a dozen stars have been measured by this method. These few are very important, however, as a means of estimating the reliability of other, less direct, methods.

How Hot?

Another question about the stars which we should like to answer is: How hot are they? For those stars whose diameters and luminosities we know, the answer can be had as easily as it was for the sun. The method in both instances is the same: From the total radiation per second, i.e., the luminosity, and the surface area ($= \pi \times$ diameter squared) we find the radiation per unit area per second by dividing the former by the latter. The temperature of a perfect radiator which would radiate at the same net rate per unit area is, then, by definition the *effective temperature* of the star. Probably the simplest way to obtain an explicit numerical value for the effective temperature of a star by this method is to make a comparison with the sun. Thus, if a star's diameter is D times as great as the sun's, its area will be D^2 times as great. If at the same time its luminosity is L times as great, the radiation per unit area per second will be L/D^2 as much. Therefore, since the sun's radiation per square centimeter per second is $0.0000572 \times (5770)^4$ ergs according to Stefan's law, the star's rate of radiation will be $0.0000572(5770)^4 \times L/D^2$ ergs per second per square centimeter. But, likewise by Stefan's law, the star's rate of radiation will be $0.0000572 T_e^4$, T_e being its effective temperature. Equating these, we see that

$$0.0000572 T_e^4 = 0.0000572(5770)^4 \, L/D^2.$$

Canceling the like constant factors and solving for T_e by extracting the fourth root of both sides of the equation, we get for the effective temperature of the star the value

$$T_e = 5770 \times \sqrt[4]{L/D^2} \quad \text{degrees absolute.}$$

As a specific example let us consider the star Aldebaran. Its luminosity is 112 and its diameter 36 times the sun's. A little arithmetic shows that $\sqrt[4]{112/36^2} = 0.542$, so that T_e for Aldebaran is $5770 \times 0.542 = 3100°$ K, approximately. Similarly, the effective temperature can be calculated for any other star whose luminosity and diameter are known.

Whither?

Another statistic which, though it is not an intrinsic property, pertains to the individual star is its relative motion in space. Though it is a common practice to refer to the "fixed" stars, they all have some motion relative to the earth and sun. We should like to determine the speed and direction of each star's motion, both because of an interest in it for its own sake and because of further useful information we can get from it.

In practice a star's motion must be determined piecemeal. Thus, for any star which is not too faint, it is possible to measure its velocity of approach or recession, i.e., its *radial velocity*. For a great many stars it is also possible to measure by other means its velocity at right angles to the line of sight, i.e., its *transverse velocity*. A knowledge of these two *component velocities* is all that is required to determine the direction and rate of a star's motion.

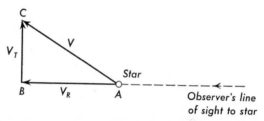

Figure 145. Any star's relative velocity V may be resolved into a radial component V_R along the line of sight and a simultaneous transverse component V_T at right angles to it.

Let us suppose that a star's radial velocity is one of approach at V_R miles per second and its transverse velocity is V_T miles per second. In 1 second the star will have moved V_R miles toward the observer and at the same time V_T miles in a direction at right angles. Of course it is actually executing both motions simultaneously, but the effect is no different from that obtained if in each second it were to first approach V_R miles from A to C and then veer off V_T miles at right angles from C to B, for example. In the latter case it would arrive at B from A in 1 second; in reality, of course, it goes with a velocity V directly from A to B in 1 second without making the diversion to C. Now, since AC is V_R miles and CB is V_T miles and since ACB is a right triangle, we know by the Pythagorean theorem that the actual distance AB traveled in 1 second is such that

$$\overline{AB}^2 = V^2 = V_R^2 + V_T^2 \quad \text{or} \quad V = \sqrt{V_R^2 + V_T^2}.$$

The angle at A between the star's space velocity and the line of sight is determined trigonometrically from the ratio of V_T to V_R.

For example, Sirius is approaching at a rate of $V_R = 5$ miles per second and has a transverse velocity of $V_T = 10$ miles per second. Therefore its space velocity is $V = \sqrt{5^2 + 10^2} = \sqrt{125} = 11.2$ miles per second. From trigonometric tables we find also that its direction of motion must make an angle of $63°$ with the line of sight in order for V_T and V_R to be in the ratio of 2 to 1.

RADIAL VELOCITY

Obviously the real problem in determining a star's motion is to determine the radial and transverse velocities. The radial velocity is comparatively simple to get. A telescope is used to concentrate the light of a star upon the slit of a spectrograph. By such an arrangement the star's spectrum can be photographed (though of course the exposure time required may be a number of hours for a faint star, even with a large telescope). Immediately before and after the star's spectrum is photographed, comparison spectra (usually of iron or titanium) are recorded by the same spectrograph just above and below those of the star. It is then possible by a direct comparison to measure accurately the wavelengths of the lines in the star's dark-line spectrum. Displacement of lines indicates the approach or recession of the star, and the rate is found by applying the Doppler principle. If the observed wavelength of a line is λ and its true wavelength is λ_0, the radial velocity of the source must be

$$V = 186{,}000 \frac{\lambda - \lambda_0}{\lambda_0} \text{ miles per second.}$$

Positive radial velocities correspond to recession, negative radial velocities to approach. The radial velocities of about 10,000 stars have thus far been measured. Velocities such as 20 miles per second are common; the greatest known at present is about 428 miles per second (the star RZ Cephei). These velocities are relative to the sun, having been corrected for the effect of the earth's orbital and rotational velocity.

TRANSVERSE VELOCITY

The transverse velocity of a star cannot be gotten quite so simply; to determine it, we must know two things, the star's rate of *apparent* transverse motion, or *proper motion,* and its distance. The proper motion of a star is measured as its change in apparent position after the lapse of 1 year; it is measured in seconds of arc. Thus the proper motion of Sirius is 1″32; in other words, Sirius' position will in 45 years be 1′ different from what it is now. The largest proper motion known, 10″25, is that of Barnard's star; in 350 years this star will have moved a full degree in the sky. Fortunately, only a handful of other stars have proper motions even approximately as great, or the constellations (Appendix 1) would become quite unrecognizable in but a few generations; as it is, ones such as Ursa Major (The Big Dipper) and Coma Berenices will look considerably different after a mere millennium.

Figure 146. PROPER MOTION AND ORBITAL MOTION OF 61 CYGNI. The negatives of two plates of the binary system 61 Cygni have been superposed to show the proper motion of the pair during the more than 39 years between the first epoch (1911.775) and the second epoch (1950.816). The accumulated angular displacement during this interval is 203″17 so that the annual proper motion is 5″204. In this same time the separation of the components has increased from 23″ (above) to 27″ (below) and the position angle increased from 129° to 140° because of their mutual orbital motions. The four comparison stars are actually about 100 times fainter than 61 Cygni whose components were reduced in brightness during the original exposures so as to make their images comparable in size to those of the comparison stars. (Courtesy K. Aa. Strand.)

Initially, at least, the interpretation of the observed proper motion of a star is ambiguous in that the star could equally well be a nearby one having a moderate transverse velocity or a more distant one moving much more rapidly. A knowledge of the star's distance settles the matter. Let us suppose that a particular star has a transverse velocity of V_T miles per second. In 1 second it will have moved V_T miles in a direction at right angles to the line of sight; in 1 year this will amount to a distance $D = V_T \times 60 \times 60 \times 24 \times 365\frac{1}{4} = 31,557,600 \ V_T$ miles. Now, by our much-used formula (p. 121) which relates the distance d from the observer to the angle μ subtended by a length D, we have that

$$D = \frac{d \times \mu}{206,265} \quad \text{miles},$$

where D is the linear length in miles, d the distance in miles, and μ the proper motion in seconds of arc. In other words, by moving D miles

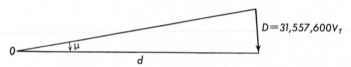

Figure 147. A star's annual linear transverse displacement D determines its proper motion μ at any distance d.

across the line of sight, the star will appear to have changed its position in the sky by μ seconds of arc; by definition, then, μ is its proper motion. Hence

$$D = 31,557,600 \, V_T = \frac{d \times \mu}{206,265}.$$

So as to have more manageable numbers, we make use of the fact that there are 19.2 trillion miles in a parsec, giving us for V_T the result

$$V_T = \frac{19,200,000,000,000d \times \mu}{206,265 \times 31,557,600}$$

$$= 2.95d \times \mu \quad \text{miles per second}$$

or

$$V_T = 2.95 \frac{\mu}{p} \quad \text{miles per second};$$

here V_T is the transverse velocity, d the distance in parsecs, p the parallax in seconds, and μ the proper motion in seconds.

As a concrete example, let us consider Sirius. Its parallax is 0″371 and its proper motion 1″32. Hence its transverse velocity is $V_T = 2.95 \times 1.32/0.371 = 10.5$ miles per second, approximately.

There remains, of course, the practical problem of measuring a star's proper motion. The most common method consists in measuring very accurately the star's position on each of two photographs, one of which was taken several years after the other. The star's difference of relative position on the two photographs represents its *accumulated* proper motion over the time interval between photographs; the difference of position divided by the number of years between photographs gives the *annual* proper motion. Thus, if a star changes its position by 20″ in 15 years, its annual proper motion is 1″33.

It is evident that the accuracy of the measurement of a proper motion is in proportion to the interval of time between photographs. Whereas the total amount of unavoidable error in the measurement of a star's position on two photographs will not depend upon when the photographs were taken, the amount of uncertainty which this introduces into the *annual* proper motion is the total error divided by the number of years elapsed; this becomes smaller as the number of years increases, and the accuracy with which proper motions can be measured is on this account continually greater.

Besides determining the magnitude of a proper motion, we can also determine its direction. It is usually expressed by stating the star's rate of motion in a purely eastward direction (its proper motion in right ascension) and its simultaneous rate of motion in a purely northward direction (proper motion in declination); west and south are the respective negatives of east and north. For instance, Capella's eastward proper motion is $+0″088$ and its northward proper motion is $-0″429$; i.e., it is moving slightly east of south. Proper motions have been determined for about 100,000 stars.

We note in passing that the stars' possession of proper motions introduces a practical complication into the measurement of their direct parallaxes; in measuring parallactic displacement, the proper motion must be allowed for. Their separate effects can be disentangled without too great difficulty, for proper motion is cumulative while parallactic displacement is oscillatory.

We have now seen how in principle it is possible to measure stars' distances, luminosities, diameters, temperatures, and motions. At the same time we have seen that in practice our methods are of very restricted usefulness. We saw, for example, that the methods given for measuring stars' distances and stars' diameters were restricted to those comparatively few stars which are sufficiently accommodating as to be comfortably near and suitably large, respectively. Fortunately, however, there exist several other methods of determining the various vital statistics of the stars. Let us consider some of the methods which, though more specialized, still possess

table 10

STAR	PARALLAX	DISTANCE	BRIGHTNESS	LUMINOSITY	DIAMETER	TEMPERA-TURE	PROPER MOTION	RADIAL VELOCITY
α Centauri A	0″.760	1.32 psc.	0.673	1.17	1.10	5,700° K	3″.67	−14 mi/sec
Sirius A	0.371	2.70	3.598	26.2	1.8	9,800	1.32	− 5
B			0.000366	0.0027	0.024	8,500		
Capella	0.063	15.81	0.731	184.	16.	5,300	0.430	+18
Arcturus	0.092	10.9	0.711	84.	23.	3,650	2.283	− 3
Rigel	0.0043	230.0	0.649	35,000.	41.	12,300	0.005	+14
Betelgeuze	0.012	83.	0.560	3,900.	420.	2,300	0.032	+13
Pollux	0.110	9.	0.291	24.	9.	4,200	0.623	+ 2
Spica	0.017	59.	0.291	1,000.	2.6	20,000	0.051	+ 3
Antares	0.015	67.	0.288	1,300.	285.	2,100	0.032	− 2
Deneb	0.003	370.	0.261	36,000.	52.	11,000	0.004	− 2
Barnard's star	0.543	1.84	0.000146	0.00049	0.087	2,900	10.27	−73
61 Cygni A	0.296	3.38	0.00643	0.073	0.59	3,900	5.21	−25
Krueger 60 A	0.257	3.89	0.000169	0.0026	0.15	3,300		
van Maanen's star	0.249	4.02	0.0000105	0.00017	0.0064	8,200	3.01	

table 11

Visual Binaries

STAR SYSTEM	A	p	a (ASTRONOMICAL UNITS)	P (YEARS)	M + m (SOLAR MASSES)
Sirius	7″62	0″371	20.21	49.94	3.47
Castor	5 .94	0 .073	81.37	380.	3.73
Procyon	4 .524	0 .287	15.76	40.65	2.37
γ Virginis	3 .746	0 .089	42.09	171.37	2.54
α Centauri	17 .593	0 .761	23.12	80.09	1.93
ξ Bootis	4 .884	0 .153	31.92	149.95	1.45
ζ Herculis	1 .369	0 .103	13.29	34.38	1.99
70 Ophiuci	4 .551	0 .199	22.87	87.85	1.55
τ Cygni	0 .85	0 .047	18.09	49.80	2.39
ξ Ursae Majoris (AB)	2 .536	0 .126	20.13	59.86	2.28
γ Coronae Borealis	0 .68	0 .030	22.67	90.0	1.44
ξ Scorpii	0 .72	0 .038	18.95	45.69	3.26
δ Equulei	0 .26	0 .056	4.64	5.70	3.07
26 Draconis	1 .50	0 .073	20.55	74.16	1.58
ψ Velorum	0 .92	0 .062	14.84	34.11	2.81
10 Ursae Majoris	0 .61	0 .070	8.71	20.8	1.53
Wolf 630	0 .210	0 .151	1.39	1.725	0.90
Krueger 60 (AB)	2 .386	0 .257	9.28	44.46	0.40

The ratio of the masses can in some instances be found. One method [6] consists in making very careful measurement of the motion of both primary and secondary components *relative to neighboring stars* in the sky. Since the actual motion of the two is about their common center of gravity, each component will be observed to revolve in an ellipse about it (Fig. 9), and because the ratio of the distances from each component to the center of gravity is equal to the inverse ratio of their masses, the ratio of the dimensions of these ellipses is likewise the inverse ratio of the masses. As a result, observation of the absolute motion of a visual binary gives a knowledge of the mass ratio.

It is found in this way that Sirius B has a mass of 0.39 that of Sirius A. Therefore, together they represent 1.39 times the mass of Sirius A. The total, as we have already seen, is 3.4 solar masses, so that Sirius A must have 3.4/1.39, or about 2.45, solar masses; the rest, 0.95 solar masses, belongs to Sirius B. Of the other visual binaries whose total masses are known, only about a score of pairs have had their individual masses determined. This is not a very large number, and therefore we shall

[6] Another method, which applies to spectroscopic binaries, will be considered later.

consider the specific results in more detail after we have considered other methods which can render our data more complete and representative.

From the masses of the stars we get, as an interesting by-product, their mean densities, provided we know also their dimensions. The mean density ρ is simply total mass divided by total volume. The most convenient way to calculate the mean density of any star is to compare it with the sun. This is very simply done, for if the star's diameter is D times the sun's, its volume will be D^3 times the sun's, and since the star has M times the

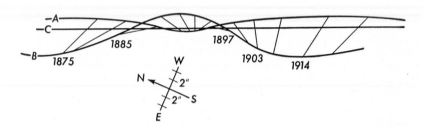

A=path of Sirius A on the sky
B=path of Sirius B on the sky
C=path of center of gravity on the sky

Figure 149. Curve *A* is the path of Sirius *A* on the sky, *B* the path of Sirius *B*, and *C* the path of their center of gravity. The latter always divides the line joining Sirius *A* and Sirius *B* in the inverse ratio of their masses.

sun's mass to distribute through D^3 as much volume, the material per unit volume will have a density

$$\rho = (M/D^3) \quad \text{times the sun's mean density}$$

or

$$\rho = 1.41 M/D^3 \quad \text{times the density of water.}$$

As an example, the mass of Sirius A is $M = 2.45$ solar masses, its diameter is $D = 1.8$ solar diameters, and therefore its mean density is $2.45/(1.8)^3 = 0.42$ times the sun's. In comparison with water, Sirius' density is therefore $0.42 \times 1.41 = 0.59$.

A small but very interesting subclass of binaries also deserves mention with the visual binaries. Though it may seem paradoxical to call them either "visual" or "binary," they are pairs of which one component is too faint to be seen. Their discovery has come from a recognition of orbital motion of the visible component. Sirius, for example, was first known to be double as a result of the wavy path it appeared to be following in the sky. In 1844, blame for its staggering was placed on a then unseen companion whose (not necessarily bad) influence led Sirius to deviate from a straight and narrow path. Eighteen years after the prediction of Sirius B it was actually seen in a new telescope, then the largest in the world.[7] The other Dog Star, Procyon, was likewise credited with a faint companion whose presence was verified many years later as the power of the newer and larger telescopes became available. Perhaps eventually all stars reputed to have very faint companions will yield to newer and more powerful instruments.

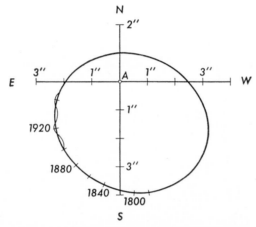

Figure 150. The star ζ Aquarii is a triple system. Components *B* and *C* revolve about component *A* in the large apparent orbit in 400 years. Simultaneously, *C* revolves about *B* in 25 years. The resultant motion of *C* about *B* is shown in the wavy line.

One of the most interesting possibilities is that some of the invisible companions are not faint stars at all but actually nonluminous planets; any body with a mass too much less than the sun's would not shine at all. Such is probably the case in the system 61 Cygni. The system consists of two visible components revolving in a period of about 720 years; each has a mass approximately 0.6 that of the sun. Celestial mechanical calculations, based on observations of 61 Cygni obtained by the use of a special high-accuracy photographic technique, have shown that one component is attended by a dark companion having only one-sixtieth the mass of the sun and revolving about it at about 2 astronomical units in a period of 5 years. This third body is small enough, only 16 times the mass of Jupiter, that we may fairly consider it to be the first planet to be discovered beyond the solar system; there is every reason to expect the discovery of more such objects in the future.

[7] The 18½-inch refractor of the Dearborn Observatory.

Eclipsing Binaries

Next we turn to the eclipsing binaries, for they permit us to make a considerable addition to our presently small collection of data. Being a new variety of object, however, they will require new methods of treatment. Let us see how astronomers' ingenuities have made eclipsing binaries tell us their dimensions and masses.

These binaries, we recall, are pairs whose orbital plane it tilted hardly at all to the line of sight. As a consequence, from where we stand each

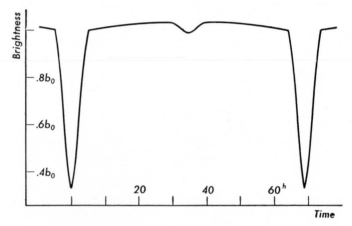

Figure 151. The star Algol (β Persei) is an eclipsing binary whose light curve is shown above. The eclipses in this system are partial. The period is about 69 hours.

star of the pair will appear to eclipse the other once per revolution. It is obviously an accident of geometry that some binaries appear as eclipsing binaries and others do not; if the earth were at some widely different point in space, the orbits of a different set of stars would appear nearly edgewise, and it would be these stars which would be observed to be eclipsing binaries. At present about 3000 eclipsing binaries are known.

Eclipsing binaries are recognized by their regular and characteristic changes of apparent brightness. A series of apparent brightness measurements is generally condensed into a graph showing how the apparent brightness varies over a period containing at least one full revolution of the stars. The length of time between eclipses of the same star is the period of revolution of the system; the graph of the binary's apparent brightness is called its *light curve* (Fig. 151). It is not to be supposed that the observations on which a light curve is based are all taken within the length of a single period. Observations made many periods apart may all be used to construct the light curve during a single period by transferring each observation to a corresponding position in the interval of the chosen period.

The light curve will indicate as a dip in apparent brightness the eclipse of each star. Usually the eclipse of one of the stars will result in a greater decrease of light than eclipse of the other, and this one is known as the *primary eclipse;* at primary eclipse the apparent brightness

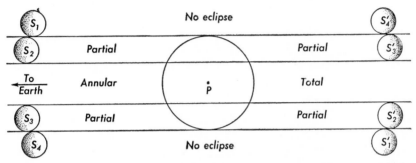

Figure 152. When the center of the secondary S is between positions S_1 and S_2 or S_3 and S_4 it will produce a partial eclipse of the primary P; half a revolution later, between S_1' and S_2' or S_3' and S_4' the secondary will be partially eclipsed. Between S_2 and S_3 the secondary would produce an annular eclipse of the primary, half a revolution later be totally eclipsed between S_2' and S_3'.

sinks to *primary minimum.* The other eclipse, sometimes creating only a barely noticeable change in brightness, is indicated in the light curve by a *secondary minimum.*

Our problem is to decipher an eclipsing binary's light curve. First of all we note that the eclipses which occur will be either both partial or one total and one annular.[8] When the secondary is on the near side of the primary, its disk will appear as far below the center of the primary as it appears above center when on the far side (or vice versa). Hence, if the secondary's apparent disk does not lie wholly on the disk of the primary at maximum phase of one eclipse, it will likewise not be wholly covered by the primary when the secondary is eclipsed half a revolution later. In this case both eclipses are partial. On the other hand, if the disk of the larger component completely covers the disk of the smaller during one eclipse, the entire disk of the smaller must appear super-

[8] With the sole exception of the unlikely case in which the two stars are identical in size and revolve in a plane seen precisely edgewise. There would then occur two total eclipses.

imposed on that of the larger at the next eclipse. In this case there is obviously one total eclipse and one annular.

The problem of analyzing the light curve of an eclipsing binary is of sufficient difficulty that we may be excused for considering a much-simplified and idealized case. Let us suppose, therefore, that the stars of the pair mutually revolve in circular orbits and that total and annular eclipses result. This case can be recognized observationally by the fact that during the total and annular phases, the light from the system will not only be reduced but wll also be constant in amount, *provided* the stars' disks have uniform brightness in all parts (we shall presently see that this is never strictly the case). There will therefore be a level portion at the bottom of both minima of the light curve.

Let us suppose that in such a system star A is totally eclipsed by star B. Then, since A is invisible during totality, we are able to measure the brightness of B alone. Knowing this and their combined brightness between eclipses gives us also the brightness of A alone. For example, suppose that a binary's apparent brightness diminishes to two-thirds of normal during total eclipse. Then component A must be responsible for one-third and B for two-thirds of their combined light.

We can now find the relative sizes of the stars. The loss of light during the total eclipse of A by B was due to the loss of light from A's apparent disk. The identically same amount of B's *disk* will be obscured by A during the annular eclipse of B by A. Hence the loss of light during annular eclipse compared with the loss of light during total eclipse will indicate the relative brightnesses of equal areas of disks of A and B. If, to continue the example, the binary dimmed to 23 twenty-fourths normal during annular eclipse (a loss of 1 twenty-fourth), the brightnesses of equal areas of the disks of A and B would be in the ratio of $\frac{1}{3}$ to $\frac{1}{24}$, or 8 to 1. Now, if B gives twice the total light of A but is only one-eighth as bright per unit area of disk, it must have 16 times as large a disk. This implies that their diameters differ by a factor of $\sqrt{16} = 4$; i.e., B has a diameter four times A's. We therefore know their *relative* sizes.

Further progress in our analysis is best made by judicious use of a little mathematics which we are content to leave to the professional. It requires no mathematics, however, to see that to what knowledge we already have of the eclipsing system, we need add only a knowledge of (1) the inclination of the orbital plane to our line of sight and (2) the relative size of the stars to their orbit to be able to predict (*a*) the durations of the total or annular phase as compared with that of the partial phase and (*b*) the lengths of the eclipses compared with the period of revolution. Clearly, the smaller star A will be wholly covered by the larger B for the maximum length of time, if A passes squarely behind B, and will be covered progressively less time the more tilted its orbital plane is to the line of sight. On the other hand, for any particular inclination of the orbit, the component A will cross before or behind B progressively higher and lower, the greater their separation. Hence the relative duration of total and annular phases to partial phase depends on orbital inclination and the components' separa-

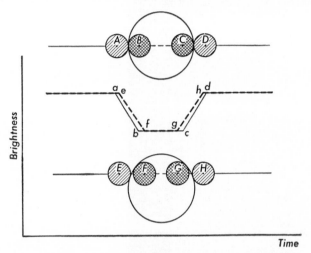

Figure 153. Points *a*, *b*, *c*, and *d* of the light curve correspond to positions *A*, *B*, *C*, and *D* of the secondary as it passes centrally in front of or behind the primary. If the eclipse is not central because of the inclination of the orbit to the line of sight, as in the lower sequence *E*, *F*, *G*, *H*, the light curve will be modified as shown. It is not difficult to visualize the changes which would result from an alteration of the sizes of primary or secondary.

tion. But so, too, does the duration of eclipse in comparison with the period of revolution, for proportionately less time will be spent in eclipse if a pair's orbit is large than if it is small. Since both the relative duration of totality and the fraction of a period spent in eclipse depend jointly on the inclination of the orbit and the stars' sizes relative to their orbit, it is possible to determine the latter from the former (by procedures we shall not describe).

It is regrettable that, for all our trouble, we have not been able to get the absolute dimensions (miles, astronomical units, etc.) of the system rather than relative ones. Fortunately there is a way to do even this for eclipsing binaries which are not too faint and whose components do not differ in luminosity by a factor of more than about three. It is then

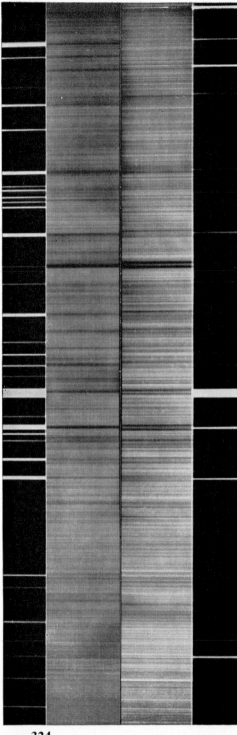

Figure 154. SPECTRO-
SCOPIC BINARY. The star
Mizar (ζ Ursae Majoris) is a
spectroscopic binary in whose
spectrum the lines of both components can be seen when their
radial velocities differ sufficiently,
as in the spectrum on the right.
(Courtesy Yerkes Observatory.)

possible to obtain the spectra of such stars, and we shall see in them the lines of *both* components.[9] From these we determine the radial velocities of *both* stars. Now they are revolving about their common center of gravity so that as one of them approaches, the other recedes. Since the rest of our information about them pertains to their *relative* orbit, the orbit of the one about the other, we take also their *relative* radial velocity, found as the velocity at which the receding component *recedes from the approaching component,* or vice versa. To illustrate, if A is approaching at 10 miles per second while B is simultaneously receding at 5 miles per second, their *relative* radial velocity must be 5 + 10 = 15 miles per second. Since we know also from the previous analysis how great is the inclination of their orbital plane and thereby the effect of foreshortening, we can at once translate the *radial* velocity into a true *orbital* velocity of the secondary about the primary.

This single datum is the key we have sought to unlock the absolute from the relative. In the simplest case, when their relative orbit is a circle, it at once gives us the absolute dimensions (in miles) of the orbit's circumference as the product of the velocity (in miles per second) by the period (in seconds); if the relative orbit is an ellipse, its eccentricity adds a mathematical complication, but none in principle, for in this case also the circumference can be calculated. In either case, the major semi-axis (in miles) can be found at once from the value of the orbital circumference (in miles). The rest is simple; since the stars' sizes are known relative to their orbit, these can now be gotten in miles. It was by this method, in fact, that the first stellar diameter was measured.

Since the mean separation of the components is now expressible in astronomical units and the period is known in years, the stars' combined mass follows. More than this, since the true motion of the pair is about their center of gravity, their actual radial velocities will be in inverse proportion to their masses, the smaller component swinging about the center of gravity as many times more rapidly and in an orbit as much larger as the larger component is more massive. Star B in our previous example would evidently have twice the mass of star A since A's radial velocity is twice B's. In other words, the radial velocities establish the mass ratio of the components and concomitantly permit the determination of their individual masses. Assembling all our information, we can then compute the stars' mean densities and, if the luminosities are known, their effective tem-

[9] The spectrum of one alone is insufficient, and if the stars differ too greatly in luminosity, only the spectrum of the brighter star can be registered.

peratures. Obviously our knowledge of these favored stars is of a high order of completeness. There are about 80 such pairs of stars.

It has been found by these methods that the star RS Canum Venaticorum, for instance, is a pair whose masses are respectively 1.86 and 1.73 solar masses while their radii are 1.63 and 5.26 times the sun's. The other quantities are determined in the standard way.

And now we must take note that we have purposely overlooked a number of factors which can greatly complicate the simple analysis we have described. Perhaps the least thorny is the effect of the eccentricity

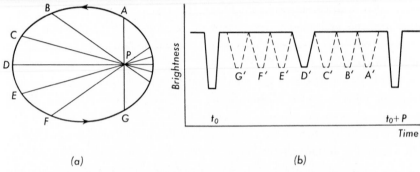

(a)   (b)

Figure 155. Figure (a) represents the relative orbit of the secondary about its primary P. When the earth is in the direction A from P, secondary minimum will be at A' on the light curve; similarly for B, B', C, C', etc.

of the relative orbit. It is easy to see what effect will result from the relative orbit's being an ellipse when one recalls that by Kepler's law of areas, the time spent by the secondary component in traversing any section of the relative orbit is proportional to the area simultaneously swept out by the line joining it to the primary. Since eclipses are observed whenever the secondary crosses the line of sight from earth to primary, this line will divide their relative orbit into two sections (Fig. 155) which may be of very unequal areas if the orbit is not a circle. As a consequence, the times between eclipses will likewise be unequal and in the same proportion. This means that the secondary minimum of the light curve need not be just halfway between two consecutive primary minima but may fall almost anywhere between, depending on (1) the orbital eccentricity and (2) the orientation of the major axis. These quantities will also determine the comparative lengths of primary and secondary eclipses; for, if the orbital velocity were constant, both eclipses would be of equal duration, but since actually the secondary is moving fastest when nearest the primary (a point called *periastron*) and slowest when farthest from the primary (a

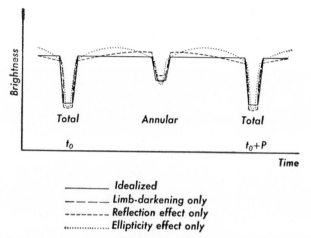

_____ Idealized

— — — — Limb-darkening only

- - - - - - - Reflection effect only

.... Ellipticity effect only

Figure 156. The solid curve represents an idealized light curve for an eclipsing binary. The broken curve (— —) shows qualitatively how this would be modified by limb-darkening alone, the dashed curve (————) shows how it would be modified by the reflection effect alone, and the dotted curve (. . . . . .) shows how it would be modified by the ellipticity effect alone.

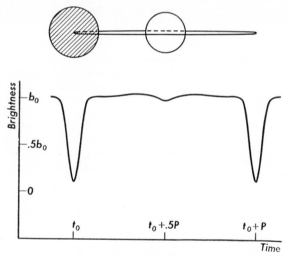

Figure 157. The light curve is that of the eclipsing binary Z Draconis. Above it is the calculated apparent orbit, showing the relative sizes of primary and secondary. The stars are actually ellipsoids with eccentricity 0.177. The luminosity of the secondary is only 0.051 that of the primary. Their period is 32.58 hours.

point called *apastron*), the durations of eclipse will have the same ratio as the orbital velocities. This ratio fixes the points at which the line of sight intersects the orbit, i.e., the orientation of the major axis.

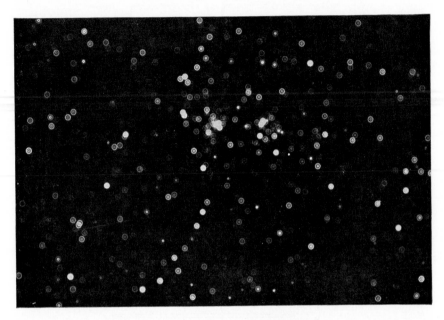

Figure 158. STELLAR COLORS ON A TIKHOFF PLATE. The double cluster in Perseus (h and χ Persei) is here shown on a *Tikhoff plate*. It is a slightly out-of-focus photograph taken with a refracting telescope over whose objective lens a central opaque diaphragm has been placed. The out-of-focus stellar images formed by an optical system of this kind are small rings rather than solid disks. The size of a ring depends upon the distance of the photographic plate from the focal plane. Because of chromatic aberration present in all refractors, rings of different colors have different focal planes and therefore are of different sizes. By filtering all but the red and blue light from the beams of starlight the red- and blue-rings may be clearly separated. Their various relative intensities distinguish stars of different colors. (Courtesy W. P. Bidelman.)

Another complication arises from the fact that stars' disks are not uniformly bright since the stars, like the sun, exhibit limb darkening. Consequently the light curve during annular eclipse will not be perfectly flat. Still another source of difficulty stems from some of the stars' being tidally elongated into ellipsoids or egg-shaped figures because of their mutual attractions at close quarters. They will present the greatest area of disk to us between eclipses, and therefore their light curves will not be flat either in or out of eclipse. This effect will be greatest for pairs whose separation is least; in fact, some pairs are known by this effect to be nearly in contact.

And finally there is the phenomenon, termed the *reflection effect,* brought about by the heating of the companionward face of either or both components. Because of the reflection effect, one side of the star becomes abnormally heated and therefore brighter than the other. Let us recall, too, that besides the aforementioned intricacies, eclipses may be partial rather than total and annular. It must be abundantly clear that eclipsing binaries present a problem that is at once knotty and at the same time of great practical importance to the astronomer. It is on account of these facts together that much time and effort have had to be given to the study of eclipsing binaries.

The binary stars have indeed proved to be most informative. Related to them, but of no particular utility, are the multiple stars. These are systems of three, four, or even as many as six stars revolving about their mutual center of gravity. It is estimated that perhaps one visual binary in twenty is also a multiple system. Sometimes three or four members of a system are visible, though more often systems' multiple nature is known only spectroscopically. Some of the most famous multiple systems are α Centauri (visual binary, the brighter component a spectroscopic binary), θ Orionis in the heart of the Orion Nebula (four components visible), ϵ Lyrae (four components visible), and Castor (three pairs visible). It is sometimes interesting to speculate on the novel features that would accompany life on a planet in such a system, but at present these stars are of only casual interest to us.

C. METHODS FOR SECONDARY STANDARDS

> *"Troll, to thyself be true—enough."*
> —IBSEN

Thus far we have been engaged in cataloguing the most direct methods for obtaining information about the stars. The details of the methods have comprised a considerable range of intricacy, but all have been straightforward in principle. In all cases, however, the methods have for some reason had to be restricted to use upon a comparatively few stars—perhaps a few dozens or hundreds, or a few thousands at best. There is no help for it; we can proceed further only by methods which, while possessing wider applicability, do so by some sacrifice in directness or on the strength of an approximate assumption. Results by these methods can give us only secondary standards. Of course the secondary standards can be and are checked against primary ones for some notion of their reliability, and it is encouraging to find them quite generally trustworthy. Let us consider some of the important methods.

Temperatures

The first applies to the determination of stars' temperatures. Our previous methods have required more information than was usually available for any given star. But, to be sure, our previous methods have given us a star's *effective* temperature, i.e., the temperature determined by the *whole* of the star's radiation; could we possibly do it with less—one or a few wavelengths, for example? We recall that the sun's "temperature" was, in fact, calculable from the intensity of radiation in any wavelength simply by using Planck's law. Unfortunately it would be quite impracticable to use the identical method on many stars, for it requires that we know E_λ, the number of ergs of radiation of wavelength λ radiated from each square centimeter of the star's surface per second. If it were necessary to determine this, we should be worse off than before, since it would require not only a knowledge of the star's total radiation per square centimeter but also a knowledge of how the energy is distributed throughout all wavelengths of the spectrum.

At the same time, this review and comparison suggests that Planck's law may be used in a different way. Since it predicts the amount of energy to be radiated in every wavelength by a perfect radiator at a given absolute temperature T, it will therefore predict the *ratios* of the intensities of radiation at any two or more conveniently chosen wavelengths, or equally well the wavelength in which the intensity of radiation is greatest. For a perfect radiator, these ratios or this wavelength will be *uniquely* characteristic of its temperature. Therefore, if the one or the other can be measured from the spectrum of a star, we can specify its temperature, provided we *assume* that stars radiate as perfect radiators.

For example, let us suppose that we choose to measure the wavelength of maximum intensity in the spectrum of a star [10] and that we find some particular value, λ_m Angstroms. Now the temperature of a perfect radiator whose radiation is most intense in this wavelength would have to be (as a consequence of Planck's law)

---

[10] Determining this wavelength is an important practical problem requiring a great amount of care and critical judgment. We omit the tedious details as unessential to the argument.

$$T = \frac{28.9 \times 10^6}{\lambda_m} \quad \text{degrees absolute.}$$

If the star were a perfect radiator, that would likewise be its temperature.

This relation is known as *Wien's law*. It indicates, for instance, that if the radiation of a perfect radiator is most intense in the wavelength 5780 Å, then its temperature must be

$$\frac{28.9 \times 10^6}{5780} = 5000° \text{ K.}$$

For the sun, Wien's law gives a temperature of 6150° K, as we have seen. This is within 7 per cent of its effective temperature, a discrepancy we can hardly afford to quibble over in cases where this method is our only one for determining temperature. Its reliability rests on how well justified we are in our assumption that stars are perfect radiators. We know, of course, that the sun is not. We find, too, that for those stars whose effective temperatures we know, it is not exactly the same as the temperature determined by Wien's law. The difference is never intolerable, however, and we are well justified in regarding the stars as approximately perfect radiators. We explicitly recognize, however, that the approximate validity of our assumption gives to the result of this method the standing of only a secondary standard.

The temperature determined by Wien's law is called a *color temperature,* as are also the possibly slightly different temperatures determined from the ratios of intensities in two or more wavelengths. The reason for this nomenclature is evident. The color of a star's light will depend on the relative strengths of the wavelengths it radiates. The ratios of intensities of the light of various wevelengths or the value of the wavelength of maximum intensity of radiation give a numerical measure of this; they are, in fact, known as *color equivalents.* Consequently stars of different colors will have different temperatures. Just as white hot iron is at a higher temperature than red hot iron, so a white hot star has a higher surface temperature than a red hot star. Thus, in order of increasing surface temperature, are deep-red Antares, orange Arcturus, yellow Procyon, white Sirius, and blue-white Rigel.

Since the color equivalents of a great many stars can be and have been determined, we are able to know the color temperatures of this many stars. We are thereby able to extend greatly our knowledge of stellar temperatures. It is to be noted, however, that our confidence in the significance of color temperatures rests on a comparison with stars whose effective temperatures have been determined by the more direct methods.

Diameters

Our second method applies to the determination of stars' diameters and depends on the preceding one. By rearranging our previous formula for the effective temperature, we see that the diameter of any star is

$$D = \left(\frac{5770}{T_c}\right)^2 \times \sqrt{L};$$

here L is the star's luminosity in solar units, T the temperature in degrees absolute, and D the diameter in solar diameters. The temperature T was previously T_e, the effective temperature, but we may identify this with the color temperature T_c if we assume, as we did a moment ago, that the star radiates as a perfect radiator; the justification and the cautions are the same as then.

As an example, $T_c = 9800°$ for Sirius, and since its luminosity is 27, we have that its diameter will be $(5770/9800)^2 \times \sqrt{27} = 1.8$ times the sun's, approximately. The same can be done for all stars whose luminosities and color temperatures are known; in practice, most estimates of stellar diameters are made by this method. We note again, however, that this method likewise rests on the same approximate assumption as that for determining color temperature; its results are therefore secondary standards.

Masses

Next we turn to attempts to determine the masses of still a few more stars. Here we shall encounter a new and different kind of inadequacy, one that is inherent in the observations rather than due to instrumental or personal limitations. The method concerns those spectroscopic binaries which are neither visual nor eclipsing binaries. Their binary character is established solely by the observation of a periodic oscillation of the radial velocity of one or both components. This oscillation is, of course, a consequence of the stars' revolution about the system's center of gravity. A graph of the radial velocity of a spectroscopic binary component over the period of at least one full revolution is called its *velocity curve*. If the spectra of both components of a spectroscopic binary are visible (as they are in about one out of every four spectroscopic binaries), we are thereby given their relative velocity, from which can be formed the *relative-velocity curve*.

A relative-velocity curve, like a light curve, gives a great deal of information about the relative orbit of the revolving pair. In a limited way,

Figure 160 illustrates how the form of a velocity curve depends on the size, shape, and orientation of the binary orbit. If we attempt the converse

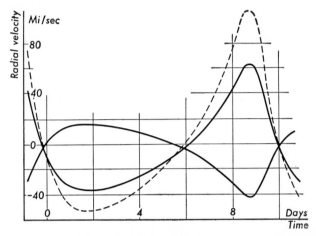

Figure 159. The solid curves are the radial velocity curves of the two components of the spectroscopic binary HR 8169. The dotted curve is their relative velocity curve. The velocity V_0 of this system with respect to the sun is the value of the velocity at which the two solid curves intersect; it is approximately -4 miles/second.

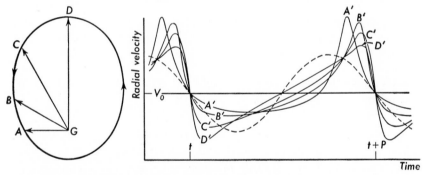

Figure 160. Curves A', B', C', and D' are the radial velocity curves of one component of a spectroscopic binary about its center of gravity G when the earth is in the respective directions A, B, C, or D. V_0 is the velocity of the center of gravity of the system. The dotted curve is the velocity curve for a circular orbit of the same major semi-axis.

problem, finding the size, shape, and orientation of the binary orbit from an observed relative velocity curve, we find it to be uniquely soluble *except* for a knowledge of the orbit's inclination to the line of sight. The exception is a result of our being unable either to see the stars separately or to witness their mutual eclipses. It is, however, a fatal exception, for lacking the inclination, we have no way of knowing the extent of the foreshortening of the orbit. Consequently its true size is unknown, and we can state only that the stars' mean distance from each other must be *at least* a certain amount, how much more, no one knows for sure. We might better reconcile ourselves to this limitation to our knowledge if it were the extent of the mischief, but it is not. For, by the same token we can know only the least

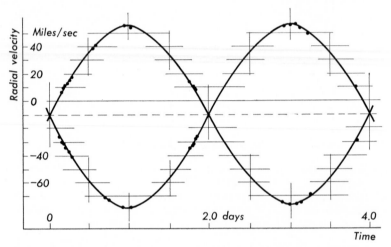

Figure 161. The velocity curves of the double-line spectroscopic binary β Aurigae show that it has a period of 4.0 days in a nearly circular orbit and that the center of gravity of the system is approaching us at the rate of about 10 miles per second.

possible value of the system's mass and the stars' individual masses; the true values are greater by a factor unknown.

Even so, this information is better than none. For example, the components of the most massive binary yet discovered (the star HD698) appear to have masses of at least 113 and 45 times the sun's, respectively. This in itself is a statistic of some value. But lower limits for the masses are not the full measure of the information to be had from spectroscopic binaries. It is possible to get also some fairly reliable *average* true masses. For we can estimate the *probability* of various orbital inclinations and therefore the probability of the *average* amount by which the true masses exceed their minimum observed values. Specifically, it is found that *on the average* the observed lower limits should be increased by about 50 per cent to give the true value. This adjustment cannot give us the mass of any single star with any greater certainty than before, but it is likely to strike quite near to the average for a group of considerable size.

And so we complete our survey of the methods which are prerequisite to our knowing anything at all of the stars; our preoccupation with means has been a necessary prelude to further progress. It should not be assumed, however, that our operational tool kit is complete. On the contrary, we shall find that what we learn by these methods will suggest new

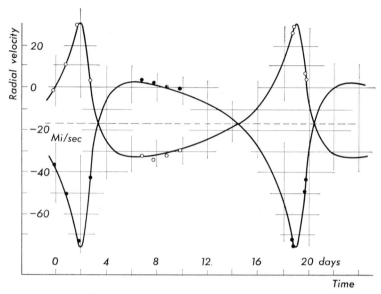

Figure 162. The velocity curves of the double-line spectroscopic binary θ Aquilae show that it has a period of 17.1 days in an orbit of eccentricity 0.6 and that the center of gravity of the system is approaching us at a rate of about 18 miles per second. The open circles represent the observed velocities of the primary, the dots those of the secondary.

methods or improvements and checks on old ones; some of these we shall consider as we are able in the following chapters.

QUESTIONS

1. Describe the principle of determining stellar distances by parallax measurment. Compare it to terrestrial distance determinations by rangefinder.
2. If the earth were to travel a square orbit rather than a nearly circular one, what would be the shape of the parallactic orbit of a star near the poles of the ecliptic? Near the plane of the ecliptic? In between?
3. A stellar parallax is sometimes defined as the angle subtended by one astronomical unit at the distance of the star. Explain.
4. With respect to parallax measurement, what advantage would a Jovian astronomer have over a terrestrial astronomer? Determine the parallax Proxima Centauri would have from Jupiter. Could it be determined with any greater absolute accuracy? Relative accuracy?
5. What is the distance of a star whose parallax is 0″.0125? Give the distance in parsecs, light years, and miles.

6. Describe the procedure by which a stellar parallax is measured. What allowance is made for the fact that comparison stars are not infinitely far away?

7. To minimize the effects of differential refraction in our own atmosphere, it is customary to take parallax plates of a star when it is near the observer's meridian. From this fact, determine the best times of day for parallax observations.

8. If a 60-watt bulb at a distance of 1 mile has the same apparent brightness as a star whose distance is 5 parsecs, determine the ratio of their true brightnesses.

9. Compared to its brightness as seen from the earth, what would be the brightness of the full moon as seen from the sun?

10. What is the luminosity of a star whose apparent brightness is 0.008 unit and whose distance is 25 parsecs?

11. If Jupiter were perfectly reflecting, what would be its luminosity? (*Hint:* What proportion of the sun's radiation would it intercept?) From your answer, comment on the likelihood that Jupiter could be seen from Proxima Centauri. What is the possibility of our seeing planets in other planetary systems, if such exist?

12. Why cannot stars' angular diameters be measured in the same way as those of the sun, moon, and planets?

13. What is the linear diameter of a star at 65 parsecs if its angular diameter is $0''002$? Give the diameter in both solar diameters and miles.

14. At what distance would a 3-inch tennis ball have the same angular diameter as Antares?

15. Find the effective temperatures of stars whose respective luminosities and diameters in solar units are: (*a*) $L = 16$, $D = 9$; (*b*) $L = 25$, $D = 0.8$; (*c*) $L = 0.25$, $D = 0.5$; (*d*) $L = 1000$, $D = 80$.

16. Determine the space velocities of stars whose respective radial and transverse velocities in miles per second are: (*a*) $V_R = +6$, $V_T = 8$; (*b*) $V_R = -12$, $V_T = 5$; (*c*) $V_R = +15$, $V_T = 20$; (*d*) $V_R = -25$, $V_T = 10$.

17. With ruler and pencil, lay off to scale on a sheet of paper arrows representing the radial and transverse velocities of the stars in the preceding exercise. With a protractor, measure for each the angle between the star's space velocity and the observer's line of sight.

18. Calculate the radial velocities of the stars in whose respective spectra lines are found to be displaced from true wavelengths λ_t to observed wavelengths λ_0: (*a*) $\lambda_t = 5400$ Å, $\lambda_0 = 5400.9$; (*b*) $\lambda_t = 4650$, $\lambda_0 = 4649.3$; (*c*) $\lambda_t = 3862.1$, $\lambda_0 = 3861.7$.

19. Find the transverse velocities of the following stars: (*a*) $d = 28$ parsecs, $\mu = 0''15$; (*b*) $p = 0''075$, $\mu = 0''375$; (*c*) $d = 145$ parsecs, $\mu = 0''061$.

20. How may proper motion be distinguished from parallactic motion? What is the procedure by which proper motions are determined? How can the measures of proper motion be improved? Can parallax measures be improved in the same way?

21. What is a visual binary? How can it be distinguished from an optical double? What measures are made on visual binaries? How are they ob-

tained? To what use are these measures put? How many observations are needed?

22. How may a visual binary's period be determined even before the system has been observed over a complete revolution? Why is it frequently desirable to do this?

23. Find the masses of the binaries to which the following data apply: (a) $a = 6$ astronomical units, $P = 4$ years; (b) $A = 1''5$, $p = 0''111$, $P = 32$ years; (c) $A = 6''19$, $d = 14.2$ parsecs, $P = 23.8$ years.

24. What is needed to obtain the individual masses of the stars of a binary system? How can this be obtained? Find the individual masses of the stars in the preceding problem, given that their mass ratios are (a) 2:1, (b) 8:3, (c) 5.6:3.8.

25. Find the mean densities of stars having the following dimensions in solar masses and solar diameters: (a) $M = 1.5$, $D = 2.7$; (b) $M = 0.75$, $D = 0.31$; (c) $M = 48$, $D = 71$.

26. What is an eclipsing binary? What measures are made on eclipsing binaries? For what are these measures used? Review the numerous factors which complicate the analysis of eclipsing binaries' light curves. Indicate what observable effects each will have.

27. Explain how, in the simplest case, the relative sizes of stars can be obtained. Apply this analysis to a system in which primary minimum (total eclipse) is one-tenth normal brightness and secondary minimum (annular eclipse) is 0.225 normal brightness.

28. What more is needed to determine the relative size of stars and orbit? Assuming a circular orbit seen edgewise, what is the relative size of stars and orbit if the eclipse lasts 30 hours from beginning to end, totality lasts 18 hours, and the period of revolution is 628.32 days? What is needed to determine the absolute sizes of stars and orbit in an eclipsing binary?

29. Find the color temperatures of the stars in whose respective spectra the wavelengths of maximum intensity are: (a) 2890 Å; (b) 4128 Å; (c) 963 Å; (d) 6500 Å; (e) 10,000 Å. What is the color of each star?

30. Find the diameters of the stars whose respective color temperatures (in degrees absolute) and luminosities (in solar units) are: (a) $T_c = 8625$, $L = 16$; (b) $T_c = 2875$, $L = 900$; (c) $T_c = 11,500$, $L = 0.081$; (d) $T_c = 30,000$, $L = 250$.

31. What is a spectroscopic binary? What observations are made of spectroscopic binaries? For what are these observations used?

32. What information can be gotten from the velocity curves of both components of a spectroscopic binary? What information cannot be gotten? How may statistical methods supplement the data on spectroscopic binaries?

33. What information can be gotten from the velocity of a single component of a spectroscopic binary? What information cannot be gotten? Under what circumstances can the velocity curve of only one component be obtained? Why are spectroscopic binaries seldom visual binaries and vice versa?

chapter 8
The Statistics
of the Normal Stars

• • •

The several methods we have lately considered have all been devised to help answer the single simple question, "What are the stars and what do they do?" Our immediate agendum consists in reviewing the best answer that can be currently given. Since the question is a large one, we shall deal first with what stars are and second with what they do. The description will apply to stars that do not distinguish themselves markedly in any respect and which therefore represent "average" members of the stellar population. We will consider later those few stars which are or do something out of the ordinary.

A. WHAT THEY ARE

"Twinkle, twinkle, little star
How I wonder what you are."
—NURSERY RHYME

The nature of a star can be found out by asking enough well-chosen questions—and by answering these questions with sufficient pertinent data. One such datum might consist of the fact that the mass of an ordinary star is comparable to the sun's—some stars having a little more, some a little less, but a few having less than a tenth or more than ten times the sun's mass. Another relevant fact is that the diameters of most stars approximate that of the sun; only exceptional ones are as small as one-tenth the sun's diameter or greater by 100 times in diameter. The range in commonplace temperatures is narrower still, a factor of five in each sense encompassing practically all. (Of course stars whose surface temperatures are sensibly less than one-fifth the sun's would shine so feebly as almost certainly to fail of discovery by present photographic means.)

The stars also show dark-line spectra as the sun does. We have, in fact, already made use of their absorption lines for determining radial velocities. These same absorption lines must furthermore tell us the stars' compositions. Again the results are reassuringly familiar—hydrogen, nitrogen, oxygen, iron, calcium, sodium, etc.—all common solar and terrestrial elements.

By now we are reasonably convinced that the stars are actually suns or that the sun is simply one of the stars. But, to be sure, there are differences among the stars; we well know they are not uniform in mass, luminosity, diameter, etc. Our real problem is therefore: What sense can we make of the differences? Is there any plan or pattern to the make-up of individual stars and is this reflected in the character of the general stellar population?

The question itself suggests that we require first to know in some fairly specific terms the character of the general stellar population. Once this has been ascertained, it may of itself suggest some fundamental regularity. We have therefore to obtain and assemble in as convenient a form as possible all available statistics of the stars. For this purpose we naturally want a statistic that is informative to the highest degree and at the same time obtainable for great numbers of stars. Astronomers have long since found that a star's spectrum is just such a one. Let us consider stellar spectra in this light.

Stellar Spectra

Stellar spectra are, like the sun's, dark-line spectra. They are not, however, all alike in appearance. Some are very like the sun's, some similar, quite a few very different. The variety is not endless, though, and nearly all the stars have spectra that can be matched detail for detail with some one of a handful of certain prototype stars. Each prototype star identifies a particular spectral class which contains all the stars of like spectra. A spectral class is given a letter designation, as stars of class A, or class K, etc. Graduated subdivisions within a letter class are indicated by Arabic numeral suffixes from 0 to 9, for example A0 or M4. Thus Vega is in class A0 and may be considered a prototype of this class.[1] It is said to have a type A0 spectrum.

One of the most significant facts concerning spectral types is that the stellar spectra grade evenly in appearance from one type into another. The prominence of characteristic features rises and wanes gradually through a sequence of properly ordered types. For example, one such feature might be the comparative strength of the hydrogen lines; they are most dominant in spectra of class A0, decreasingly strong in spectral types

---

[1] Any star of a given class may be chosen as the prototype of that class; usually it is one of the brightest or one of the most familiar.

which precede and follow it in the spectral sequence. The spectral sequence was only briefly alphabetical. Its present and long-standing order is O, B, A, F, G, K, M, R, N, and S.[2]

Before attempting to understand the significance of the spectral sequence, let us see what some of the features of the several types are. For the present we shall omit consideration of types O, R, N, and S, which contain only a very small percentage of the stars. Class B is characterized by the presence of lines of neutral helium, silicon ionized from one to three times, a number of other ionized elements, and strong hydrogen lines. The lines due to helium disappear, and those of most of the highly ionized atoms are weaker in class A, while the hydrogen lines are stronger and easily dominate the spectrum. As we progress to type F, there is a decline in the strength of the hydrogen lines and the emergence of many lines of metals—iron, calcium, sodium, strontium, manganese, etc. —usually both neutral and ionized. Class G stars show more and stronger lines from the metals, particularly the two lines of Ca^+ designated as the H and K lines, whereas hydrogen lines are less strong than in class F. The lines H and K become extraordinarily strong in class K, outdoing all other lines, and lines of the metals are in general stronger than those of hydrogen. In this class there first appear molecular bands, groups of many regularly but closely spaced lines due to molecules, appearing to all effects in spectrographs of moderate size as deletions of intervals of a number of wavelengths (10–20 Å). In class M the molecular bands are much stronger and the most prominent are due to molecules of titanium oxide (TiO).

A continuous sequence such as is presented by the spectral sequence could hardly have been expected a priori. How is it to be explained? For one thing, the differences between two spectral classes are not to be explained, in general, as an effect of different chemical abundances in the stars of the two types (for qualifications and exceptions, see pp. 414, 464). For, if in different stars the various elements were present in appreciably different proportions, the gradation from one spectral type to another would not be unique; any given class might shade into neighboring classes in as many ways as there are ways of varying the proportions of its chemical elements. This is not observed; on the contrary, the remarkable continuity of the spectral sequence argues decisively for a uniformity of chemical composition among the stars.

Fortunately we are offered a clue to the spectral sequence by considering examples of stars with spectra of the various classes. For example,

---

[2] A simple and entertaining way to remember this series of letters is by means of the following mnemonic: the spectral types are given in order by the first letters of the words in the sentence "Oh, Be A Fine Girl. Kiss Me Right Now. (Smack!)"

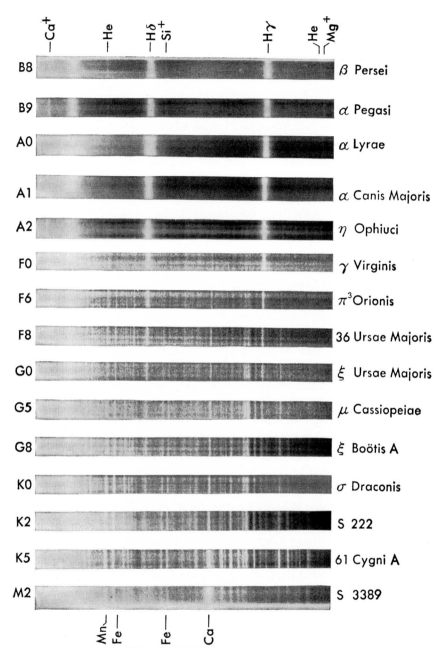

Figure 163. STELLAR SPECTRA. This series of fifteen stars illustrates the principal characteristics of representatives of various spectral types. It shows also the gradualness of the progressive changes in their identifying features. These, like most reproductions of stellar spectra, are negatives; absorption lines therefore appear light, the continuous background appears dark. (Courtesy Yerkes Observatory.)

blue Spica and Rigel are B stars, blue-white Vega and Sirius are of type A, yellow-white Procyon type F, the sun and yellow-orange Capella type G, red-orange Arcturus and Aldebaran type K, and red Antares and Betelgeuse type M. We are at once struck by the fact that the spectral sequence is an arrangement according to color, and we have already seen that color indicates temperature. Therefore the spectral sequence must be primarily a temperature sequence. Let us see if this will explain the differences which occur serially in the spectral sequence.

The high temperature of the B stars is required to excite helium, to ionize silicon three times, and to cause hydrogen to absorb strongly. The lesser temperature of the A stars is insufficient to produce lines of helium or its ion. At the same time the lines of hydrogen are in contrast even stronger because fewer hydrogen atoms have been disqualified through ionization. In stars of type F the increase in un-ionized hydrogen atoms is more than offset by a greater decrease in the number of excited hydrogen atoms, and therefore the lines of hydrogen are not as strong as in class A. On the other hand, most of the metals, which are easily ionized, gain so appreciably in singly ionized atoms that their lines appear in considerable numbers; in the hotter stars these same metals would be more highly ionized and could produce few or no lines in the visible wavelengths. The trend noted in the F stars continues to the relatively cooler G stars in which the hydrogen lines are still weaker and the lines of the metals still stronger. The increase in the number of Ca^+ ions at the expense of Ca^{++} is shown strikingly by the much greater strength of the H and K lines of Ca^+; since these are resonance lines, they benefit most by the increase of Ca^+ ions. The number of Ca^+ ions is a maximum at the temperature of the K stars, and therefore the H and K lines are strongest in this class. By now hydrogen has become so weakened and the metals so strengthened that the metallic lines are stronger than those of hydrogen. Moreover, in the cooler K stars a few of the atoms can unite to form certain molecules which at higher temperatures would be unable to survive the more violent collisions and the more intense radiation. In the M stars the H and K lines wane because fewer calcium atoms remain ionized at the lower temperature. But at these lower temperatures progressively more molecules are tolerated and the molecular bands gain greatly in strength, particularly the hardier or more abundant ones like titanium oxide and zirconium oxide.

This interpretation of the spectral sequence is, we see, self-consistent. We can thus make use of the fact that not only does surface temperature determine the spectral type of a star, but conversely, the spectral type will accurately indicate the temperature. Consequently, by means of the stars whose effective temperatures and color temperatures are already known, the temperature of each spectral type can be calibrated. Table 12 indicates the effective temperature of a number of spectral types. We now have a comparatively simple means of determining the temperatures of a great many stars—simply determine their respective spectral types.

table 12

SPECTRAL TYPE	EFFECTIVE TEMPERATURE
B	12,000–25,000° K
A	8,000–11,000
F	6,200– 7,800
G	4,600– 6,000
K	3,500– 4,900
M	2,600– 3,400

The Hertzsprung-Russell Diagram

Spectral type also shows a striking correlation with luminosity. The relation between them is shown to best advantage in a diagram called the *Hertzsprung-Russell diagram* [3] (after the Danish and American astronomers who "discovered" it). It is a graph in which vertical position indicates luminosity and horizontal position specifies spectral type. If the individual stars of known luminosity and spectral type are represented by dots on such a graph, it will be found that they do not fall haphazardly over the entire diagram but are concentrated almost exclusively in a diagonally placed belt; this belt is known as the *main sequence,* and the great majority of the stars belong to the main sequence. It is obvious from the Hertzsprung-Russell diagram that the most luminous stars of the main sequence are likewise its hottest; in fact, they are the most luminous stars because they are hottest, the diameters of main sequence stars being all of comparable size. The sun, Proxima Centauri, and the bright components of Sirius and Procyon, are all main sequence stars.

The overwhelming majority of stars belong to the main sequence. There are, however, a few stars whose positions on the Hertzsprung-Russell diagram fall unmistakably above those of the main sequence stars of the same spectral type; evidently they are notably more luminous than other stars of the same temperature. They could be so only by being much larger in size. Such stars are appropriately designated as *giants.* This term is applied to any star of greater luminosity than the same main sequence

[3] Also known as the spectrum-luminosity diagram.

type; it is not incorrect, however, to think of them also as stars of comparatively large diameter. Arcturus, among the more familiar stars, is a giant. Still another step in luminosity above the giants is an even smaller class called the *supergiants*. The supergiants are the largest and most luminous stars known. Among them are such stars as Rigel, Deneb, Betel-

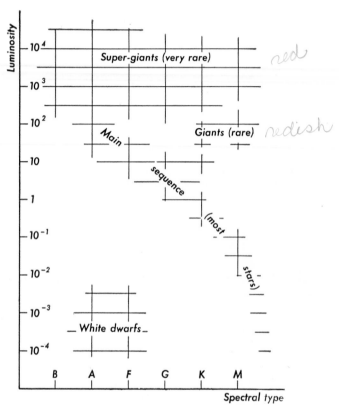

Figure 164. In this schematic Hertzsprung-Russell diagram, the areas not covered by coordinate lattice contain few or no stars. The sun occupies the position at unit luminosity, spectral type G2.

geuse, and Antares. The supergiants appear scattered across the top of the Hertzsprung-Russell diagram. All stars of the main sequence are, for contrast, called *dwarfs*.

Information Obtainable from Spectral Types

To be quite candid, it is only by loose usage that we can refer to giants or supergiants as "of the same spectral class" as main sequence stars (dwarfs). As might be expected, stars so different in size and luminosity do show small but definite differences in their spectra. These differences are called *luminosity effects* (Fig. 165). They consist of such distinctions as greater or lesser strength of certain telltale lines or sharpness or diffuseness of characteristic lines, particularly those of hydrogen.

The origin of the luminosity effects lies in the fact that the giant and supergiant stars have large diameters. Since their diameters are much

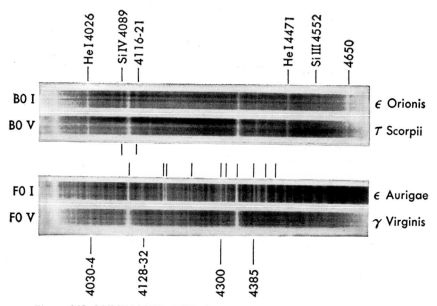

Figure 165. LUMINOSITY EFFECTS. Luminosity effects in the spectra of stars of type B0 and F0 are evident in the spectral lines identified by the markers. (Courtesy Yerkes Observatory.)

greater in proportion than their masses, they will have smaller surface gravities than the dwarfs.[4] Consequently their atmospheres are, by comparison, less compressed and the pressures within them are very much lower than even in the solar atmosphere. This is the immediate cause of the "luminosity" effects. In the first place, pressure broadening is much less. In the second place, ionization takes place more readily at the lower pressure simply because ions and free electrons are then given less opportunity to recombine. Hence the gases will either be more ionized in a giant at the same temperature or equally ionized at a lower temperature.

[4] The surface gravity of a star will be M/D^2 times the sun's, where M and D are in solar units.

Therefore, though the spectrum of a giant may possess the identifying features of some particular spectral class, it will certainly differ in lesser details since the populations of the states of its atoms cannot possibly be identically the same as in the gases of a dwarf's atmosphere. In fact, it is a general rule that the temperatures of giants are lower than those of dwarfs of the "same" spectral class. Table 13 gives the effective temperatures of giants and dwarfs of the spectral classes from type G on.

Rather than having invariably to apologize for our loose usage of the term "spectral class," we can make an explicit recognition of the differences between the spectra of giants and dwarfs by a slight refinement in their designation. This is done by affixing a *luminosity class* designation to the letter type.[5] Luminosity classes are denoted by Roman numerals: I for supergiants, II and III for giants, IV for subgiants, and V for dwarfs. Thus supergiant Deneb is type A2 I, giant Dubhe is G8 II, giant Aldebaran is K5 III, subgiant Procyon is F5 IV, and dwarf Vega is A0 V.

A complete spectral classification therefore contains implicitly some highly valuable information. In particular, a careful determination of spectral luminosity class fixes a star's luminosity to within about 60 per cent. This is really much better than it seems at first glance; it is actually a quite remarkable standard of precision.

table 13

SPECTRAL TYPE	T_e	SPECTRAL TYPE	T_e
dG0	6000° K	gG0	5200° K
dG2	5710	gG5	4620
dG5	5360	gK0	4230
dK0	4910	gK5	3580
dK2	4650	gM0	3400
dK5	3900	gM2	3200
dM2	3200	gM4	2930
		gM6	2750
		gM8e *	2590

* For the significance of the suffix "e," see p. 391.

Much of the power and usefulness of this method of classification rests in its being applicable to a great many stars about which little information would otherwise be obtainable. The method of spectral luminosity determination is enormously useful, for example, in finding distances

[5] It is also frequently done by prefixing a "d" for dwarfs, "g" for giants, and "c" for supergiants.

to. Upon these, whose distances have been determined in some way, depends a statistical method which is extended to the rest.

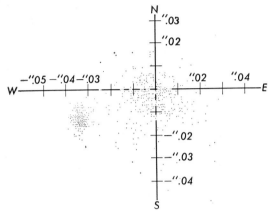

Figure 169. The distance and direction of each dot from the intersection of the coordinate axes indicate respectively the magnitude and direction of the proper motion of a star of a region in the constellation Cancer. Stars of the galactic cluster Praesepe are clearly segregated in the cluster of points in the lower left quadrant. (This diagram does not show how the stars are placed on the sky.)

Figure 170. The arrows originating in each of the stars of the Hyades have the respective directions of these stars' proper motions and their lengths are in proportion to the magnitudes of the proper motions. Their common parallel motion is in the direction of the cross at *C* upon which the arrows converge. Knowledge of the true direction of space motion, the proper motion, and the radial velocity then permits the distance of the Hyades to be determined.

The statistical method for getting the distances of the farther clusters depends upon the fact that among the nearby clusters those which are alike in total membership and in apparent concentration are of approximately equal diameter. Though the actual diameters range from about 1.5 parsecs to 15 parsecs, over three-fourths of all clusters have diameters between 2 and 6 parsecs, with a majority at about 3.5. Assuming that what is true of the nearby clusters is also true of the farther ones, we can estimate the distances of any of them simply from their apparent diameters, for the apparent diameters are less in proportion to their distances. The nearest cluster is about 40 parsecs away; the farthest that can be seen is about 7000.

From the volume occupied by a cluster and a count of the number of stars in it, one can calculate the density of stars within the cluster. The exceptional cluster M67 has a density of 140 solar masses per cubic parsec. At the center of M11 there are in each cubic parsec more than 80 stars as luminous as the sun; an observer there would have every night the impressive view of at least 40 stars as bright as or brighter than Sirius. To be sure, very few clusters are as populous as these, most having an average density of only a few tenths of a star of the sun's luminosity per cubic parsec. This is to be compared, however, with the corresponding density in the sun's neighborhood of only about 0.01 star of luminosity as great as the sun's.

Like the molecules of the onetime lunar atmosphere, the stars of a cluster one by one tend to acquire the velocity of escape in consequence of their mutual encounters. The rate of escape is governed by the density of the cluster. Clusters with densities of at least 0.6 solar mass per cubic parsec will persist for very long periods of time. Less dense clusters will evaporate in a few tens or hundreds of millions of years. Clusters like M67 and M11 will persist almost indefinitely.

Two conclusions may be tentatively drawn from these considerations. In the first place, since clusters of low density will dissipate in short astronomical times, it may very well be that those low-density clusters we now see are of relatively recent origin; on the other hand, high-density clusters may well be very old. In other words, the stars of different clusters may in fact be of different ages. In the second place, present membership in a cluster implies past membership traceable back to a common origin. In other words, stars of any given cluster are probably of a single age and were formed from the same material. We may expect of them, then, a homogeneity not found among the general field stars. Confirmation of both these expectations—age differences among different clusters, and uncommon homogeneity within each cluster—may be sought for in their respective Hertzsprung-Russell diagrams.

The homogeneity of cluster stars is at once evident from the small scatter of the plotted positions of the stars in a Hertzsprung-Russell diagram. Of course it is only for the nearer clusters that a true Hertzsprung-

Russell diagram can be constructed, for spectra cannot be had of the stars in the fainter, more distant clusters. In place of a Hertzsprung-Russell diagram, one constructs for the distant clusters an equivalent color-brightness diagram. In these, apparent brightness is reckoned vertically, and some color equivalent (p. 330) is reckoned horizontally. Each cluster star is entered upon the diagram at a point corresponding to its apparent bright-

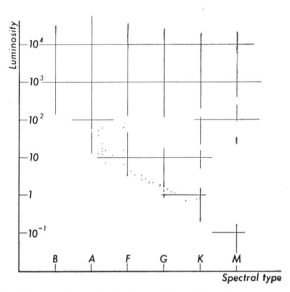

Figure 171. Stars of the galactic cluster Coma Berenices, about 75 parsecs distant, appear as points superposed on the general Hertzsprung-Russell diagram. Note the absence of giants and super-giants. Information on late-type dwarfs is lacking because these stars are so faint.

ness and color. The final result is a diagram very similar to a Hertzsprung-Russell diagram, for color equivalent is a measure of spectral type and at a common distance apparent brightness is proportional to luminosity. Such a color-brightness diagram is shown in Figure 172; its similarity to a Hertzsprung-Russell diagram is clear.

The color equivalent most often used in these diagrams is called *color index*. It is arbitrarily taken as two-and-a-half times the logarithm of the ratio of the visual brightness to the photographic brightness, provided these brightnesses have been (by convention) adjusted to be equal for stars of type A0. This is a possible definition because the ordinary photographic plate is, in comparison to the eye, more sensitive to blue light, less sensitive to red. Consequently plate and eye will have slightly different views of all stars not of type A0; this difference, as specified by color index, is a measure

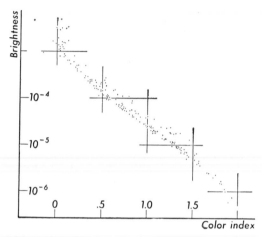

Figure 172. This color-brightness diagram is of the galactic cluster Praesepe in Cancer. The brightnesses used are photographic rather than visual.

table 14

Color Indices *

SPECTRAL TYPE	COLOR INDEX	SPECTRAL TYPE	COLOR INDEX
B0	−0.23		
B2	−0.20		
B5	−0.15		
B8	−0.06		
A0	0.0		
A2	+0.07		
A5	0.22		
A8	0.34		
dF0	0.42	gF0	0.42
dF2	0.47	gF2	0.47
dF5	0.55	gF5	0.55
dF8	0.60	gF8	0.73
dG0	0.65	gG0	0.85
dG2	0.70	gG2	0.96
dG5	0.82	gG5	1.12
dG8	0.94	gG8	1.24
dK0	1.03	gK0	1.37
dK2	1.20	gK2	1.59
dK5	1.34	gK5	1.86
dM0	+1.69	gM0	2.06

* These color indices are based upon photographic and visual effective wavelengths of 4270 Å and 5570 Å, respectively.

increases. This gives rise to an interzone in which the hydrogen content diminishes steadily from its greatest value at the boundary of the original envelope to the minimum value momentarily possessed by the well-mixed shrunken convective core itself. In a star of ten masses, corresponding to a main-sequence star of spectral type B1, the radius of the core would shrink from its original value of 23 per cent (containing 24 per cent of the mass) to almost nothing. As this happens, the luminosity and radius will both increase slightly.

When the content of the convective core falls to about 1 per cent hydrogen, the core can no longer provide energy fast enough to replace what the star's surface radiates. Were this state of affairs to endure, each layer of the star would give up a portion of its thermal energy and its temperature would drop. In that event, the pressure would fall in proportion and the two great forces which maintain the star's equilibrium would be out of balance. The force of gravity would have the upper hand and the star would shrink. This is exactly what happens, gradually and continuously. By contracting, the star trades gravitational energy for radiant energy. At the same time, the compression which attends the contraction raises the temperature throughout; part of the sacrificed gravitational energy is retained as thermal energy while the rest is being radiated.

The interzone now comprises almost the whole of the original convective core. The contraction lasts only long enough to raise the temperature of the interzone to the point at which the remaining hydrogen will generate energy rapidly enough to stay further contraction. In this state, much of the energy is generated in a thin shell about a largely inert core. It is not long, in fact, before the hydrogen-burning shell is the sole supplier of energy for the star. The shell must therefore advance toward the surface of the star, eating the substance of the outer hydrogen-rich envelope and leaving in its wake an ever-growing helium core.

Since the core no longer has any energy sources of its own, there is nothing to maintain its center at a higher temperature than its periphery; one might therefore expect it to assume throughout the same temperature as the energy-generating shell that surrounds it. However, such an isothermal core cannot, with the density distribution which it then has, support the press of the remainder of the star. It therefore continues to contract, rising in temperature the while. As the central temperature approaches 100 million degrees, an entirely new thermonuclear reaction is initiated; it is known as the *triple-alpha process*.

The triple-alpha process takes its name from the fact that it involves three helium nuclei or alpha particles. It consists of the two reactions

(1) $$He_2^4 + He_2^4 \rightarrow Be_4^8 + \gamma$$

and

(2) $$Be_4^8 + He_2^4 \rightarrow C_6^{12} + \gamma.$$

In the first, two helium nuclei form an unstable Be_4^8 nucleus. The synthesis at a temperature of 10^8 degrees is for the first time rapid enough that the unstable Be_4^8 nuclei cannot disintegrate faster than they can be formed. There is therefore a small proportion of these nuclei which can react with the abundant He_2^4 nuclei to form the stable C_6^{12}. As with the synthesis of helium from hydrogen, energy is released, though hardly more than one-fourth as much.

The star is now constructed of a helium-burning core outside which is a hydrogen-burning shell surrounded by an envelope unchanged in composition. These complex internal adjustments bring about a simultaneous rapid expansion of the envelope. The star thus moves to the right in the Hertzsprung-Russell diagram, and in such short order that very few stars are ever caught in the act. On this account, the Hertzsprung-Russell diagram has an apparent vacancy between the upper main sequence and the giant branch. What careers these stars pursue thereafter is not yet known, but there is strong circumstantial evidence that they become various species of the class of peculiar stars (see Chap. 9).

The lifetimes of the free-spending upper main-sequence stars are not very great by astronomical standards—from a few millions to a billion years. This means that all such stars now observable are comparatively young. They are in sharp contrast to the long-lived main sequence stars of late spectral type whose careers to the present have been virtually uneventful. Between these extremes lie the stars of intermediate mass (1.5 or 2.0 solar masses, for example) whose distinctive evolutions can be followed in some detail and which presage many of the eventual states of stars like the sun and lower main sequence.

A star of intermediate mass proceeds more deliberately toward a state of core exhaustion. As before, there will be formed a helium core surrounded by a thin energy-producing shell blanketed by a hydrogen-rich envelope. A difference of some consequence, however, is the fact that at every step the central temperature is lower and the central density is substantially higher than for stars of the upper main sequence. Indeed, the central densities approach 20,000 to 30,000 times the density of water. Even completely ionized matter cannot retain its compressibility at such density, and we must henceforth reckon with the occurrence of an unfamiliar fourth state of matter, the *degenerate state.*

The degenerate state of matter is one in which individual nuclei no longer claim governance of particular electrons; all electrons are held in common by all nuclei. Matter in the degenerate state thus constitutes a

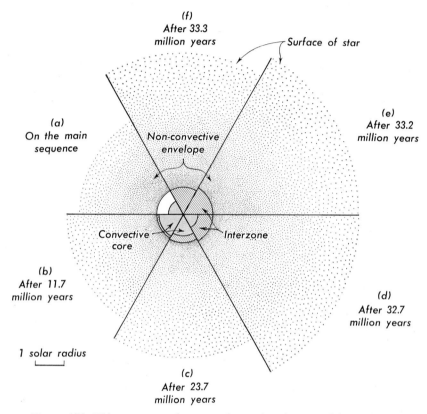

Figure 175. This sequence of sectors shows the changes of internal structure which a star of large mass may be expected to undergo. The latter stages occur in rapid succession. The mass is 10, the initial radius 3.63, and luminosity 3000, in solar units. It begins at (a) with a central density of 7.8, a central temperature of 27,700,000° K.

sort of "fluid crystal." Because of the high density usually associated with degenerate matter, it is sometimes also called the "crushed state." By enormous compression, one superatom is formed of the parts of many single atoms. Within the superatom the laws of atomic physics hold even as they do within single atoms. The degeneracy of matter is thus an essentially atomic phenomenon, not to be understood except by the special rules of atomic physics. It is to such a state that the matter at the center of the core of an aging star of intermediate mass is driven as the density encroaches upon the realm of crushed matter.

At the time of the first appearance of degenerate matter at the center of the star, the star's convective envelope covers half to three-quarters of the radius and a fifth to a third of the mass. The core extends through only 1 or 2 per cent of the radius but contains about 23 per cent of the mass. As more of the hydrogen is burned in the thin advancing shell, the mass of the core rises to nearly 60 per cent and the central temperature reaches 40 million degrees. At the same time, the luminosity increases from about 100 to more than 1000 times the sun's. The star expands by an amount which depends upon the abundance of the heavier elements in its envelope, but which is in any case sufficient to place it in the region of the red giants. Because the radius of the core has remained almost constant. the central density has risen to more than 100,000 times the density of water.

To illustrate the remarkable structure of one of these red giants, consider a model of 1.3 solar masses in which hydrogen has been exhausted in the inner 26 per cent. It will have a luminosity of 226 times the sun and a radius of 21 solar radii (Figure 176(c)). The innermost 0.08 per cent of the radius contains 24 per cent of the mass of the star and comprises the degenerate helium core. The energy of the star is generated by hydrogen burning in the narrow zone between 0.0012 and 0.0015 radii, containing about 0.1 per cent of the mass. The non-convective core includes 28.5 per cent of the mass and extends to 8 per cent of the radius. The central density is nearly 350,000 but drops to one-thousandth of that value at one-thousandth of the radius. The central temperature is about 40,000,000° K.

One of the important consequences of the appearance of degenerate matter at the center of the star is that such matter is less compressible than a normal ionized gas. The core is therefore able for a time to support the remainder of the star, unlike the core of the more massive stars whose cores do not become degenerate at this stage. Hence the hydrogen-consuming shell expands at a pace that must be extremely rapid to meet the needs of so luminous a star. By the time a star of 1.2 solar masses has exhausted the hydrogen in about 50 per cent of its mass, it has become a supergiant of luminosity 5000. It must then also suffer structural changes, including a contraction of the core and an increase of the central temperature to the ignition point of the triple-alpha process.

The triple-alpha process becomes important when the core of the star reaches a temperature of approximately 80,000,000° K. Initially, the liberated energy heats the core but causes no expansion because the core is degenerate. The higher temperature causes the helium to be burned even more rapidly, the helium burning faster begets an even higher temperature, and so on. By the time the temperature in the core reaches 300,000,000° K, energy is being released at a rate of 10^{13} solar luminosities. The entire process is so rapid that this phase of the star's life is termed the "helium flash." The helium flash is so brief that the released energy has no opportunity to escape from the star. This energy therefore works to expand the star, re-

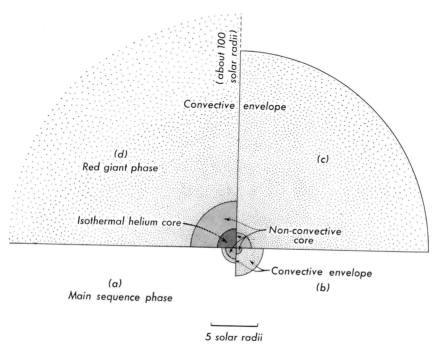

Figure 176. The evolution of a star of intermediate mass is indicated in this sequence of cross sections. Note that the red giant phase is far too large to show on the same scale as the others.

ducing the pressure and density of the core so greatly that the matter once again becomes nondegenerate. It may be anticipated that the star then enters a "second childhood," repeating in parallel fashion much of its earlier history. It does so in much less time, however, for helium provides less energy than hydrogen.

The Evolution of the Stars

We can now anticipate what effects will accompany the aging of stars of different masses. Every star can be expected to consume its hydrogen, alter its internal chemical composition and structure, and eventually brighten and expand. This course may be traced in fair detail for stars which range the full length of the main sequence. The career of each may be followed in the Hertzsprung-Russell diagram over an evolutionary track along which the star moves inexorably upward and to the right from the main sequence. It is most important, however, that the stars of different masses follow their respective evolutionary tracks at very different paces; massive stars attain the giant stage in a few hundred million years or so, whereas dwarfs may not depart sensibly from the main sequence even after many billions of years. This has an important bearing upon the character of the stars of a galactic cluster, for example.

The stars of a cluster are assumed to begin their lives at almost the same time and with almost the same chemical composition. They therefore lie upon a narrow main sequence. The first to leave it are those at the top, followed closely by those just below, and so on down to some point at which the evolutionary changes have not yet become apparent in the luminosity or radius of the star. Here is the point at which the cluster stars turn off from the main sequence. In a color-brightness diagram, the cluster stars would at any moment be arrayed along a *time line,* a curve connecting points of the same age along the various evolutionary tracks. Every time line will coincide in its lower parts with the main sequence. Its turn-off point, however, will occur at a point which sidles down the main sequence, rapidly at first but then with diminishing speed. The depth of a turn-off point is thus an index of age, as we originally guessed it might be. Moreover, calculations of the lifetimes of stars of different masses on the main sequence will serve to calibrate the turn-off points so that the ages of the clusters may be read from their color-brightness diagrams. This method is not yet one of high accuracy, but it is reliable enough to show that the double cluster in Perseus is probably less than ten million years old and that the cluster M67 is perhaps seven billion years old. Other clusters lie between these extremes. Clearly, the theory of stellar evolution and the study of galactic clusters are intimately related.

White Dwarfs

Though the changes in structure which follow the giant stage in a star's development cannot yet be described, the ultimate state of every star is little in doubt. The history of a star, as far as it has been possible to follow it, has been dominated by several trends. First, the nuclear fuels (hydrogen and later helium) have dwindled steadily. Second, an isothermal core has become an increasingly dominant part of the star's structure, comprising an ever larger portion of the entire mass. Third, contraction has compressed the core to such an extent that it is of inordinately high density, so high as to lapse into the strange degenerate state. It is difficult to imagine how any of these trends might be arrested or reversed. There would thus seem to be no way that a star could fail, in time, to become a totally impoverished, isothermal, small, extremely dense, degenerate star. Such are the white dwarfs.

Of the approximately 400 white dwarfs presently known or suspected, the parallaxes of 26 are known, 4 belong to a cluster of known distance, and 10 are components of binary systems whose distances can be estimated from the luminosities of normal companions. The luminosities of these white dwarfs range from 0.025 downward to 0.00004 solar luminosities. Thus the white dwarfs derive their name from the fact that they have colors similar to the stars of spectral types B to F, but in contrast to the latter, are less luminous by a factor of ten thousand to several hundred thousand times. Because the white dwarfs are so underluminous, they occupy a position in the Hertzsprung-Russell diagram far below that of normal stars of the same color.

The color temperatures and luminosities imply very small radii for these stars; they range from about five times the earth's diameter for the largest to about one-third the earth's diameter for the smallest. They are therefore intrinsically faint because they are so small. Probably the most astonishing thing about them, however, is that in spite of their planetary dimensions, they must have stellar masses. Because the masses of stars are so difficult to come by, the masses of only three white dwarfs are known: Sirius B has 0.98 solar masses, Procyon B 0.4 solar masses, and 40 Eridani B 0.43 solar masses. These are presumed to be typical. Only by a theoretical relation between mass and radius can the masses of others be estimated at present.

A white dwarf of typical dimensions would have a surface gravity about a hundred thousand times that of the earth. A man whose weight at the earth's surface is 150 pounds would weigh 7500 tons at the surface of the star. Acting upon the star's own atmosphere, the high surface gravity compresses it to a thickness of only a few hundred feet; within this distance its density diminishes outward by a factor of a billion. The velocity of escape would be about 2500 miles per second. The mean density would be approximately 350,000 times that of water, and the central density would be 40 tons per cubic inch. All but the outermost 100 miles or so must be in the degenerate state.

The 80 known spectra of white dwarfs are varied. Some show no lines at all. In others, lines of hydrogen are visible. Still others contain identifiable lines of helium, calcium, magnesium, and iron. Recognition and identification are rendered difficult by the fact that the extremely high atmospheric pressure broadens most lines almost to oblivion. Thus the strongest hydrogen lines have equivalent widths of 40 Å. However, most lines are so shallow that they drop to half their central intensities only at a distance of 10 Å from the center of the line.

The very high surface gravity of the white dwarfs is responsible for a most interesting and important spectral effect in addition to the great pressure broadening; this is the *gravitational red shift*. All spectrum lines are shifted to the red in proportion to the wavelength. The effect is thus indistinguishable from a Doppler effect corresponding, on the average, to a recessional velocity of 12 miles per second. The two effects can be separated only for those white dwarfs which have normal companions whose average radial velocity is the true average radial velocity of the white dwarf itself.

The explanation of the gravitational red shift is that it signifies a loss of energy by the photon; for, the energy of a photon is proportional to its frequency and a red shift implies a diminution of frequency. The lost energy is sacrificed in overcoming the enormous gravity at the star's surface; for comparison, consider how arduous it would be for a man to escape from such a star by climbing a ladder. In principle, there is a gravitational red shift in the spectrum of the sun and every normal star, though their surface gravities are so much less than that of a white dwarf that the actual effect is too small to measure with certainty.

The extremely low luminosities of the white dwarfs virtually certify the absence of any hydrogen in the interior of the star. Hydrogen in the atmosphere is perhaps explicable on the grounds that the last small remnant has floated to the top as the heavier atoms drop to the interior under the tremendous force of gravity.

The bizarre properties of the white dwarf stars are crowned by a distinctive mass-radius relation. Among the normal stars, mass determines luminosity and radius is more sensitive to chemical composition. Among the white dwarfs, the chemical composition is the same for all, at least to the extent that they contain no hydrogen; what is more, they flagrantly violate the mass-luminosity relation. Instead, the mass of a white dwarf determines its radius but the larger the mass, the *smaller* the radius. This seemingly contrary relation is a direct consequence of the particular relation that exists between the pressure and the density in degenerate matter. Here is an instance of a large-scale phenomenon that can be understood only upon the basis of the laws of atomic physics.

Consider the effect of adding mass to any white dwarf. The extra weight will crush the degenerate matter still further. The star will shrink—and by an amount that is more than the volume of the material added. By adding more and more matter, the star could be made smaller and smaller. In fact, the star could be reduced to a point by the time the total mass had reached about 1.2 solar masses! There is therefore an upper limit to the mass of a white dwarf; it is about 1.2 times the mass of the sun.

The three white dwarfs whose masses have been determined from observation have masses less than the theoretical limit. The masses of the rest are inferred from the mass-radius relation. The mass-radius relation has also some interesting observational implications. It predicts that because the more massive a white dwarf, the smaller its radius, the surface gravity will increase beyond all bound as one approaches the mass limit. This in turn implies that the red shift in the spectra of white dwarfs near the mass limit would be so great as to shift the spectrum entirely out of the visible region!

The white dwarfs are coasting slowly to extinction. They have no internal resources of energy except the small store of thermal energy which is a remnant of former times; they cannot even contract further, since the radius is fixed by the mass-radius relation. The internal temperature of a white dwarf is several million degrees, almost the same throughout. This residual heat is lost slowly through the thin blanket of nondegenerate matter forming the skin of the star. The slow rate of loss ensures a very gradual decline and a long, moribund future.

The low luminosity of the white dwarfs limits the study of them to those within a relatively small distance. Judging from this restricted sample, they constitute at least 2 per cent of all stars. Allowance for possible future discoveries leads to estimates that run as high as 10 per cent. The number and proportion will inevitably increase.

With the white dwarfs, the course of stellar evolution has come full circle. It presumably began with a star of homogeneous composition. The development of internal inhomogeneities marked the periods of the star's subsequent career. Only in the final, white-dwarf stage have the inhomogeneities once again disappeared, this time in the uniformity of inevitable exhaustion.

The Globular Clusters and Stellar Populations

THE GLOBULAR CLUSTERS

A study of the constitution of the stars has made it clear that the observable characteristics of a star are determined by the total mass of the star and its chemical composition, as the Vogt-Russell theorem requires. At the same time, it is equally clear that the chemical composition is not a matter of mere total abundances of the chemical elements but of their distribution through the body of the star as well. Both these factors vary as the star ages.

A confirmation of the theory of stellar structure is to be found in a study of the galactic clusters, whose ages are to be inferred from the turn-off points of their color-brightness diagrams (see p. 357). Nearly all such clusters are relatively young, however, inasmuch as very few are dense enough to withstand for a cosmically long time the dissipative effects to which they are continually subject. Only the densest clusters can be astronomically old and those which are, born in the long ago, may possibly not have had the same initial chemical composition as later comers to an evolving universe. This is a possibility to bear in mind as we consider the *globular clusters.*

Though there may be as many as 2000 globular clusters in our Milky Way galaxy, at present less than 120 are known. In general, they contrast with galactic clusters by their apparent compactness and very great number of members. Their appearance on photographs made with large telescopes is best likened to swarming bees or a celestial popcorn ball. Accessible to observers in the middle northern latitudes are such fine specimens as M13 in Hercules and M3 in Canes Venatici. Brightest of all is ω Centauri in the southern hemisphere.

The distances of globular clusters are all more than 5000 parsecs and therefore somewhat difficult to determine; a few instances exist of discrepancies as great as a factor of five or ten times in independently derived distances of the same clusters. The distances of most globular clusters are gotten from observation in them of certain special variable stars called Cepheids (see p. 394). In only four globular clusters have Cepheids not yet been found. Cepheids are one hundred or more times more luminous than the sun (and therefore visible to great distances in large telescopes), relatively easy to identify because of their characteristic periodic changes in brightness, and—most important of all—subject to an empirical relation between mean luminosity and period. They therefore declare both

Figure 177. GLOBULAR CLUSTER M13 IN HERCULES. This is the brightest and best known of the globular clusters in middle northern latitudes. (Courtesy Yerkes Observatory.)

their presence and their true brightnesses to the observational astronomer. From the true and apparent brightnesses their distances can be inferred. Cepheids in clusters thus indicate clusters' distances.

The nearest globular cluster is nearly as far as the farthest observable galactic cluster. Three are well beyond the customarily assigned bounds of the galaxy, one at a distance from the sun of 130,000 parsecs. The majority are at a distance not more than a few tens of thousands of parsecs.

The apparent diameters of the globular clusters are somewhat indefinite, for continually longer photographic exposures show a continually greater extent of cluster. The apparent diameters commonly assigned to these objects range from about that of the moon (30') for the largest clusters down to a bare 2' for the smallest that can be recognized. The range in true diameter which this implies is from about 16 to 190 parsecs, with an average between 60 and 80 parsecs.

When the diameter of a cluster is known, the density of stars in it may be judged. In doing so, however, one must reckon with the fact that in many clusters the congestion of stars is so great that only about the outer fringes of the cluster is it possible to distinguish individual stars. Even so, nearly 45,000 separate stars have been counted in M3. Estimates which make reasonable allowance for such inability to resolve a globular cluster into all its individual members suggest that the mass of M3 must be approximately 245,000 solar masses. Estimates for other clusters give results which range from about 10,000 solar masses for the very smallest clusters to 6,700,000 solar masses for M22.

From the diameters and masses it is possible to conclude that the average star density in a globular cluster is roughly half a star per cubic parsec. At the center of a cluster, however, it is 50 stars per cubic parsec. In especially large and rich clusters it may be hundreds or even thousands of times this amount. In the middle of the great globular 47 Tucanae the light of the stars is equivalent to several thousand full moons, comparable to twilight!

In spite of the extraordinary congestion within a globular cluster, collisions between stars are unknown and must certainly be rare. Even in a globular cluster the stars are separated by distances equal to tens of thousands of their own diameters. On the other hand, the stars of the cluster must interact strongly enough with each other that their total energy is distributed amongst them quite evenly, as it is amongst the molecules of a gas. It seems likely that those clusters having a large total energy will be least compact, like a gas at high temperature, whereas those clusters having a smaller total energy will be more dense, like a cool gas. Clusters with an over-all motion of rotation will also be slightly bulged, like the rotating earth; all have small ellipticity.

Paralleling the considerable range in clusters' diameters and the large range in total masses is a very great spread in total luminosities. The small-

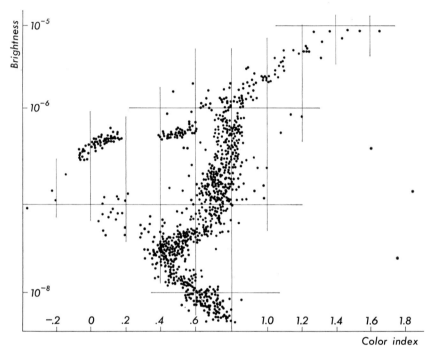

Figure 178. The color-brightness diagram of the globular cluster M3 illustrates the features which are characteristic of many globular clusters. Each dot represents the data for a single star of the cluster.

est dwarf globular has a luminosity of merely 7500 as contrasted with the most luminous cluster, ω Centauri, which is about 1,300,000 times as bright as the sun. The mean luminosity is about 75,000. It is a strange fact that as much as 90 per cent of the light of the cluster is supplied by stars brighter than the sun, comprising as little as 10 per cent of the total mass. To gain some insight into this unexpected feature of the globular clusters, we consider next their color-brightness diagrams.

The color-brightness diagrams of the globular clusters are constructed in the same way as for galactic clusters, out of apparent brightnesses and a color equivalent such as color index. The observational difficulties are greatly aggravated, however, by the extreme faintness of the individual stars and by their mutual congestion. Nevertheless it is found that the stars of a globular cluster range in color from blue to brick red. The brightest stars are red, not blue, and have a luminosity of about 1500 times the sun.

The color-brightness diagrams of all globular clusters appear to be basically the same. The main sequence is thus far known only for three

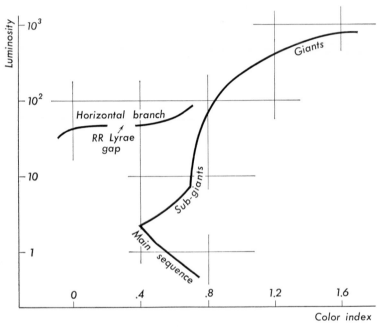

Figure 179. The principal features of the Hertzsprung-Russell diagram of globular clusters are shown schematically in this figure. Note the horizontal branch and the absence of an upper main sequence.

of the brightest clusters. This is because its upper part is entirely absent; it begins about halfway down in comparison with a similar diagram for normal field stars. Contributing further is the fact that the stars of the main sequence in a globular cluster are subdwarfs, two to five times less luminous than normal dwarfs of the same color. The giant branch in the color-brightness diagram turns off from this truncated main sequence in a manner suggestive of the giant branch of an old, dense, populous galactic cluster. It curves sharply upward and to the right, the cluster's brightest members lying at the upper tip of the giant branch. Arching to the left from the red giant branch is a horizontal branch corresponding to a luminosity of approximately 100. The Cepheids are the exclusive occupants of one small segment of this branch. Such color-brightness diagrams are currently available for about a dozen globular clusters.

The distinctive form of the color-brightness diagrams (and therefore of the Hertzsprung-Russell diagrams) of globular clusters is to be explained as a consequence of these objects' great age. It has already been seen that only dense clusters can survive for long times, and the advanced turn-off point of the main sequence is evidence that they have. Various clusters are estimated to have ages upward of 5×10^9 years. It may be surmised that the horizontal branch represents the corridor through which the spent red giants make their exits to the ultimate white-dwarf state. If this is the case, globular clusters must have large numbers of white dwarfs; M3 is estimated to contain almost 50,000 of them.

STELLAR POPULATIONS

The stars of at least some globular clusters are distinguished in yet another way. The spectra of individual stars, more informative than mere colors, show unusually weak lines of the metals and cyanogen (CN), slightly enhanced lines of hydrogen. These anomalies are not to be explained except as genuine abundance differences; the metals, as well as carbon and nitrogen, are of genuinely low abundance in the red giants of some of the globular clusters. In M92, for example, they are only about one-tenth as abundant as in the stars of M13. It is difficult to resist the suggestion that the primeval matter from which the oldest globular clusters were formed had not yet been enriched with a substantial seasoning of the elements heavier than hydrogen and helium. Such theoretical models of metal-poor stars as are available support this surmise. Metal-poor stars are indeed subdwarfs in their initial stages. On the other hand, the only globular cluster known to possess normal M stars (47 Tuc) is one in which the metal abundance is one of the highest for globular clusters.

The contrast which the stars of the globular clusters offer to the more familiar field stars and the stars of most galactic clusters has been made the basis of a classification into two *populations,* I and II. The majority of field stars comprise population I and include the normal dwarfs from spectral types A to M, the blue giants and all supergiants, stars found in the galactic clusters. The stars of population II are typified by the stars of the globular clusters—subdwarfs, red giants having weak metal and cyanogen lines, slightly stronger hydrogen lines. We shall later find differences of motion and distribution through space to reinforce the distinctions here made. For the present, however, we can say that the stars of population I are young and metal-rich, those of population II are old and metal-poor. Stars of intermediate characteristics also exist.

B. WHAT THEY DO

"Which way ought I to go to get from here?"
"That depends a good deal on where you want to get to," said the Cat.
"I don't much care where—" said Alice.
"Then it doesn't much matter which way you go," said the Cat.
— Lewis Carroll

The Solar Motion

As we have noted previously, the "fixed" stars move, and we can determine in detail the motions of many, in part the motions of many more. From a consideration of the available results, what can we say of the stars' motions in general? Do they mill about like fish in a pond, or should they better be compared to salmon running upstream? We can very easily settle the matter by considering their radial velocities. If we are set in the midst of an assemblage of stars whose motions are entirely helter-skelter, then in any quarter of the sky we should see equal numbers approaching and receding. In fact, the average of their (positive) recessional velocities and (negative) velocities of approach should be zero or very nearly so.

On the other hand, if we are amongst stars which, though moving in all directions, are at the same time drifting systemically in one direction, their motion will appear rather different to us. If we look in the direction from whence they come, a majority will be observed to be approaching; in the opposite direction a majority will appear to be receding. In either of these directions the average radial velocity will be numerically equal to the general speed of drift. At the same time, in any direction at right angles to the direction of drift, the purely line-of-sight velocity will have an average value of zero (or nearly so), since the radial velocities in these directions contain no part of the drift velocity and will be as often positive as negative.

How is it with the stars themselves? Using the criteria we have just set up, we conclude that the stars within a few hundred parsecs of the sun are drifting toward a point in the constellation of Columba ($\alpha = 6^h$, $\delta = -30°$). Their average speed is 12 miles per second. It is understood, of course, that many of the individual stars may have motions quite different from the average, both in direction and amount; it is the average of the group, however, which determines the general character of their collective motions.

In point of fact, we have been guilty of a slight presumption in stating that the stars of the sun's neighborhood are drifting by it (and us). With

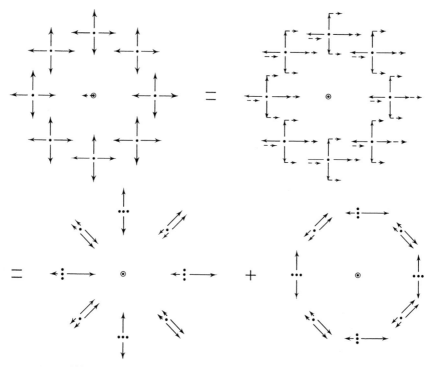

Figure 180. From the sun, moving through a field of stars whose velocities are randomly distributed (as in upper left), it will seem that the velocities are distributed asymmetrically about a stationary sun (upper right), as may be judged either from radial velocities (lower left) or transverse velocities (lower right).

the proper modesty we should prefer to think of the sun as moving amongst its neighbors with a speed of 12 miles per second toward a point in the constellation of Hercules (specifically, toward $\alpha = 18^h$, $\delta = +30°$); this point is called the *apex of solar motion* and its opposite in Columba the *antapex.* Though it is literally true that the two interpretations will represent equally well what is observed of the stellar motions, we hesitate to assume that the sun alone among a vast number of stars is at rest. Therefore we think of the sun as moving 12 miles per second toward the apex of solar motion. Buzzing about it as it goes are the nine major planets and the many lesser bodies of the solar system, somewhat like flies harassing a trotting horse.

Secular and Mean Parallax

It must be evident that the sun's well-established motion relative to its astronomical neighbors will give to each of them an apparent reflex motion; the observed space velocity of each will be 12 miles per second too large in the direction of the antapex. Consequently, if this velocity

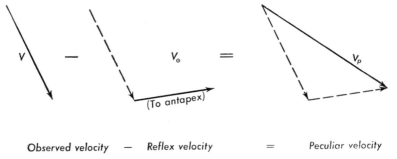

Observed velocity   —   Reflex velocity   =   Peculiar velocity

Figure 181. A star's peculiar velocity, V_p, is its observed velocity, V, from which has been discounted the reflex solar velocity, $V_\odot$.

is deducted from the space velocity (with due allowance for direction), we shall obtain the velocity of each star relative to the average of the whole group. The result is called the *peculiar velocity* of the star. In consequence of the way in which the peculiar velocities of stars are determined, it follows that the average peculiar velocity of all the stars in the neighborhood of the sun must be zero.

This fact may be turned to our advantage; it permits us to improve and add to our present statistics. To see most simply how this can be done, let us consider the stars at right angles to the directions of the apex and antapex. These stars, let us recall, have the largest average proper motion of any in the sky; this is, of course, only an apparent effect, due to the sun's moving by them some 4 astronomical units a year. In other words, we are observing these stars from positions in space which are 4 astronomical units farther apart every year. Here is a base line that is both large and cumulative. Evidently the apparent transverse motion of stars everywhere but at the apex is in part a genuine transverse motion (due to the transverse component of its peculiar velocity) and in part a parallactic displacement toward the antapex (called *secular parallax*) due to the sun's motion. If the secular parallax could be determined, the stars' distances would be known.

Unfortunately the secular parallax of an individual star cannot be had, for there is no way of knowing what part of its transverse motion is peculiar motion and what part is reflex parallactic motion. This ambiguity disappears, however, when we consider the average motion of a group, for we know that their average peculiar velocity is zero. If we consider a group of stars all nearly at right angles to the direction of the apex, their transverse velocities toward the antapex will be

$$V_{TA} = V_{TAP} + V_{TAR} = V_{TAP} + 12,$$

V_{TAP} being the peculiar transverse velocity toward the antapex, $V_{TAR} = 12$ miles per second being the reflex transverse velocity due to solar motion. On the other hand, it is still true that

$$V_{TA} = 2.95\mu_A d \quad \text{miles per second,}$$

μ_A being that part of the proper motion in the direction of the antapex. Comparing the two expressions for V_{TA}, we see that

$$V_{TAP} + 12 = 2.95\mu_A d \quad \text{miles per second.}$$

If we now average both sides for the whole group, remembering that the average peculiar velocity $V_{TAP} = 0$, we shall find that

$$\overline{\mu_A d} = \frac{12}{2.95} = 4.1,$$

$\overline{\mu_A d}$ being the group's average of $\mu_A d$.

At this point we are forced to allow an approximation, namely, that $\overline{\mu_A d} = \overline{\mu_A} \times \overline{d}$; that is to say, we suppose the average of the product of μ_A and d to be equal to the product of the averages of μ_A and of d. This would be the case if all the μ_A's were equal or if all the d's were equal; as a rule this is not so, but the assumption is kept for lack of a better one. Keeping in mind both the statistical and approximate nature of our final result, then, we can finally conclude that

$$\bar{d} = (4.1/\bar{\mu}_A) \quad \text{parsecs.}$$

The related quantity $\bar{p} = 1/\bar{d}$ is called the *mean parallax*. By a proper modification of the formula, the mean parallax of stars anywhere in the sky may be had.

To be entirely honest, somewhat unexact relations such as this are resorted to with some reluctance, but there is no help for it. On the other

table 15

BRIGHTNESS (b)	MEAN PARALLAX * ($\bar{p}$)	MEAN DISTANCE ($\bar{d}$)
0.05	0".0230	43 parsecs
0.01	0. 0138	72
0.005	0. 0111	90
0.001	0. 0064	156
0.0005	0. 0051	196
0.0001	0. 0030	333
0.00005	0. 0024	417
0.00001	0. 0017	588

* The mean parallaxes here given are actually those for stars within 20° of the plane of the Milky Way (p. 432).

hand, let us not take too reserved a view of such results, for they are extremely useful and, moreover, surprisingly reliable. Especially is this so when we choose a fairly homogeneous group of stars such as all those of the same apparent brightness, for the true distances of a number of stars of the same apparent brightness should be more nearly equal than if the apparent brightnesses were widely different within the group. This is precisely the condition for obtaining a more reliable average. Table 15 shows the mean parallaxes of stars of different apparent brightnesses. The significance of mean parallaxes may be still further increased by limiting consideration to stars of the same spectral class.

Mean parallaxes are particularly useful as indices of the distances of certain types of uncommon stars, all of which are too far away to be

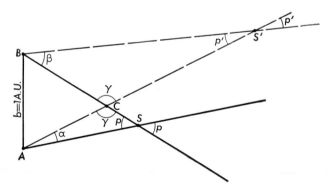

Figure 182. Points A and B are at the extremities of a base-line one astronomical unit in length. The *relative* parallax, p_r, of a near-by star S with respect to a distant star S' is the difference of the angles β and α; i.e., $p_r = \beta - \alpha$. The absolute parallax of S is angle p, that of S' is p'. From the relation of triangles $BS'C$ and ASC it is evident that $\alpha + p = 180 - \gamma = \beta + p'$ or $p = (\beta - \alpha) + p'$, whence $p = p_r + p'$.

accessible by other more direct means. Mean parallaxes are also indispensable for obtaining *absolute parallaxes*. Most parallaxes, as measured, represent the relative apparent annual displacement of nearby stars with respect to distant ones in nearly the same direction in the sky (Fig. 182). From the table of mean parallaxes we see that the background stars have their own parallaxes, which can now be intelligently allowed for. By such allowance *relative parallaxes* may be converted into absolute parallaxes; it is only from absolute parallaxes that stars' true distances can be found. The solar motion thus provides a means of getting important information that could not easily be had if the sun were at rest among its neighbors.

The Distribution of Peculiar Velocities

The sun has a peculiar velocity of 12 miles per second toward the apex of solar motion in Hercules. The other stars in its neighborhood have an average peculiar velocity which by definition is zero. How may we characterize the varied peculiar velocities of the sun and its neighbors? Perhaps one of the easiest ways to visualize the character of the motions of the group of stars whose peculiar velocities are known is to imagine them all collected at some starting point and released simultaneously. Assuming that their respective peculiar velocities would not be affected by this imaginary experiment, we could use their positions after a lapse of 1 year as indicators of these stars' speeds and directions of motion. Of course their distribution about the starting point would bear no relation to their present distribution through the space in the sun's neighborhood; it would show only how these stars' velocities are apportioned in direction and magnitude. In particular, if we think of the stars as marking the positions of raisins in a cake, we would find the cake to be elongated in one dimension and slightly elliptical in cross-section. Such a distribution is described as *ellipsoidal,* and the longer axis of the ellipsoid points to the two *vertices of star streaming.* The stars (raisins) are found to be concentrated toward the center of the ellipsoid (cake), their number thinning out rapidly toward the boundary.

If we give separate consideration to various homogeneous groups of stars, we find that they depart significantly from their joint norm. In general, stars of early spectral type have a comparatively small range of velocities, whereas those of late spectral type show a large spread; even their apices are different. Associated with this latter difference is the fact that the stars of large velocity have a strikingly asymmetric motion relative to the rest. The stars whose peculiar velocities are in excess of 40 miles per second all appear to move toward that half of the sky centered on a point in the Milky Way about midway between Sirius and the Southern Cross. These stars are called the *high-velocity stars*.

The spectra and Hertzsprung-Russell diagrams of the high-velocity stars show these stars to be of population II. On the other hand, the stars of lowest average velocity are population I stars of young galactic clusters. It is evident that stars' motions as well as their chemical compositions are correlated with their ages. Indeed, stars' motions serve as a second means of differentiating the two population types. Corroborating this conclusion is the observation that the globular clusters of extreme population II have both the largest peculiar velocities and the greatest dispersion of velocities of any group of stars.

QUESTIONS

1. Review the evidence which indicates that the stars are suns.
2. What kind of spectra do the stars show? How are they classified? Describe the principal features of the classes of the spectral sequence.
3. How is it known that differences in spectral type are usually not evidence of differences in chemical composition? What is the evidence that the spectral sequence is a temperature sequence? How does the temperature variation along the sequence account in detail for the changes in spectroscopic features?
4. Sketch a schematized Hertzsprung-Russell diagram. How does it make necessary a distinction between giants and dwarfs? How is this distinction taken account of in the nomenclature?
5. What are the luminosity effects? Are they directly due to differences in luminosity? Explain their origin in detail.
6. Find the distances and spectroscopic parallaxes of stars whose respective brightnesses (in brightness units) and luminosities (in solar units) are: (*a*) $b = 0.222$, $L = 1.998$; (*b*) $b = 0.0007$, $L = 0.1372$; (*c*) $b = 0.03$, $L = 14,700$; (*d*) $b = 0.000015$, $L = 0.00918$. Which of these spectroscopic parallaxes would you expect to be of greater accuracy than the corresponding directly measured parallaxes?
7. Explain how objective prism spectra are obtained. What are their advantages and disadvantages compared to slit spectra?
8. How is the dynamical parallax of a binary system obtained?
9. What are galactic clusters? How are cluster members distinguished from nonmembers?
10. How are the distances, diameters, and densities of galactic clusters determined? What is the evidence that galactic clusters are not chance associations of stars? How long may any cluster be expected to survive? What determines this? What two important conclusions follow from this?

11. What is color index? How does one interpret a cluster's color-brightness diagram? What inferences may be drawn from such diagrams?

12. Describe the method by which the internal structure of a star can be computed. How does this kind of analysis lead to the Vogt-Russell theorem? State the theorem. To what conclusions does it lead?

13. How does the constitution of the sun compare with that of other stars? Contrast the sun to more massive stars.

14. What is the carbon cycle? What are the reactions of the carbon cycle? How does the carbon cycle differ from the proton-proton process? In what respect is it similar? Could it also be called the nitrogen cycle?

15. What is the constitution of a giant star? How does such a star evolve? How does it reach the giant stage? What new energy-generating process probably takes place for the first time in giant stars? What new state probably appears for the first time in giant stars?

16. How do the color-brightness diagrams of galactic clusters corroborate theory in explaining stellar evolution?

17. What is a white dwarf? Where does it fit in the stellar evolutionary scheme? In what respects is it abnormal? Of what is it composed?

18. What is the gravitational red shift? How is it explained?

19. Why would one not expect to find a white dwarf whose mass is almost 1.2 solar masses? How many white dwarfs are known? How common are they? Are the last two answers consistent?

20. What are globular clusters? How do they differ from galactic clusters? How are their distances determined? What are their diameters? Their star densities? Their luminosities? Masses?

21. What is remarkable about the color-brightness diagrams of globular clusters? How are they explained?

22. How do galactic and globular clusters afford a basis for a classification of stellar populations?

23. Explain the principle of the method of determining the solar motion. Describe the details of two methods for finding the position of the apex of solar motion. How does one determine the velocity of solar motion?

24. Comment on the following questions: (*a*) Which is really moving—the sun or the stars? (*b*) How long will it be before the sun arrives at the apex of solar motion?

25. What is secular parallax? What is the meaning of the term? For what stars can mean parallax be best determined? In what respect are mean parallaxes especially useful? From what limitations do mean parallaxes suffer?

26. Determine the mean distances and mean parallaxes of star groups whose respective mean proper motions toward the antapex are: (*a*) $0''.1$; (*b*) $0''.0164$; (*c*) $0''.0023$.

27. Explain the ellipsoidal distribution of peculiar velocities. What has it to do with the distribution of the stars?

28. In what ways does the motion of the high-velocity stars set them apart? Do they differ in other respects?

chapter 9
The Peculiar Stars

● ● ●

As we have seen, the course of events in the life of a normal star is fairly well understood. The period covered in the currently available theory of stellar evolution extends from the young star's arrival upon the main sequence to a point midway in its career as an aged giant. During this entire time, those changes which take place in the star are so gradual that their progress is far beyond our power to observe. Not so with many of the very young stars or the very old stars! They exhibit changes in a time short enough to be appreciated in a human lifetime or less. On this account they are called variable stars, or simply *variables*.

The only variations which are obvious without the aid of astronomical equipment are changes in luminosity. These are evident as changes in apparent brightness. The discovery of variables is, in fact, largely a search for stars whose brightnesses change. Except for the dramatic appearance of an infrequent exploding star, brightness variations among stars visible to the naked eye are modest, even subtle. This is borne out by the fact that the first recorded mention of a variable star was in 1596, the second not until 1672, and the third only in 1784. By 1915, however, 1687 variables were known, and in 1955, 13,745 had been discovered. Photography offers the best means of finding them, for in photographs taken at different times the variables are likely to attract attention to themselves by their unequal images on the different plates.

Variables are given a nomenclature of their own. The first discovered variable of a given constellation is known, arbitrarily, as R of that constellation, as R Aquarii; the second is S, as S Geminorum; the third as T, as T Pyxidis (etc.). After Z comes RR, followed by RS, etc.; and when RZ is reached, the next is SS, etc. If still more designations are needed in any constellation, they continue with AA, . . . AZ, BB, . . . BZ, . . . , to QZ (excepting combinations with J). In some instances this is not yet enough, so that the 334 letter combinations are continued with the further designations V335, V336, etc., as V444 Cygni.

Establishing the variability of any star is ordinarily of no particular value except insofar as it identifies the star as one deserving further observation. The further observations begin with an extended series of determinations of the star's apparent brightness. These must be made frequently enough and extend over a sufficient length of time to establish the general character of the variability. The observations, made by visual estimate, by photographic determination, or by a photometer (the most accurate of which employ photoelectric cells), are used to construct a light curve just as for eclipsing binaries. It is by their light curves that most types of variables (as well as eclipsing binaries) are identified. The variations in luminosity displayed by a light curve require accompanying variations in radius and surface temperature. These will be detected respectively by measures of radial velocity or of color and spectral type. Indeed, in some few cases, the spectra rather than light curves provide the principal evidence of an abnormal activity or state.

It is clear, then, that luminosity fluctuations or spectral abnormalities may be expected to identify stars which in the evolutionary sense are either very young or very old. All the very old stars are or have been giants. A large proportion of the variable stars are therefore giant stars. Among stars visible to the naked eye, about 3 per cent are variable. However, a majority of the naked-eye stars are giants, so that the actual proportion of variables is far less than 3 per cent; in view of the vast distance to which giants may be seen, perhaps only one star in a million is a variable. This scarcity is undoubtedly an index of how brief is the period of a star's infancy or demise.

Let us consider those seemingly peculiar stars which we have reason to regard as either very young or very old.

A. THE VERY YOUNG STARS

"Interesting if true, and interesting anyway."
—MARK TWAIN

T Tauri Stars

Perhaps the youngest stars of which we have any knowledge are the T Tauri stars. Their brightnesses vary erratically by a factor of 2 to 40 times and within the space of a few hours. Though they are of all spectral types from B to M, most are of early type. They are sometimes called nebular variables because of their uncommon incidence in the neighborhood of clouds of unformed gas and dust called nebulae (see p. 452). Though at one time it was suggested that the nebula may have obscured the star in an inconstant manner, as is the sun by a cloud in our sky, the star's relation to the nebula is probably not so direct. It is more likely that the star has formed in the recent astronomical past from some of the nebular matter. It is presumed to be in the process of settling down to the routine of life on the main sequence. Contraction may only now have brought its interior to a temperature sufficiently high to ignite nuclear reactions which consume certain of the light elements such as lithium, beryllium, and boron.

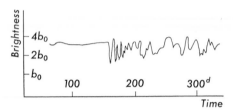

Figure 183. This figure shows schematically the general features of the light curve of a T Tauri variable.

The nuclear reactions of these elements with hydrogen in the star's outer layers may produce the observed luminosity variations.

Rotating Stars

To discriminate other young stars from all the rest, we may be guided by the fact that population II stars are very old. Therefore young stars can belong only to population I. Since the possession of an upper main sequence is an exclusive characteristic of population I, and since these stars are relatively short-lived, we may be sure that the stars we find here are comparatively young.

A feature peculiar to many of these stars is an extensive broadening of all the spectrum lines, giving them a "washed-out" appearance and actually obliterating many of the faint ones. Stars having such spectra are called n-stars, most familiar among them being Altair. The width and shallowness of the n-stars' spectrum lines are readily explained as due to the rapid rotation of these stars. It is easy to see (Fig. 185) how rotation would bring about the observed effect: Unless we are looking at a star's pole of rotation, one limb of the rotating star will be approaching the observer, the other limb will be receding, and there will be portions of the disk whose respective radial velocities are equal to each value between these extremes; consequently, because of the range of their Doppler shifts, the absorption lines of different parts of the star's disk will not fall one atop the other in the composite (observed) spectrum but will be strung out to a greater "width" with a lesser "depth." The resulting rotational

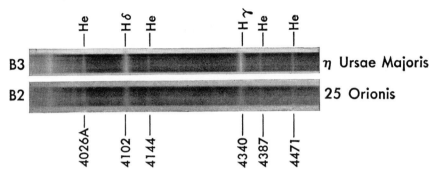

Figure 184. ROTATIONAL BROADENING OF SPECTRAL LINES. The spectra of both these stars show rotationally broadened lines. The star η Ursae Majoris (at the end of the handle of the Big Dipper) has an estimated minimum equatorial rotational velocity of 125 miles per second. The broader lines of 25 Orionis indicate that it is rotating even more rapidly. (Courtesy Yerkes Observatory.)

broadening gives to the absorption lines a distinctive contour that is distinguishable from other effects.

One can even make a reasonable estimate of the minimum linear equatorial velocity [1] of rotating stars, since the amount of rotational broadening

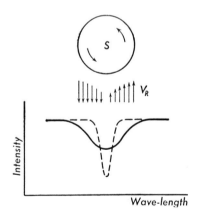

Figure 185. S is the pole of a rotating star. The arrows V_R show by their lengths the radial components of the rotational velocities at selected points along the star's equator. Since not all parts of the star's surface have the same radial velocity, the spread of Doppler displacements will spread the normal profile of any line (dotted curve) into a rotationally broadened line profile (solid curve) of the same equivalent width.

depends on the rotational velocity. The average equatorial rotational velocity of main sequence stars of types B8 to A2 is 110 miles per second.

[1] Minimum, since the radial component of a rotational velocity decreases as the tilt of the axis of rotation to the line of sight decreases. It is the same effect of projection which limits us to a knowledge of the minimum mass of a purely spectroscopic binary.

A feature of approximately one star in eight of spectral type A is the anomalous strength of the lines of many of the metals; in recognition of this peculiarity these stars are designated as Ap stars. Their strong hydrogen lines qualify them as A stars, their metal lines imply abundances of certain elements up to 1000 times greater than normal, and they are bluer than is proper for an A star. Further, the width of the spectrum lines is less than average, though there is a continuous transition from normal to peculiar spectra. Among those stars whose lines are least broadened by rotation, it is possible to detect the Zeeman effect, just as in sunspots. The amount of the effect shows these stars to have magnetic fields two or three times as strong as an average sunspot.

The magnetic forces are thought to be the key to these stars' several peculiarities. Presumably these stars were formed from matter having the normal cosmic proportions of the elements. However, strong magnetic forces in their atmospheres have accelerated hydrogen nuclei to very high speeds, thereby creating ultrahot areas possibly like outsize solar flares. Considerable numbers of neutrons will be formed in these very hot spots. Because of the ease with which most nuclei absorb neutrons, most of the neutrons will be swallowed up in a short time. In this way, nuclei most prone to capture neutrons will be transmuted into other, possibly unstable, isotopes; nuclei least prone to capture neutrons will be little affected and tend to increase in relative proportion. These are some of the very atoms which are anomalously abundant. There is some precedent for such a process on a small scale, for solar flares have shown a slight surplus of heavy hydrogen. At the same time, the hot spots will radiate optically in such manner as to contribute disproportionately to the blue region of the spectrum, thereby creating the observed color discrepancy of the Ap stars.

A distinctive subclass of the Ap stars are the magnetic or spectrum variables. The spectrum anomalies of most Ap stars do not vary in time; in a spectrum variable, however, the peculiar lines fluctuate in intensity. For example, in the spectra of some the lines of ionized europium wax and wane while those of ionized chromium behave contrarily. These spectral variations are attributed to two large equatorial spots brought alternately into view by rotation. Ions and atoms with different magnetic properties associate themselves primarily with one or the other of the spots according to the spots' respective magnetic polarities. During each rotation of such a star we see successively the "chromium magnetic pole" and the "europium magnetic pole." All spectrum variables also show brightness variations in the same period but by amounts not in excess of

20 per cent. There are synchronous radial velocity variations whose nature depends upon the identity of the atom by whose lines it is measured. Among the brighter stars, Cor Caroli (α Canum Venaticorum), Alpheratz (α Andromedae), and Alioth (ϵ Ursae Majoris) are spectrum variables.

Shell Stars

Another group of very young stars are those which belong to classes O, B, and related types. Those of class B are uncommon, but stars of class O are genuinely rare, there being only a few hundred known.[2] The high surface temperature of the hot stars, 30,000° K to 100,000° K, is the source of a number of interesting phenomena peculiar to these classes.

One such phenomenon is *atmospheric turbulence*. The outer layers of many of these stars must be in violent commotion, for there is observed in their spectra a Doppler broadening of the spectrum lines such as would be caused by outrushing and inrushing clouds of atmospheric gases. Since the parts of the star's atmosphere which are rising from or falling toward its photosphere will have appreciably different radial velocities, they will therefore possess a variety of Doppler displacements. The resulting superposed absorptions will thus extend over a greater number of wavelengths than usual. It is by this effect that turbulence is recognized. We can well imagine that the atmospheres of such hot stars as these seethe furiously.

More spectacular than the phenomenon of turbulence is the formation of expanding or rotating shells of gas about some O and B stars as well as a very few A stars. Since these shells (also known as *extended atmospheres*) can, of course, not be seen as such, it is interesting to see how their existence has been demonstrated. Attention was first attracted to these stars by the presence of emission lines[3] in their spectra. Moreover these were no ordinary emission lines, for they were superposed on broader, weak absorption lines and bisected by sharp, narrow, dark lines. These features are usually and most conveniently represented graphically by a line profile (Fig. 186), which is simply a graph of the intensity of radiation over an interval of spectrum containing the line. A line profile is generally gotten by means of an instrument known as a microphotometer, which

---

[2] The determinative spectral characteristics of type O are hydrogen lines weaker than in type B, lines of neutral and ionized helium, and lines of doubly and triply ionized oxygen and nitrogen.

[3] The occurrence of emission lines in a stellar spectrum is noted by suffixing an "e" after the star's spectral type. We are therefore considering stars primarily of types Be and Oe. About 400 are known.

measures intensities with the aid of a photocell. At first glance, a Be or Oe emission-line profile is likely to strike one as a weird and startling variant of normal stellar-line profiles. However, it contains the information which leads to its own interpretation.

In the first place, the wide and shallow absorption lines have been rotationally broadened. On the other hand, the central emission in any

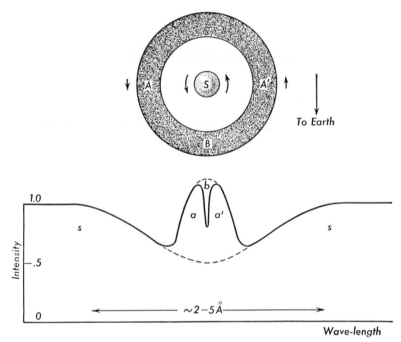

Figure 186. The rotating star S produces the rotationally broadened line profile *ss*. Superposed on it is a less broadened emission line *aa'* whose source is the more slowly rotating shell AA'. Part B of the shell, lying in the line of sight between earth and star, creates an unbroadened absorption core *b*.

line is observed to be less broadened by rotation than the background absorption and therefore must originate in gases detached from the main body of the star. Such detached material must form a shell about the star. Because the diameter of the shell is greater than the diameter of the star, the shell will not rotate as rapidly as the star, as either Kepler's law of areas or harmonic law would predict. (This result, a consequence of Newton's laws of motion, is generally expressed by saying that angular momentum is conserved.) Because of the slower rotation, the emission lines of the shell will not be so greatly broadened. It is partly because the emission is confined to a smaller range of wavelengths and the absorption spread over a greater range of wavelengths that the emission can, in its range, exceed the absorption, thereby producing a superimposed visible emission line. And finally, the narrow central absorption line will be formed by that part of the shell which is directly between the disk of the star and the observer. It acts in exactly the same way as the solar atmosphere, and since here the gases of the shell are moving along across the line of sight, it will form an absorption line entirely without rotational broadening. We can thus account for all the principal features of these unusual lines in the Be and Oe stars.

How are such shells formed? The stars' rapid rotations suggest that possibly these stars spin so rapidly as to throw off shells or rings much as a spinning wheel throws off droplets of water.

But why should shells be formed almost exclusively by O and B stars? Undoubtedly their high temperatures are related as a cause or a symptom of their instability, for all shell stars have such high surface temperatures that the temperatures are usually difficult to determine well. The stars are alike too, in being giants and supergiants, though generally not of uncommonly large diameter. Their shells are estimated to have diameters about five to ten times those of the enveloped stars. From the high luminosities these stars are presumed to be comparatively massive.

Besides the types of shell stars so far described, there are some which usually show no emission lines but are recognized from more subtle evidences known as *dilution effects*. Dilution effects consist in unusual strength or weakness of certain sensitive lines, as, for example, some of He, Si^+, and Mg^+. Their strength or weakness is caused by the fact that although the quality of radiation in unit volume of an extended atmosphere or shell (as judged by the relative intensities of radiations in the various wavelengths) may be like that at the photosphere of the star, the quantity of radiation (as measured by its absolute intensity) will be much less. Consequently the populations of the various atomic states will differ materially from those in a normal photosphere, and different line strengths will be the result. The star Pleione of the Pleiades is an example of a shell star known by dilution effects. Dilution effects also demonstrate that some stars possess shells only temporarily.

Not only single stars have shells; some binary systems have shells and the results are oftentimes unusual. The system of β Lyrae, for example, consists of a giant B9 and a giant F star (subtype unknown). They revolve in a period of 12.9 days and are near enough to each other that their atmospheres are in contact. This has been shown to result in a flow of gases from the larger B9 component to the lesser F component. However, it

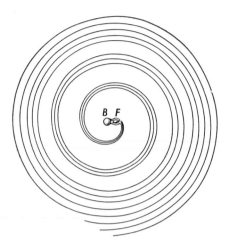

Figure 187. In the β Lyrae system material from the B star streams to the F star, part of it being lost to both, spiralling along the lines of flow to form a ring of tenuous gas surrounding the system.

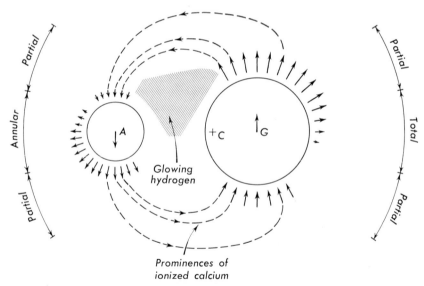

Figure 188. A model of this sort explains the observed behavior of the eclipsing binary UX Monocerotis. As the A and G stars revolve about their center of gravity C the observer far to the right will witness total and partial eclipses as indicated.

seems likely that not all the gases which stream from the B star are captured by the F star; some are probably lost, to spiral gradually outward and form the system's shell (Fig. 187).

A second system of unusual interest is the eclipsing binary UX Monocerotis. This pair consists of a dwarf A3 star and a larger subgiant G2 star. They mutually revolve in slightly less than six days and are separated by a little more than one diameter of the larger star (about 6.6 solar diameters). The peculiarities in their spectra and the changes which these undergo indicate that the pair is surrounded by a ring of gases which arise in the forward face of each star and terminate at the back side of its companion. These arches of stellar matter are thought to result from large-scale prominences, huge hydrogen prominences stemming from the front of the A star, ionized calcium prominences streaming out from the face of the G star. Perhaps these stars offer a clue to the origin of shells and streams about all shell stars.

B. THE VERY OLD STARS

"I know all the facts of life, but I don't know if they're true."
—CHON DAY

The white dwarf stars are assuredly the oldest stars in the evolutionary sequence; their careers are wholly behind them. Treading close behind are several types of stars whose falterings both mark them as old and recommend them as objects of special interest to the stellar pathologist. We shall consider those which pulsate, explode, and expand.

Pulsating Stars

CLASSICAL CEPHEIDS

Prototype of the pulsating stars are the typical Cepheids, so named for δ Cephei, the first of them to be discovered. Its brightness varies periodically by approximately a factor of two once every 5^d9^h. The light curve is characterized by a fairly rapid rise from minimum to maximum brightness, a much slower decline; it is clearly unlike that of a simple eclipsing binary. The periods of classical Cepheids in general range from 27^h for BQ CrA to 45^d4^h for SV Vul. Their light curves have a shape which depends upon the length of the period; those with longest period have the most asymmetrical light curve.

Accompanying the changes in brightness of a Cepheid are simultaneous variations of radial velocity. The velocity curve, determined as for a spectroscopic binary, has the same period as the light curve; about 200 are known. The shape of a velocity curve is much like a mirror image of the light curve (see Fig. 190). The ratio of the amplitudes of the light and velocity curves is approximately the same for all.

A Cepheid also undergoes changes of color during each period, being reddest at minimum and bluest at maximum. This color change indicates

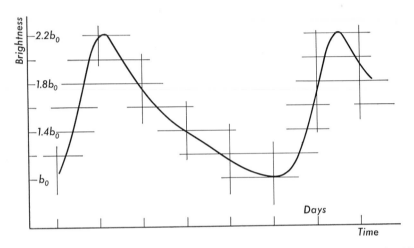

Figure 189. The characteristic shape of a Cepheid light curve is shown in this light curve of δ Cephei.

a temperature variation estimated to amount in some cases to nearly 1000 degrees. The spectral types change correspondingly, the mean type ranging from F6 to G8 in order of increasing periods. At minimum light, the spectra are almost indistinguishable from those of nonvariable supergiants; at maximum they are abnormal. They show that the stars' atmospheres are in a state of turbulence and that they possess an appreciable magnetic field.

These related variations cannot be accounted for by assuming that the Cepheids are eclipsing binaries, for light and velocity curves show that if they were, the orbit of the secondary would fall within the primary. It is concluded that they are pulsating stars which expand and contract like a beating heart. The variations of radial velocity are due to alternate approach and recession of the star's surface as its diameter increases and decreases by about 3 per cent or less. The changing diameter and temperature are responsible for the fluctuations of luminosity.

population II variables; the effect is seldom detectable among the typical Cepheids. Considered in more detail, the available evidence suggests that the emission lines of the W Virginis stars may be due to shock waves generated in the atmospheres of these stars by the pulsation. Shock waves are known to be a very efficient means of heating and compressing gases.

LONG-PERIOD VARIABLES

The most numerous of the pulsating stars are the long-period variables, of which more than 4000 are known. They derive their name from the

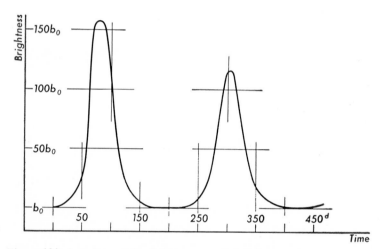

Figure 193. A section of the light curve or R Boötis provides a typical example of a light curve of a long-period variable.

fact that their periods are comparatively long, ranging from 70 days (AU Tauri) to 1379 days (BX Monocerotis), with an average of about 270 days. Their light variations are not as rigorously periodic as those of the Cepheids. The light curve of a long-period variable (Fig. 193) may show moderate differences even between successive cycles, and the intervals between maximum light may be unequal by as much as a month.

One of the striking features of these stars is the comparatively large range in apparent brightness between maximum and minimum light. A factor of 20 is considerably less than average, and a factor of 4000 is known for at least one, the star χ Cygni. This large change of apparent brightness is known to be due primarily to the fact that these stars, without exception, have low temperatures. At maximum their temperatures are between 2200° K and 3300° K, and at minimum they are between 1650° K and 2500° K, with a range of 600° K to 800° K. Most of the energy of the long-period variables is thus radiated in the infrared, and the visible light is merely the tail on the spectral dog. A temperature variation of several hundred degrees thus wags the tail far more than the dog; the luminosity range in all wavelengths together is generally not more than a factor of 3. The differences between the ranges of total and visual luminosity is exaggerated to some degree by absorptive molecules which are abundant in the atmospheres of such cool stars.

The fact that these stars have low surface temperatures implies that they will be of spectral types M, R, N, and S, with an occasional K. The

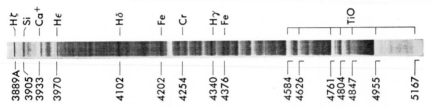

Figure 194. SPECTRUM OF A LONG-PERIOD VARIABLE. This negative of the spectrum of the famous long-period variable Mira (*o* Ceti) shows many of the prominent molecular bands of TiO so characteristic of the majority of long-period variables. It shows also emission lines of H, Si, and Fe. The brightness of the star was increasing at the time this spectrum was taken. (Courtesy Yerkes Observatory.)

spectra of the M stars are dominated by the absorption bands of TiO. The R and N stars show in their spectra the bands of molecular carbon (C_2), and in the R stars the bands of cyanogen (CN) are strong as well. Spectra of the S stars are distinguished by the bands of zirconium oxide (ZrO). These distinctions appear to be evidence of genuine abundance differences among these classes of stars. In the R and N stars, called the *carbon stars* or C stars, carbon is more abundant than oxygen, so that all the oxygen is taken up in carbon monoxide (CO) molecules whose absorption bands are not in the visible region; in normal stars, there is an excess of oxygen from which TiO may be formed. If, however, zirconium is more abundant than titanium, abundant zirconium oxide will make the star one of type S. Among the C stars, those with a superabundance of carbon form CN as well as C_2; these are the R stars, whose subdivisions range in a temperature sequence. The N stars probably form a sequence according to limited carbon abundance. Curiously, in the N stars some as yet unidentified absorptive molecule so beclouds the spectrum in wavelengths shorter than 3800 Å that the stars appear a very deep red color corresponding to a temperature of a mere 1000° K; the strength of atomic lines, however, indicates a temperature of about 2500° K. An oddity of the S stars is the identification of spectrum lines of the radioactive element technetium, which virtually disappears by spontaneous disintegration within a few million years. This element must have been created within the star in astronomically recent times.

A characteristic feature of the spectra of long-period variables of all classes is the appearance of emission lines about midway between maximum and minimum; they disappear by the succeeding minimum. The relative strengths of these lines are anomalous and the intermittency of their appearance can perhaps be explained by supposing that the emission lines originate from inner levels of the stars' atmospheres and that molecular

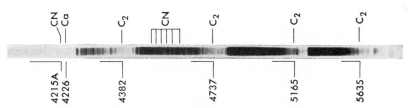

Figure 195. SPECTRUM OF A CARBON STAR. The carbon star HD 52432 whose spectrum is shown here is of type R5. The strong absorptions are by carbon (C_2) and cyanogen (CN) molecules. (Courtesy Yerkes Observatory.)

absorption of overlying layers temporarily cuts off the radiations from these levels during part of each cycle. The bright lines are cut off, in fact, when the temperature of the atmosphere is least and molecules are present in greatest numbers. The cause of the emission lines is not known; possibly they are due to shock waves, as has been suggested as the source of the emission lines of the population II Cepheids.

Like the Cepheids, the long-period variables of longer period have later spectral types. It is interesting, too, that the stars of longer period have the stronger emission lines.

The long-period variables have velocity curves of small amplitude; the famous variable Mira, for example, has a radial velocity which varies less than 8 miles per second about the mean. The pulsation of these stars is beyond any doubt, however, for the variation of the diameter of Betelgeuse has been measured with a stellar interferometer. The velocity curve inferred from the absorption lines is similar in shape to the light curve, whereas the velocity curves from emission lines vary for different elements.

The long-period variables show a seemingly strange period-luminosity relation: the visual luminosity decreases with increasing period. This is an illusory effect, however, for the stars of longest period are of those of lowest surface temperature and therefore of lowest surface brightness.

If account is taken of all wavelengths, these stars are all supergiants with luminosities of more than 20,000 times the sun's.

The long-period variables show an intermediate velocity distribution to that of the Cepheids and the RR Lyrae stars. Those of the latest spectral type and longest period are probably of population I; those of shortest period and earliest spectral type are probably of population II. They probably represent an advanced stage in the evolution of massive stars in both populations. The abundance differences amongst the C, M, and S stars are found only in very old objects.

A sort of bridge between the Cepheids and the long-period variables seems to be afforded by the *RV Tauri stars,* of which some 70 are known.

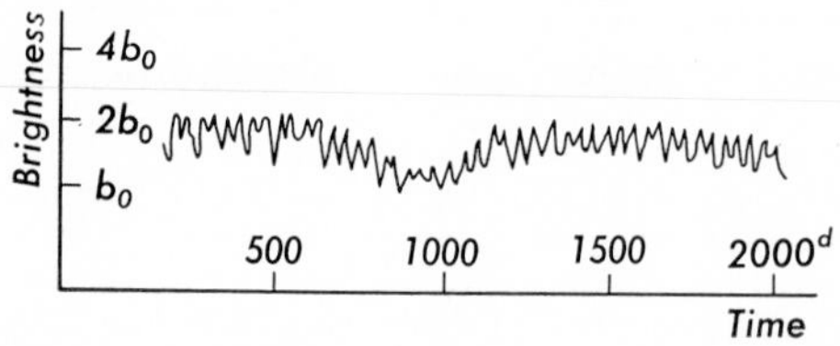

Figure 196. Both the long and the short periods are evident in this section of light curve of RV Tauri.

They are often described as semiregular, for their fluctuations in brightness, though not entirely predictable, are often repetitive with a determinate average period. Consecutive maxima may be conspicuously different, however (Fig. 196). Moreover, the average brightness at maximum and minimum may itself undergo long-period fluctuations of 3 to 4 years. The spectra, of types F to K, are suggestive of those of Cepheids, and the stars show similar radial velocity variations. They show an inverse period-luminosity relation like the long-period variables, with the brightest seeming to fall on an extension of the period-luminosity relation for the W Virginis stars. Their periods range from 33 to 146 days.

Explosive Stars

MILDLY EXPLOSIVE STARS

The mildest sort of stellar explosions at present known are those exhibited by a group of dwarf K and Me stars known as the UV Ceti stars. They flare up within a few seconds or minutes and subside within hours or less. UV Ceti itself has been known to brighten as much as 250 times within 20 seconds, returning to normal about 2 hours later. Since the luminosities of these stars are as low as 0.00004, their flares are impressive only in a proportionate sense; possibly many stars' luminosities change by as much or more, but the variation goes unnoticed except amongst stars of very low intrinsic brightness. The flare stars show emission lines of hydrogen and ionized calcium. Many are components of binaries. This suggests that the outbursts may take place in the space between the components.

Next in line are the U Geminorum stars, which increase in brightness within about 24 hours and decline slowly. Although the outbursts of these stars are entirely unpredictable, they have characteristic average frequencies

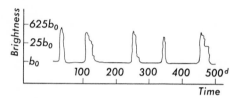

Figure 197. The light curve of a U Geminorum star may be recognized by the intermittent outbursts of varying height and separation.

ranging from once every 13 days (for AB Draconis) to once every 340 days. U Geminorum itself suffers an outburst every 97 days on the average, but the actual interval may be anything from 57 to 201 days. Its brightness increases about 150 times. The less time between outbursts, however, the less the increase in luminosity at the subsequent outburst. Maxima 10 to 20 days wide alternate with maxima only 3 to 8 days wide. These stars are bluish-white with wide emission lines at minimum. The latter are overtaken by the continuum and become absorption lines at maximum. The entire class may be binaries and their unstable nature may be a consequence of being double.

NOVAE

One can surmise that if a star were to exhibit outbursts only after many years or centuries, the violence of the explosion would surpass that of the U Geminorum stars by several orders of magnitude. Such is the case with the novae, or "new stars." Novae are stars that, without warning, flare up from long-standing obscurity to temporary brilliance. About 150 novae have thus far been observed in our stellar system. The rate of their discovery has constantly accelerated because of the increasing power of more and better telescopes as well as to more systematic vigilance. The current rate of discovery is from one to two novae per year. It is conservatively estimated, however, that in our star system, there are annually probably at least two dozen, most beyond present powers of observation.

Until recently most novae were designated by the constellation and year in which they appeared, as Nova Aquilae 1918. Latterly, however, as it came to be recognized that novae could be legitimately classed as variables, they have been given designations befitting that status, as DQ Herculis or V 356 Aquilae.

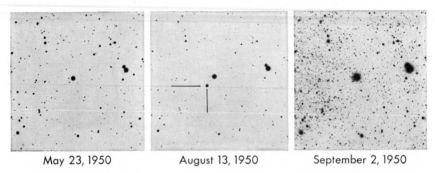

May 23, 1950   August 13, 1950   September 2, 1950

Figure 198. NOVA SCORPII 1950. The appearance and subsequent disappearance of a nova in Scorpius is shown in these three photographs. The first photograph preceded the outburst. Less than a month after discovery of the nova on August 7, 1950, it had faded into invisibility, as shown in the third photograph. (Courtesy McDonald Observatory.)

Figure 199 shows a schematic light curve which indicates the changes in luminosity of a nova in the course of an outburst. As the figure indicates, there is an almost abrupt initial increase in luminosity from its value in the pre-nova stage to a luminosity that is typically about 4000 to 6000 times greater. Then, after a brief hesitation, the nova brightens rather more slowly by another factor of 5 to 10 times. Having attained a maximum luminosity 25,000 to 50,000 times its pre-outburst value, the nova begins to fade fairly rapidly. This initial decline, to about one twenty-fifth the maximum brightness, is followed by a transition period wherein novae are most prone to display individuality; some merely fade less rapidly, some exhibit marked fluctuations in brightness, a few take the opportunity to sink to a deep minimum and then partially recover. At the end of the transition period, the nova is about one–two-hundred-fiftieth of its maximum brightness and enters then upon a long final decline (possibly showing minor irregular fluctuations) by which it eventually returns to its pre-nova luminosity.

The durations of these various phases of a nova's development vary

Continuously Ejecting Stars

THE P CYGNI STARS

The ejection of mass achieved so dramatically by the novae may well be accomplished inconspicuously on a similar scale by several other types of peculiar types of stars such as the P Cygni stars, the Wolf-Rayet stars, and the planetaries. The P Cygni stars are so named for their prototype, P Cygni. The P Cygni stars, like the Oe and Be stars, show hydrogen and helium lines (and frequently others) that are combinations of emission and absorption but which have a very different sort of profile (Fig. 204). Sharp absorption lines are always at the violet edge of usually wider emission lines. By reference to the Doppler principle, we conclude

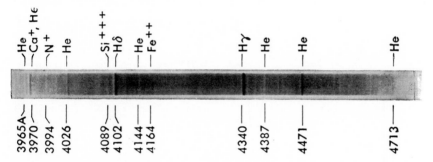

Figure 203. SPECTRUM OF P CYGNI. The spectrum of P Cygni shows numerous emission lines (dark lines on the negative) having absorption lines just to the violet of them. From the absorption lines alone one would classify P Cygni as not earlier than B0 nor later than B2. (Courtesy Yerkes Observatory.)

that gases directly between the star and us (the ones forming the absorption) are approaching the most rapidly. This would be the case if the star were surrounded by an expanding shell of gases that was being continually driven out from, and replenished by, the star. For, although the shell must expand equally fast in all directions, the full effect of the expansion will appear as approach only along the direction to the observer, while in other directions it will effect varying proportions of sidewise motion or even recession. It is these latter parts of the shell which originate the emission.

Evidently P Cygni stars complement the Oe and Be stars; the one group expands, the other rotates, but both are surrounded by shells. A distinctive feature of the P Cygni stars is, however, that apparently little or no part of their absorption lines is formed in the stars' photospheres —if indeed they have well-defined photospheres. Though it admits radiation of the continuous background, the expanding shell appears to be effectively opaque to direct photospheric line radiation. This conclusion is arrived at from the observation that whereas we see to great depths in the expanding shell, in even the deepest of these layers the material is definitely a part of the shell and is flowing out from the star, as shown by

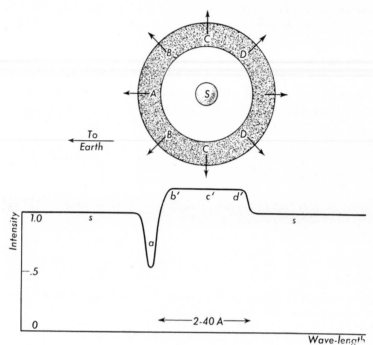

Figure 204. The star *S* is surrounded by an expanding shell. The star provides the continuous background *ss* of the line profile of a typical P Cygni or Wolf-Rayet line. The region *A* of the shell is responsible for part *a* of the profile, and similarly for *B* and *b, C* and *c,* etc. The emission feature *bcd* is very narrow in P Cygni stars, sometimes many angstroms wide in Wolf-Rayet stars.

the profile of lines originating in them. Thus lines of doubly and triply ionized nitrogen and silicon can come only from the inner, hotter layers, and even these layers are expanding.

There is an interesting difference between the inner and outer layers of the P Cygni shells, namely, the outer layers of the shell are expanding more rapidly than the inner. As it is ejected, material of the shell is evidently accelerated, possibly by radiation pressure.

THE WOLF-RAYET STARS

The P Cygni stars are outdone in violence by the still hotter, related Wolf-Rayet stars (discovered jointly by Wolf and Rayet in 1867 at

Paris). Their emission lines are enormously wide, 20 Å to 30 Å, having faint absorption lines at their violet edges (Fig. 205). The great displacements of the absorption lines indicate velocities of ejection as high as 2000 miles per second.

These stars, of which less than a hundred are known, are assigned to spectral class W. One group of them shows spectrum "lines" of He, He+, O^{++}, O^{+++}, C+, and C^{++}, but no N; at the other extreme, another

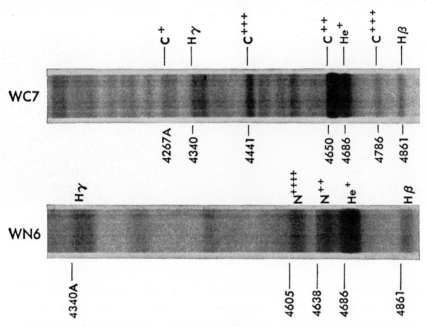

Figure 205. WOLF-RAYET SPECTRA. The spectrum of a Wolf-Rayet star (HD 192103) of the carbon sequence and the spectrum of a Wolf-Rayet star (HD 191765) of the nitrogen sequence both show the characteristic wide emission bands. (Courtesy Yerkes Observatory.)

group shows lines of N^{++}, N^{+++}, and N^{++++} rather than those of carbon, which are only faintly present. The two groups are distinguished as stars of types WC and WN, respectively. Here, as in the R and N stars, there seems to be a variation in the abundance of carbon and perhaps also of nitrogen.

Both the P Cygni stars and the Wolf-Rayet stars have surface temperatures so high that they are difficult to determine reliably; they range from 30,000° K to 80,000° K. They are giants and supergiants, but because of their high temperatures their radii are not uncommonly great. The shells are estimated to have diameters about five to ten times those

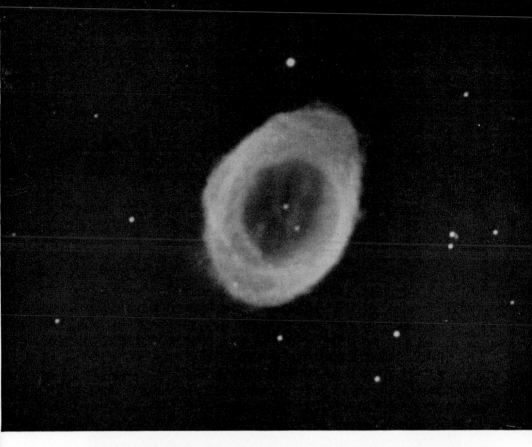

Figure 206. RING NEBULA IN LYRA. The Ring Nebula in Lyra is probably the best known planetary in the northern sky and can be seen in telescopes of modest size. (Mt. Wilson-Palomar Observatories Photo.)

of the enveloped stars. From their high luminosities, they are presumed to be comparatively massive. Some kinship with novae seems to be implied by the fact that the object η Carinae, which is now a P Cygni star, is also a former nova.

THE PLANETARIES

It might at first seem that only by an exercise of poetic license could we classify the planetary nebulae (Fig. 206) among stars, even peculiar ones. The logic of including them will be clearer, however, after we have noted many similarities between the planetaries and several of the kinds of peculiar stars. To begin with, it would be well to note first that the term *planetary* is used in purely descriptive fashion. Planets and planetary nebulae both show round disks in a telescope; this superficial resemblance is the full extent of their similarity.

We should note, too, that the disk of a planetary is but a husk or shell enclosing a star called the *nucleus* of the planetary nebula. These nuclei, almost invariably faint, are hot stars of type O or W; they are among the bluest stars known. In luminosity and spectral type they are much like post-novae.

All the planetaries are distant objects, being from 1000 to 10,000 parsecs away. Their apparent diameters range from about half that of the moon to barely perceptible disks. Actually they are enormously large, from 30,000 to 150,000 astronomical units in diameter. Their spectrum lines show them to be expanding at a rate as high as 25 miles per second. They may be rotating as well, a possibility suggested by the apparent flattening of some.

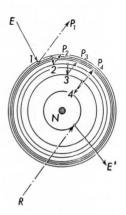

Figure 207. An ion with nucleus N captures a free electron E in an excited orbit at 1, emitting a photon P_1. As the electron cascades to permissible excited orbits at 2, 3, and 4, the atom emits photons P_2, P_3, and P_4. The atom then absorbs a high-energy photon R to release the electron E', and repeat the process. In this way photons such as R are broken into several smaller-energy photons such as P_1, P_2, P_3, and P_4. This process is fluorescence.

The average luminosity of planetary nebulae, exclusive of nuclei, is about 100. It is interesting that to the eye and the photographic plate a planetary nebula is always many times brighter than its nuclear star. We cannot conclude from this, however, that the nebular shell is itself responsible for this extra radiation. The explanation is found in several much subtler mechanisms, one of which is *fluorescence*. Since the planetaries afford us such a striking and important yet comparatively simple demonstration of fluorescence, let us consider the phenomenon in more detail.

Fluorescence depends upon the central star's production of large quantities of very short-wavelength ultraviolet radiation. When this radiation is absorbed by neutral hydrogen atoms, for example, the atoms become ionized. The electrons freed in this way do not maintain their independence indefinitely, however, but recombine at length with some ion. In the process, a photon will be released. Often the reradiated photon will be the same kind of short-wavelength ultraviolet radiation that originally set the electron free, but sometimes it will be of a longer wavelength. This will happen whenever the recaptured electron is caught in one of the larger permissible electron orbits about the capturing nucleus. By subsequently cascading down to the smaller permissible orbits, the electron causes the atom to radiate the remainder of its original energy in smaller doses of still longer wavelength. The result will have been to convert a single short-wavelength photon into two or more longer-wavelength photons. That is the essential feature of fluorescence.

But fluorescence is more than just an interesting phenomenon; it gives us a means of determining the temperatures of the nuclei. The temperatures of the nuclear stars are otherwise very difficult to determine, for the greatest part of their radiations is in the ultraviolet at wavelengths so short as to be excluded by the earth's atmosphere. Wien's law shows, for example, that a perfect radiator at about 58,000° K would radiate with maximum intensity at only 500 Å, and the temperatures of the nuclear stars are (as we shall see) not uncommonly as high as 50,000° K to 100,000° K.

The argument by which the temperature is determined is quite direct. It is assumed (and with reason) that every photon sufficiently energetic to ionize a neutral hydrogen atom will do so and that each such photon will eventually be transformed by fluorescence into two or more longer-wavelength photons, of which exactly one will appear in the visible region of the spectrum. Evidently the combined strength of the visible hydrogen lines from the nebula is a measure of the number of ionizing photons radiated by the star. At the same time, the strength of the star's own visible radiations is a measure of the number of visible photons which it radiates. By Planck's law the ratio of the number of ionizing photons to visible photons is uniquely characteristic of the star's temperature, so that by comparing observed and computed ratios, the temperature of the nucleus can be determined. The hottest nuclear star yet found has a surface temperature of about 200,000° K.

As a consequence of fluorescence, little if any of the nuclear star's ionizing radiation makes its way through the nebular shell. In fact, the limits of this high-frequency radiation can be made visibly apparent in a slitless spectrogram of a planetary (Fig. 208). Such a spectrogram, taken with a spectrograph whose slit is so wide as to admit the whole image of the nebula rather than just a slice of it, consists of a set of images of the nebula in each of the wavelengths emitted by the planetary. The position of each image identifies the atom or ion in whose light it is formed. Significantly, the various images from any particular atom or ion are much alike in size and shape, but images in the radiations of different kinds of atoms or ions may be markedly different in size. For example, the images due to He$^+$ are not as large as those in the light of He. This is because photons energetic enough to ionize helium soon become transformed by fluorescence into radiations no longer capable of so doing, though they are still powerful enough to excite neutral helium atoms to radiate. Helium is not alone in being visibly stratified; the other elements have images whose sizes are in the reverse order of the difficulty of producing and exciting their radiations. Such an effect is reminiscent of the Wolf-Rayet stars.

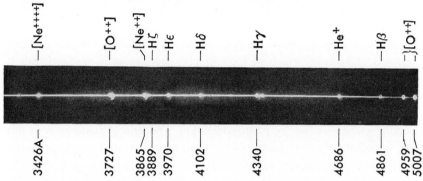

Figure 208. SLITLESS SPECTRUM OF A PLANETARY NEBULA. Since planetaries have emission spectra, the use of a slit in the spectrograph is no longer necessary. Planetary images in each of the discrete wavelengths present appear strung along the spectrum of the central star. Wavelengths are given below, identifications above. Square brackets denote forbidden lines. Note the unequal sizes of images of various wavelengths. (Courtesy Yerkes Observatory.)

There is one very strange feature about a certain few of the lines of many of the planetary nebulae. In short, these lines should not be there. For example, O^{++} and N^{++} produce a few selected lines of their normal spectra, while numerous others that would be expected to appear at the same time are conspicuously absent. The puzzle was solved by some ingenious spectroscopic sleuthing. It was discovered that the O^{++} ion possessed an absorption line at 304 Å within a thousandth of an angstrom of one of the fluorescent emission lines of He$^+$. Because of the unusual strength of the fluorescent radiation, great numbers of O^{++} ions are excited by it, and by their own fluorescence they produce the anomalous observed radiations. As though such a coincidence of wavelengths were not sufficiently remarkable by itself, the N^{++} ions readily absorb the fluorescent radiations of O^{++} at 374 Å and are thereby excited to produce their own fluorescent radiations; this seems to be the atoms' version of a double play.

But one of the most interesting things about the nebular radiations is that the two strongest lines in many of the nebulae are forbidden lines not directly produced either by ionization and recombination or by coincidence fluorescence. Their origin was for so long a mystery that they were, in fact, ascribed to an unknown substance called nebulium; nebulium has since been found to be O^{++}.

But why should O^{++} produce strong forbidden lines in planetary nebulae and not in the laboratory? Furthermore, why are there not also strong permitted lines of O^{++} present? The answer to the latter question depends upon the fact that it requires considerably more energy to excite the permitted radiations of O^{++} ions than it does to excite their forbidden lines. For all practical purposes the difference is prohibitive, for the excitation energy is gotten in this instance by robbing fast-moving free electrons of however much of their kinetic energies as is required; this is the same process as takes place in a laboratory discharge tube or a neon sign.

The amounts of energy involved are limited by the average energies of the electrons set free by photo-ionization. The hijacked energy is in this case sufficient only to excite the O^{++} ion to one of its metastable states. The result is the emission of a forbidden line, as in a nova shell, since the planetary is very rarefied. In brief, the nebulium lines are forbidden lines excited by electron collision, and their great strength is possible only because of the very low density of the nebula. They are the product of a third mode of excitation, the other two modes being fluorescence after photo-ionization and fluorescence after coincidence absorption.

It is an interesting corollary to the existence of strong forbidden radiations that the temperature of the nebula itself is kept much below that of the nuclear star, for the forbidden radiations have been made possible only at the expense of the kinetic energy of the particles of the nebular gas. It is the kinetic energy of these particles, however, which is measured by the temperature, and if the kinetic energy is limited (as by collision excitation), so is the temperature. As a matter of fact, the strength of the forbidden lines has been used to calculate the average kinetic energy of the nebular gas and therewith the temperature. It is found by this means that the planetaries have temperatures of 8000° K to 16,000° K.

The forbidden lines are likewise very helpful in that their strengths permit estimates of the extremely low density of the nebula; there are only a few thousands to a few tens of thousands of atoms per cubic inch. This density times the measured volume of a planetary gives for it a mass that is about equal to the sun's.

These interesting and unusual objects are rare specimens; there are about 400 known. Their rarity may stem from the fact that they are pos-

thought to be maintained by the decay of radioactive isotopes formed at the time of the original explosion. Chief among them is C_6^{14}, radioactive carbon. Only one two-thousandth of the mass of the Crab Nebula need be C_6^{14} to maintain the nebula's luminosity over long periods; it would fall to 40 per cent of its present brightness only after 7000 years. What is more, fast-moving electrons released in the radioactive decay are probably responsible for the obliteration of the absorption lines, even as in the solar corona. The decay of carbon also results in excited nitrogen atoms whose strong emission lines are a peculiarity of the Crab Nebula. Similarly, lines of ionized sulfur are almost certainly to be credited to the radioactive generation of excited sulfur ions.

If these hypotheses are borne out, supernova relics of the past 80,000 years should be still detectable. In this length of time, there may have been as many as 800 supernovae. The Loop Nebula in Cygnus (Fig. 211) may be one such; significantly, this nebula has no visible central star. The strong radio source Cassiopeia A may be another.

It is not to be supposed that every type of stellar peculiarity is herewith encompassed in our summary of the peculiar stars. It is hoped, however, that the major categories have been surveyed in a fashion that will exhibit their intrinsic fascination and provide such acquaintance as will be useful for the further examination of the large-scale universe.

QUESTIONS

1. What are intrinsic variables? How are they distinguished from eclipsing binaries? What designations are given them?
2. Why are the T Tauri stars, the rotating stars, and the shell stars thought to be young?
3. By what means is the rotation of a star made known? Can all rotating stars be detected in this way? Which cannot and why? Why are the estimates of equatorial rotational velocity all minimal? How does rotation help to explain the spectrum variables?
4. Draw a schematic line profile for a rotating Be star. Account for each of its principal features.
5. What are dilution effects? Why do they occur? In what respects are they like and unlike luminosity effects?
6. What characterizes the light curve of a Cepheid? The velocity curve? How do the light and velocity curves show that the Cepheids are not eclipsing binaries? What are they?
7. What is the period-luminosity relation? Why is it important?
8. How do population II Cepheids differ from those of population I?
9. List the similarities and differences between the Cepheids and the long-period variables. Why do the long-period variables show such a large range

of apparent brightness? To what spectral types do the long-period variables belong? What spectral anomalies do they show?

10. Sketch a schematic light curve for a nova. Indicate the approximate durations of each of the several significant stages. Describe the accompanying spectral changes. What is the interpretation of the nova phenomenon on the basis of the light curve and spectrum observations? How appropriate is the term "nova"?

11. What are forbidden lines? How do they originate in a nova?

12. How luminous are novae at maximum? Before outburst?

13. What kinds of stars are likely to become novae? Is the sun one of them? How may novae be related to the U Geminorum stars? The white dwarfs?

14. Draw a schematic line profile of a P Cygni star. Account for each of its principal features. What evidence is there that P Cygni stars and Wolf-Rayet stars may be related to novae?

15. What are planetaries? How large are they? How luminous?

16. How is a planetary able to appear so much brighter than the nuclear star which is its source of energy?

17. Explain how the temperature of a planetary nucleus is determined. What is it?

18. What is a slitless spectrogram? What do slitless spectrograms of planetaries show?

19. Explain the three different mechanisms responsible for the spectrum lines of a planetary.

20. What are the temperatures of planetaries and how are they determined? What are the densities of planetaries and how are they determined?

21. How are the ages of planetaries estimated and what are they? What relation may this bear to the rarity of planetaries?

22. How do supernovae differ from normal novae? How common are they? What stars in our galaxy are known to have been supernovae? How can they remain several hundred times more luminous than the sun for many centuries?

Figure 212. GROUP OF GALAXIES IN LEO. This field shows four bright and numerous faint galaxies as well as a number of more sharply outlined foreground stars. (Mt. Wilson-Palomar Observatories Photo.)

part III
The Universe

•••

chapter 10
Galaxies

• • •

A. THE MILKY WAY GALAXY

*"I saw eternity the other night,
Like a great ring, of pure and endless light
All calm, as it was bright."*
—HENRY VAUGHAN

The Distribution of the Stars

We have been occupied with an examination of the properties and activities of the stars, both singly and severally. However, there is one important feature of the stellar population which we have entirely overlooked, namely, its distribution through space. It is as though in taking a census of the United States we had recorded the name, age, occupation, weight, height, etc., of every person but had failed to note their addresses or even the states in which they live. From an incomplete survey of this kind we can get no notion of where the population is sparse, where dense. So, for the stellar population, we ask: *What is the three-dimensional distribution of the stars?* More than that, does this distribution change with time, and if so, how and why?

It is from the answers to questions such as these that we can expect to find out something of the scale and plan of the local universe as well as clues to its past and future history. It would appear that at least getting the distribution of the stars in space should be a relatively simple and straightforward matter of measuring the distances and noting the directions of the stars. And so it might be but for several difficulties. Perhaps the first to beset us is the practical difficulty of merely obtaining any desired datum for all the many millions of stars that can be reached with even moderate-sized telescopes; this is not a problem of principle, of course, but one of time and effort. Then there is the further difficulty that even the sun, which according to our present knowledge is of slightly above-average luminosity, could not be seen at a distance of over 10,000 parsecs in the largest existing telescopes. Hence from the earth a celestial census-taker gets ever more sketchy statistics from the outer provinces, and for most purposes must confine himself to a domain of a few thousand parsecs radius or less; this is a serious restriction.

These limitations, though irksome, need not be fatal. They may be in a good part circumvented by availing ourselves of statistical and indirect methods of obtaining the information we want. As a matter of fact, such methods will give us somewhat more information than we have bargained for, introduce us to unsuspected features in the system of stars, and create new problems in the process of solving the old ones.

THE STARS' APPARENT DISTRIBUTION

Whatever the stars' true distribution through space, we see the projection of this distribution on the celestial sphere whenever we look at the sky. Even from this depthless two-dimensional distribution of stars we can get information of great value. Plain to the naked eye, for instance, is the existence of the Milky Way, shown by any small telescope to be an aggregation of innumerable faint stars. This rather narrow belt of stars divides the sky very neatly into hemispheres, one centered upon the point at $\alpha = 12^h49^m$, $\delta = +27°$, the other centered upon the opposite point at $\alpha = 0^h49^m$, $\delta = -27°$. These points are designated as the north and south *galactic poles,* respectively, and the great circle midway between them is called the *galactic equator,* marking the *galactic plane.* The galactic plane centrally bisects the Milky Way. It is often convenient to refer stars' positions to the galactic plane and poles, and for this purpose one uses the coordinates galactic latitude and longitude. *Galactic latitude* is measured in degrees from the galactic plane toward the north and south galactic poles; *galactic longitude* is measured in degrees eastward from the point at $\alpha = 17^h42^m$, $\delta = -29°$, where the stars are densest upon the sky.

We can make immediate use of galactic coordinates to consider the relative concentration of stars toward the galactic plane. As a measure of this concentration we shall arbitrarily take the ratio of the number of stars of specified brightness within galactic latitudes 0–20° to the number of stars of the same brightness within galactic latitudes 40–90°. Among stars just visible to the unaided eye, stars in the lower galactic latitude group are $2\frac{1}{2}$ times as frequent as in the high-latitude group, and our ratio is thus 2.5. Stars a hundred times fainter show a concentration of 2.9; those still a hundred times fainter have a yet larger galactic concentration of 5.8; and the faintest stars to be seen in the largest telescopes exhibit a 16.2-fold concentration toward the galactic plane.[1]

[1] These and many other of the statistics which follow are derived from portions of sky which are believed to form a small but representative part of the whole. Two

of the way from center to rim, some 8200 parsecs. The star clouds toward the galactic center, where the density of stars is twice that at the sun, mark a galactic nucleus which broadens to about 4500 parsecs thickness and has an over-all diameter of roughly 12,000 parsecs. Enveloping this central stellar disk is a corona studded with globular clusters and cluster Cepheids to a distance of 20,000 parsecs (and sometimes more) from the galactic center (see Fig. 232).

The Dynamics of the Galaxy

A fact of key importance concerning the stellar galactic disk is that it rotates; the disk owes its flattened shape, as do the rings of Saturn, to its rapid rotation about the galactic center. For such rotation there is convincing internal evidence. To understand the nature of this evidence, we first note that the galaxy may conceivably rotate (1) after the manner of a wheel, all parts turning through the same angle in the same time and all having the same period, or (2) in the fashion of the planets about the sun, those bodies near the center revolving more rapidly and in a shorter period. Actually these modes represent two extremes, of which probably neither is adhered to by the galaxy. The former would be expected if the material of the galaxy were spread uniformly throughout it, whereas the latter requires that practically the whole of the galactic mass be concentrated at the galactic center. Since the evidence we already have is inconsistent with either extreme, it seems safe to say that galactic rotation will be in a manner intermediate to these extremes. It will serve our purpose, however, merely to recognize that the various parts of the galaxy will probably not maintain fixed distances from each other as do the parts of a wheel.

Then how will it look to us? We can expect parts of the galaxy nearer the galactic center to rotate about it in less time than we ourselves do (though perhaps, unlike the planets, not as much less as Kepler's harmonic law would require), while parts of the galaxy farther out will take longer. This state of affairs could be represented by a set of concentric merry-go-rounds, each of which takes longer for a single round than any of those within it. Any rider will find himself being overtaken by riders closer in but will pass by riders farther out. If he were to analyze the velocities of other riders *relative to himself,* he would observe these results (Fig. 215): (1) Riders directly toward or away from the center of rotation would show a purely transverse instantaneous motion, have zero instantaneous radial velocities. (2) Riders directly ahead or behind would keep their distances indefinitely and show no average transverse *or* radial velocities. (3) Riders closer in would approach from behind, i.e., show negative radial velocities, or increase their distance if ahead, i.e., show positive radial velocities. (4) Riders farther out would be overtaken if ahead, i.e., show negative radial velocities, or be left still farther back if behind, i.e., show positive radial velocities. In other words, if the parallel be transferred to the rotating galaxy, we should find a characteristic and predictable variation of both radial velocity and proper motion of the stars as we "box the compass" in the galactic plane. This expectation is borne out (most clearly

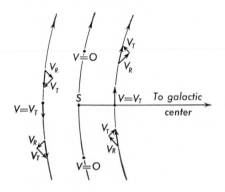

Figure 215. Because of galactic rotation, the sun, at *S*, is being overtaken and left behind by stars nearer the galactic center, overtakes and leaves behind stars farther from the galactic center. The figure shows how this relative motion affects the apparent radial velocity V_R and the transverse velocity V_T.

in the radial velocities, which are easier to obtain) by observations of giants of all types, supergiants, long-period variables, planetaries, and galactic clusters. Other types of objects cannot be seen to a distance great enough to give useful evidence. There can hardly be any doubt of galactic rotation.

At what speed does the sun revolve about the galactic nucleus? To determine this, we must measure the motion of the sun relative to some set of bodies which do not revolve about the galactic nucleus or, at worst, do so slowly. The galactic corona or halo of globular clusters is probably such a set of bodies, for it is distributed with nearly spherical symmetry about the galactic nucleus; appreciable rotation about the galactic nucleus would flatten the corona even as it does the disk itself. The radial velocities of the globular clusters range from -225 to $+182$ miles per second. In conjunction with the clusters' respective directions in space, this is found to imply that the sun is moving toward galactic longitude 90° with a speed of approximately 120 miles per second. There is reason to think, however, that the clusters in turn may be rotating about the nucleus with a speed which would add about 25 miles per second at the sun's distance from the galactic center. Thus the total velocity of galactic rotation of the sun is probably 145 miles per second or so. At this speed the sun executes one galactic rotation in about 230 million years.

For confirmation of so important a result, we may refer the motion of the sun to the nearer external galaxies. Their approaches and recessions may be most simply accounted for by supposing the sun's speed of galactic rotation to be 140 miles per second, a figure in excellent agreement with our previous one. Further, galactic rotation of the sun may now be seen

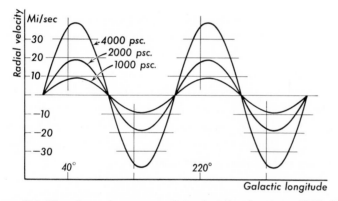

Figure 216. The observed average radial velocities of stars at 1000, 2000, and 4000 parsecs are dependent on galactic longitude in a way indicated by these curves. Such curves are sometimes used to ascertain the distances of remote stars from their radial velocities when other methods fail.

to account for the strongly asymmetric motion of the high-velocity stars; these are actually stars of the galactic halo which are being speedily left behind by the galactic rotation of the sun and its neighbors. In reality, therefore, it is we and not the high-velocity stars who have the high velocity. There are also several useful features of galactic rotation which can be exploited for considerable information. One is that, within limits, the radial velocities of distant objects give a measure of their distances. Except in those directions where we expect the radial velocity to be zero, the radial velocities due to galactic rotation should increase in proportion to the distance. Observations of objects whose distances are known establish what is to be expected in any direction for the radial velocity of a star at any distance. This standard can then be applied to any other object whose distance is desired.

Another and very important result that can be gotten from the observations of differential rotational velocities is an independent determination of the distance to the galactic center and of the mass of the galaxy. The method of doing so is based upon Kepler's harmonic law. Thus the mass of the galactic nucleus and the sun's distance from it will determine the sun's period of revolution; the period and mean distance of the sun determine its velocity. At the same time, the mass of the galactic nucleus and the distance of a star 1000 parsecs farther from the nucleus than the sun will fix the rotational velocity of that star about the nucleus. The difference between the two orbital speeds is the relative velocity of the sun and star. The rotational velocity of the sun and the relative velocity of the sun and stars in other parts of the galaxy therefore depend upon the mass of the galactic nucleus and its distance from the sun. When the former two are known from observation, the latter two can be inferred. The distance so determined is substantially that found previously. The mass of the galactic nucleus, and therefore for practical purposes the mass of the entire galaxy, is in round numbers 10^{11} solar masses. If the sun is taken to be an average star, we conclude that there are about 10^{11} stars in the Milky Way Galaxy. Impressive as such a figure is, it is nevertheless also true that the density of stars might be increased a millionfold without even incurring serious risk of their collision.

The Interstellar Medium

Our description of the galaxy thus far has had to be somewhat circumspect because it has ignored a very important component of the Milky Way, the *interstellar medium*. This is unformed matter between the stars, most of it in the form of a tenuous gas, the rest of it an even thinner cloud of dust particles. Occasional concentrations of interstellar matter in the vicinity of bright stars provide some of the most spectacular celestial sights in the form of diffuse nebulae. For convenience let us consider, in order, the interstellar gas, interstellar dust, and diffuse nebulae.

INTERSTELLAR GAS

The first evidence that anything at all existed in the apparently dark and vacant spaces between the stars came in the year 1904. It was discovered then that the spectrum of the star δ Orionis showed a peculiar K line of ionized calcium. To begin with, this line was peculiar in that a very sharp K line is abnormal for an early B-type star such as δ Orionis. More than this, the K line was the only line in the spectrum of this spectroscopic binary which did not take part in the periodic Doppler displacement. Clearly the line could not have originated in the atmosphere of either component of δ Orionis; it must have been formed by atoms between these stars and the earth, and for this reason it is called an *interstellar line*.

Interstellar lines have since been found in the spectra of a considerable number of stars, many not binaries. For the most part, these lines are most easily identified in the spectra of stars of early type, whose own lines are few and often very broad and shallow. All together, 15 atomic lines and 11 molecular bands of interstellar origin have been identified. They include lines of sodium, potassium, iron, ionized titanium, and the mole-

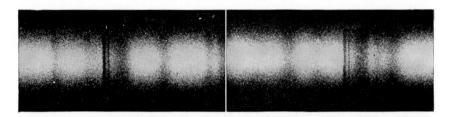

Figure 217. INTERSTELLAR LINES. The interstellar Ca+ line H (right) and K (left) show double in the spectrum of the binary υ Sagittarii. The diffuse stellar absorption lines contrast plainly with the sharp interstellar lines. (Mt. Wilson-Palomar Observatories Photo.)

cules CN, CH, and CH+ as well as ionized and neutral calcium. Six diffuse interstellar bands 4 Å to 10 Å wide remain unidentified.

All known interstellar absorption lines are resonance lines; i.e., these lines arise from an excitation of the atom in its ground state or state of lowest energy. It is on this account that no interstellar absorption lines of hydrogen are found. The resonance lines of hydrogen lie far in the ultraviolet, hidden from view by the earth's atmosphere. Nevertheless the presence of hydrogen in the interstellar gas is indicated by the lines of the molecule CH. The strength of these lines establishes that, as in stellar atmospheres, hydrogen is overwhelmingly the most abundant constituent of the interstellar gas by a factor of 100,000 or so.

As might be expected, nonresonance emission lines of hydrogen have been found in extensive areas of the Milky Way. From the same regions there are often forbidden lines of O^+, O^{++}, and N^+. These emission lines must be produced by the same means as the emission lines of the planetary nebulae, namely, by the ionization, recombination, and fluorescence of hydrogen and by the electron excitation of O^{++} and N^+. As in the planetaries, these processes are possible in the very tenuous interstellar gas since the rarity of a photo-ionization or a collisional excitation is offset by the fact that ions remain unmolested for a long enough time to work out their own salvations.

About the very hot stars, hydrogen is almost wholly ionized to distances up to 500 light years. The hot stars thus give rise to huge volumes of gas radiating emission lines of hydrogen. They may be most conveniently traced out in the light of the red line of hydrogen. Nine such ionized hydrogen regions are known within 1000 parsecs of the sun, many more beyond. Like planetaries about their nuclei, the ionized hydrogen regions are far brighter in the visible region of the spectrum than are the associated stars. They are indeed objects of great luminosity, visible in other galaxies as well as in our own.

Very hot stars are rare, however, and as a consequence, about 95 per cent of all interstellar hydrogen remains neutral and therefore dark. It is from the tincture of other atoms in the interstellar gas that much of what is known of it has been learned. One of the most important features of these interstellar lines is the fact that they are compound, showing as many as seven components. From this it may be inferred that the gas along the line of sight is assembled in discrete clouds, each with its own radial velocity and Doppler shift. On the average, a line of sight in the galactic plane would intercept eight to a dozen such clouds every 1000 parsecs. The average diameters of such clouds are a few tens of parsecs.

It is evident that the greater the distance of a star, the stronger should be the interstellar lines in the spectrum of that star. It is indeed found that the intensity of the interstellar K line as measured by its equivalent width is approximately proportional to the distance of the star in whose spectrum it is observed; each thousand parsecs increases the equivalent width about a third of an angstrom. It must be admitted, however, that the interstellar gas cannot be of uniform composition, for the interstellar lines of different elements have strengths which vary in their proportions from star to star.

By a process simpler in detail but fundamentally similar to the one used to determine the abundances of the elements in the solar atmosphere, it is possible to determine the density of the interstellar gas from the strength of its absorption lines. For example, an analysis of the interstellar lines in the spectrum of χ^2 Orionis indicates that the interstellar gas between it and the earth has an average density of about 0.6×10^{-23} ($0.6/10^{23}$) grams per cubic centimeter. In other terms, it represents approximately 50 atoms per cubic inch. This, however, is only an average. Within a cloud the density may be 200 atoms per cubic inch, elsewhere much less.

To appreciate how tenuous the interstellar gas clouds are, we may note that within a volume equal to that of the earth, the amount of interstellar gas will be only about 7 pounds. Ordinarily we should regard such a low density as a near-perfect vacuum, but between the stars we call it the *interstellar medium*. Although the tenuity of the interstellar gas may seem remarkable, its amount in aggregate is truly astonishing. It probably comprises about 6 per cent of the galaxy's 100 billion solar masses.

The importance of the interstellar gas is even greater than its mass might suggest, however, for it serves as a tracer by which the extent and structure of the galaxy may be investigated. The hot stars of early type and their associated clouds of ionized hydrogen may be mapped to considerable distances within the galaxy. Their local distribution shows unmistakably a pattern of arms like those visible on the great Andromeda galaxy and others. The more extended distribution of the clouds of neutral hydrogen may be discerned even to the limits of the galaxy in many directions, however, by means of a particular hydrogen radio radiation, the emission at wavelength 21 centimeters (about $8\frac{1}{4}$ inches).

That hydrogen should have such an emission line was first predicted theoretically in 1944. It was noted then that what is customarily regarded as the ground state of the hydrogen atom is actually two states differing in energy by a very minute amount. A transition from the higher to the lower state results in the emission of the 21-centimeter radiation, a spectrum line very remote from the visible region, falling instead within the radio range. A hydrogen atom excited by collision with another atom to the upper state would spontaneously emit a 21-centimeter radio radiation only after about 11 million years, on the average. Were not the infrequence of radiation by individual atoms offset by the enormous number of hydrogen atoms, this radiation would be undetectable. Even so, the total intensity of 21-centimeter radiation over the earth's entire surface is only 1 or 2 watts, less than half the power of a single flashlight battery. This means that the radio telescopes used to study the 21-centimeter line of neutral interstellar hydrogen must be able to detect signals as faint as 10^{-18} ($\frac{1}{10^{18}}$) watts.

Though discrete emission lines of radio wavelength have been predicted for two other kinds of atom or molecule, the 21-centimeter line is thus far the only such line known to observation. Its role in the investigation of the structure of the galaxy depends upon the fact that, as an emission line of accurately known wavelength, it will exhibit any Doppler shift which the motion of its source may impose upon it. The radial velocity of any cloud is believed to be that of galactic rotation to within 5 miles per second. This is important for two reasons: (1) Were there no relative displacement

of the emissions of different clouds, the radiations of clouds beyond about
5000 light years would more probably than not suffer an absorption in the
intervening gas and the identity of its original source would be obliterated;

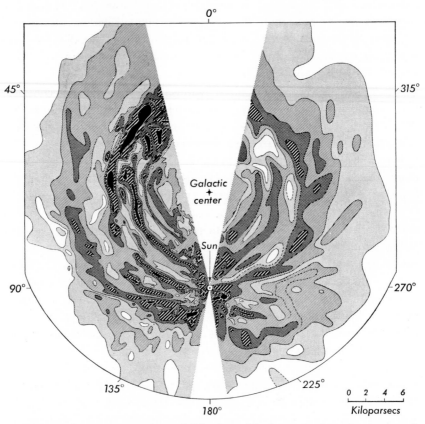

Figure 218. This map of the distribution of hydrogen in the galaxy was made
from radio observations of the 21-centimeter radiation. The darker areas are regions
denser in hydrogen. In the vacant sectors, the radial velocity due to galactic rotation
is effectively zero. (Adapted from figure by courtesy of Dr. F. J. Kerr, Radiophysics
Division, C.S.I.R.O.)

and (2) the distances of the clouds can be told from their radial velocities,
as have the distances of certain bright stars (see p. 439).

Like an artillerist mapping enemy gun positions, the radio astronomer
can plot the distance and direction of the hydrogen clouds over a large
portion of the galaxy. The results of such work show dramatically (see
Fig. 218) the complex spiral form of the Milky Way. The sun is found

to lie on the inner edge of a spiral arm, one passing through Orion and stretching away toward Cygnus. At the same time, an entirely new feature of galactic dynamics is revealed. The gas clouds within 3000 parsecs of the galactic center stream out from it with velocities from 25 to 100 miles per second. This apparent expansion seems to characterize stars of population I even out to the sun; if it is assumed that the sun, its neighbors, and adjacent gas clouds are receding as a group from the galactic center with a speed of 4 miles per second, the map of the galaxy's arms shows a symmetry which it otherwise lacks.

Radio telescopes also detect considerable continuous radiation from the galactic halo or corona; similar radiation originates in the halo of the Andromeda nebula. It is termed *synchrotron radiation* inasmuch as it is thought to be due to the deceleration of very rapidly moving electrons in a large-scale magnetic field of the galaxy; a synchrotron does the same thing on a much smaller scale. The strength of the radiation together with estimates of the strength of the magnetic forces in the galaxy seem to imply that the atoms of coronal gas must have velocities such as they would in a gas at $1,000,000°$ K and that a small proportion of the electrons have still higher velocities.

INTERSTELLAR DUST

It is reasonable to expect that in the vast low-density clouds of interstellar gas, some of the atoms and molecules will clump together into small particles. Such particles are variously called dust, smoke, grains, or fog. Their absorption of radiation is not limited to a few weak sharp interstellar lines as is that of the interstellar gas; they effect a continuous absorption of starlight. On this account, they produce a variety of obscuration effects. Such, for example, are the striking intricate dark lanes in sections of the Milky Way (Fig. 219). These seemingly vacant areas are actually the silhouettes of irregular clouds of interstellar dust.

The most conspicuous absorbing clouds are nearby. More distant clouds show feebler contrast to surrounding areas because of the presence of numerous foreground stars. Thus the distances and extents of such clouds can be roughly gauged by means of star counts; a paucity of faint stars in a given area of the Milky Way indicates a nearby cloud, whereas a moderate number give evidence of a more distant cloud. The relationship may be exhibited in a *Wolf diagram* (so named for the astronomer who first devised one). This is simply a graph showing the number of stars, per unit area of sky, which have an apparent brightness of any particular amount (Fig. 220). In directions where there is no obscuring material,

Figure 219. REGION ABOUT RHO OPHIUCHI. Lanes of dark absorbing interstellar matter are silhouetted against star clouds of one of the richest regions of the Milky Way. Of the bright objects near the center, the red supergiant star Antares is the one on the lower left. (Courtesy Yerkes Observatory.)

the fainter, more distant stars should increase in number about as the volume of space which includes them. Such an area of sky indicates the standard rate of increase of the number of fainter stars.

The Wolf diagram of a neighboring region will be materially different if there is a dust cloud in this direction, for beyond the near side of this cloud all stars will be dimmed. Hence, from this point on, the number of fainter stars will be less than normal and the rate of increase of still fainter stars will slacken until we begin to include the stars which lie entirely beyond the cloud. The presence of an interstellar dust cloud thus introduces a "bend" into the curve of the Wolf diagram. The faintness of the stars at which the bend is initiated provides an index (from their mean parallax) of the distance of the near side of the cloud. The amount by which the bent portion appears to be displaced from the standard curve measures the cloud's total obscuration. From this and the point at which the normal rate of increase of fainter stars resumes, we have the corrected brightness of the stars on the far side of the cloud, and with it, their distance. In this manner we have found the approximate distance, extent, and effectiveness of an interstellar dust cloud. As an example of the results of this method we can say of an absorbing cloud in the constellation Scutum that it commences at about 180 parsecs, extends to about 265 parsecs, and dims the light of stars beyond it by a factor of about 20 times.

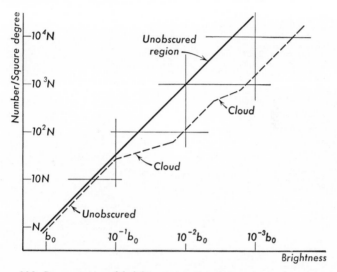

Figure 220. Star counts and brightness measurements are used to construct Wolf diagrams, of which this is an example. From Wolf diagrams one seeks to learn the distance, extent, and effectiveness of clouds of absorbing interstellar dust.

Though the method of star counts and Wolf diagrams is a valuable and informative one, the results of this method are not to be taken too literally, for one can never be certain that the star counts of a standard region are wholly free of the influence of absorption or that there may not be real differences in the numbers of stars of two regions. Moreover, interstellar dust is not limited to starkly silhouetted clouds. The galactic clusters gave one of the first demonstrations of this fact. To understand how, imagine the color-brightness diagram of a cluster superposed upon a Hertzsprung-Russell diagram so that the various color indices coincide with their respective equivalent spectral types and so that the main sequence of the cluster lies in the standard position relative to the luminosity scale. Since all stars of the cluster are at virtually the same distance, the graduation of the

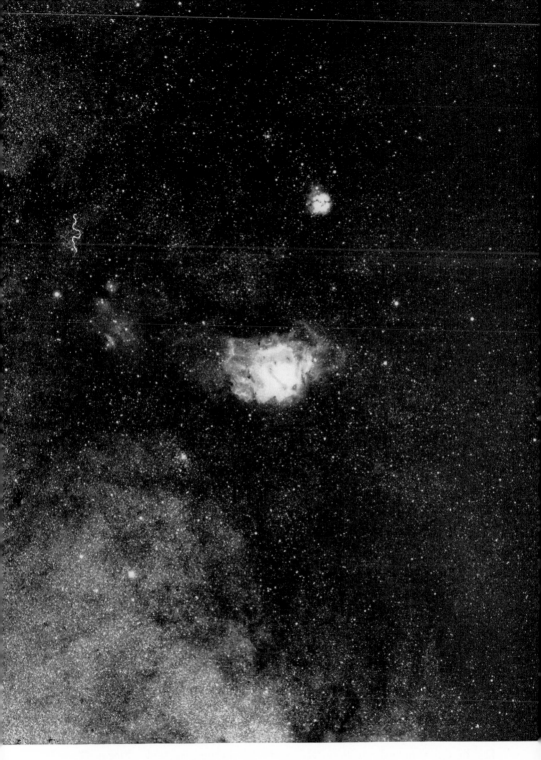

Figure 221. STAR CLOUDS IN SAGITTARIUS. The large bright object at the center is the diffuse nebula NGC 6514. Above it is the Trifid Nebula, shown in more detail in Fig. 229. (Mt. Wilson-Palomar Observatories Photo.)

Figure 222. NEBULOSITIES NEAR GAMMA CYGNI. Bright and dark diffuse nebulae provide mutual contrast in a region of the summer Milky Way. (Mt. Wilson-Palomar Observatories Photo.)

brightness scale will differ from that of the luminosity scale only by the common factor $1/d^2$. In other words, one may choose for any brightness the corresponding luminosity and compute the cluster's distance from the formula $d = \sqrt{L/b}$. If space is transparent, this method should be one of more than ordinary accuracy. It disagrees, however, with the distance one would expect from the apparent diameter of the cluster. The former distance is greater than the latter by an amount which increases with distance.

The discrepancy is to be explained as due to the fact that, on account of interstellar absorption, the faint clusters appear fainter than they should. Then, if their abnormal faintness were credited to distance alone, the distance would be overestimated more and more the farther the cluster. It has been concluded from this that interstellar dust exists as a thin generally pervasive layer affecting the transparency of space in every direction. From such dimming of clusters and other high luminosity objects, it is known that absorption of light by dust clouds near the galactic plane reduces the light from sources at 1000 parsecs to one-half or even one-fifth of its original intensity. Its total effect is startling; an estimated 90 per cent of all starlight from the galaxy is obscured from us by dust clouds, else full starlight would equal the brightness of the full moon.

The same dust which absorbs light will also redden it, just as dust in the earth's atmosphere both absorbs and reddens the sunlight which passes through it. The amount by which the light of a distant star is reddened by interstellar dust is expressed numerically as a quantity called *color excess*. It is simply the difference between the observed color index of a star and the normal unreddened color index of a star of the same spectral type. Thus, if a star whose normal color index is 0.5 were found to have a color index of 0.6, its color excess would be $0.6 - 0.5 = 0.1$.

Reddening offers independent evidence of the presence of interstellar dust. This is important because the amount of reddening of individual stars can be readily measured free of the uncertainties of the statistical determinations of the amount of dimming. Coupled with the fact that obscuration increases with reddening because both increase with amount of interstellar dust, this allows more accurate estimates to be made of the dimming of remote objects. Star clusters afford an example of a critical application of the determinations of color excesses; in order to construct a correct color-brightness diagram, the member stars' color indices must be decreased by the amount of their color excess and their brightnesses must be increased by the associated dimming factor.

The distribution of interstellar dust is one of the most important subjects of investigation in galactic astronomy. About 30 to 40 per cent of the area of the Milky Way is spread with the projection of known clouds of all degrees of contrast. However, irregularity is one of the most pronounced characteristics of the interstellar dust. For example, reddening shows a strong dependence on galactic longitude. It also shows a dependence upon distance, as can be clearly seen in a reddening-distance diagram (Fig. 223). Such a diagram is a graph of the color excesses of stars in a certain small area of sky plotted against their respective distances. Sometimes reddening increases in rough proportion to distance, sometimes shows abrupt increases at certain distances.

Inasmuch as there is no established relation between color excess and the intensity of the interstellar lines, it must be concluded that the dust is less uniformly distributed than the gas. The dust tends to concentrate in clouds, of which there is an average of one about every 10,000 cubic parsecs. Most clouds have radii in excess of 5 parsecs, some considerably more. A line of sight in a representative direction in the galactic plane could be expected to intercept about six dust clouds in 1000 parsecs. An estimated two-thirds of the obscuration near the galactic plane is due to dust within 6000 light years; the remaining 20,000 light years to the galactic center is relatively free of clouds.

From the relative effectiveness of the interstellar dust as absorber and as reddener we can judge the average size of the grains. Particles of the smallness of molecules redden considerably but dim little, as in the earth's

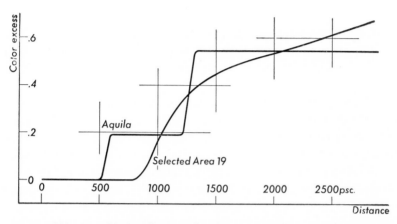

Figure 223. A reddening-distance diagram can provide valuable information about the distribution of interstellar dust in depth. It may also show, as this figure does, the diversity of distribution.

atmosphere; particles as large as buckshot would absorb or scatter light almost exclusively, redden it almost not at all. Between these extremes is interstellar dust, whose absorbing and reddening powers correspond to spherical particles about one ten-thousandth of an inch in diameter.

The observed dimming power of the dust clouds suggests for them an average density of about 10^{-26} times the density of water; it is thus only about $\frac{1}{300}$ as dense as the interstellar gas. The average amount of dust in a volume equal to that of the earth would be only about a third of an ounce. However, an entire cloud would have a mass of 10 to 100 solar masses. This figure affords a reasonable check upon the estimate of the density, for appreciably greater density would increase the mass of the dust clouds to such amount that the motion of neighboring stars would be affected to a degree that would be in contradiction to the observations.

These estimates are necessarily rather uncertain since the chemical composition of the grains is unknown. However, there is a possibility that the compounds or elements which constitute the interstellar grains will become known when identifications have been made of a number of diffuse interstellar bands whose source is undetermined. These absorption features are unlike any known atomic or molecular lines, and since the strength of at least some of them appears to be proportional to the amount of reddening, it seems safe to assume that they originate in the dust clouds. Guessing that the over-all composition of the interstellar medium is similar to that of the sun, one can hazard the conjecture that interstellar grains contain 100 parts of water, 30 parts of molecular hydrogen, 20 parts of methane, 10 parts of ammonia, 5 parts of magnesium hydride, and a sprinkling of other compounds as impurities.

The receipt of faint, scattered light from interstellar dust clouds provides a suggestive clue. It shows that the particles behave like a cloud of tiny mirrors, as would snowflakes, fine sand grains, or powdered rosin, rather than as absorbers like the dark silver grains on the strongly exposed parts of a photographic negative. This indicates that interstellar grains are for the most part of nonmetallic substance (such as sand) rather than of metal (like iron or silver).

Another pertinent detail is the fact that the interstellar grains partially polarize transmitted starlight. Crudely put, this means that the particles differentially sort the undulations of a light wave in the horizontal and vertical planes; a crystal of Iceland spar or a piece of polaroid will do the same thing. The observed polarization of starlight implies that the grains are probably needleshaped and oriented perpendicular to the galactic plane by a force which can only be supposed to be a general galactic magnetic field.

The dust clouds now in existence must be astronomically young, for they are thought to spawn stars within about 100 million years. Presumably they form from the material of a gas cloud, a surmise suggested by the fact that the relative proportions of gas and dust are almost the same everywhere. An upper limit to the size to which grains may grow is set by the fact that grains will be vaporized in the course of the collision of dust clouds. Any particular grain may survive an average of nine collisions with clouds before succumbing; its life expectancy is therefore about 100,000,000 years.

DIFFUSE NEBULAE

The diffuse nebulae are some of the most beautiful objects in the sky. Most are so faint, however, that only a long-exposed photographic plate can show their intricate details. They are glowing condensations

Figure 224. THE ORION NEBULA. The great Orion Nebula is visible to the naked eye in the sword of Orion. It envelops and is illuminated by the quadruple star θ Orionis. (Mt. Wilson-Palomar Observatories Photo.)

Figure 225. THE HORSEHEAD NEBULA. The silhouetted outline of the horsehead appears near the center of this photograph made by a three-hour exposure with the 100-inch Hooker reflector. An extensive absorbing cloud accounts for the smallness of the number of faint stars on the left. The bright aura at the top is the edge of the image of the star ζ Orionis. (Mt. Wilson-Palomar Observatories Photo.)

within the interstellar medium. Almost without exception, each engulfs a star. The inference is that the involved star is the ultimate source of the nebula's radiation. If this is so, we might fairly expect that the extent to which the star can effectively illuminate the nebula will be proportional to the luminosity of the star. Though neither the true luminosity of the star nor the true extent of the nebula can be determined without knowing their common distance from us, the apparent brightness of the star and the apparent area of the nebula both vary inversely as the square of the distance from us. Consequently, no matter what their distance, the two should be proportional. Observations establish that this is substantially the case; we therefore conclude that the bright diffuse nebulae derive their light from a neighboring star or stars and are not self-luminous.

The probability that a dark cloud of interstellar gas and dust will be near enough to a bright star to become a diffuse nebula is estimated to be but one chance in 2000. Limitation of the distance to which a star can illuminate a nebula accounts for the frequent association of dark and bright nebulae. The dark nebulae are the silhouettes of nebular clouds too distant from the illuminating star. One of the most striking of the dark nebulae is the famous Horsehead Nebula in Orion (Fig. 225). It is, however, but one of the more prominent details in a large region of bright and dark nebulae; such nebulae tend to occur in clusters.

The diffuse nebulae and their associated stars are probably not physically connected, and the relation between them is fortuitous and transitory. Nevertheless the star determines the nature of the nebular spectrum, which may be either an emission or an absorption spectrum. Specifically, if the spectral type of the star is earlier than B1, the nebula will have an emission spectrum; if the spectrum of the star is later than B1, the nebula will have an absorption spectrum. The emission lines can be excited in nebular gas only by short wavelength radiation such as is provided in sufficient abundance only by stars at least as hot as those of type B0. Indeed, the ultraviolet radiations of B0 stars will create about them spheres of ionized hydrogen some hundred light years in radius. As a result, about two-thirds of the 300 or so diffuse nebulae presently known have been discovered on photographs taken in the light of the red line of hydrogen, a line which is produced by the extensive recombination of ionized hydrogen. We may at the same time conclude that the absence of interstellar emission lines in an area of the Milky Way is more probably evidence of the scarity of hot stars there than of a lack of interstellar gas.

The emission lines of a diffuse nebula are produced by the same processes as take place in the planetaries. On the other hand, the absorp-

Figure 226. CONE NEBULA. This photograph of the Cone Nebula by the 200-inch Hale reflector was made after a preliminary photograph with the Palomar Observatory 48-inch Schmidt telescope showed the nebula to be an object of special interest. It is in the constellation Monoceros. (Mt. Wilson-Palomar Observatories Photo.)

tion spectrum of a nebula is produced entirely by the embedded star and is seen by reflection from the nebular dust particles, just as sunlight reflected from the moon shows the solar spectrum. There can be little doubt that this is the case, for the absorption spectrum of a diffuse nebula is invariably of the same spectral type as that of the associated star; moreover, nebula and star agree very closely in color when emission lines are absent.

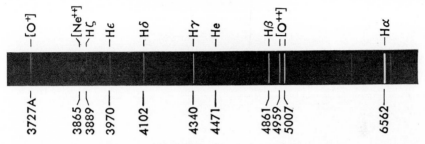

Figure 227. NEBULAR EMISSION SPECTRUM. This is the bright line spectrum of the Orion Nebula (Fig. 224) from about 3700 A to 6600 A (wavelengths shown below). The "nebulium" lines at wavelengths 4959 A and 5007 A are often designated as N_2 and N_1. Square brackets about an identification of element indicate that the associated lines are forbidden. (Courtesy of the Observatory of the University of Michigan.)

The existence of both *emission nebulae* and *reflection nebulae* shows that the nebulae are mixtures of dust and gas. A wide range of the local conditions of excitation, motion, and composition shows, however, that the mixture may be quite inhomogeneous. Curiously, the two types of nebulae show slightly different relations between their apparent area and the brightness of the enveloped star.

Emission nebulae appear to be of the same chemical composition as the normal stars of population I. There are observed in their spectra the normal lines of H, He, C, N, O, and possibly Si and Fe. In addition there have been identified forbidden lines of Fl, Ne, S, Cl, A, K, Ca, Fe, and possibly Ni.

The distances of the bright diffuse nebulae are found by estimating the amount of absorption of the light of the exciting star and making proper allowance for it in the spectroscopic parallax. For instance, the Orion nebula is thought to be at about 540 parsecs. If so, it must have a diameter of about 30 parsecs; all other known diffuse nebulae are smaller.

The intensity of the emission lines permits an estimate of the density of the nebular material. It is probably a few hundred atoms per cubic

Figure 228. MESSIER 16. Mixed bright and dark diffuse nebulosities make up the nebula M16 in Scutum. Note the small discrete absorbing masses that appear to have broken free of the main nebular clouds. (Mt. Wilson-Palomar Observatories Photo.)

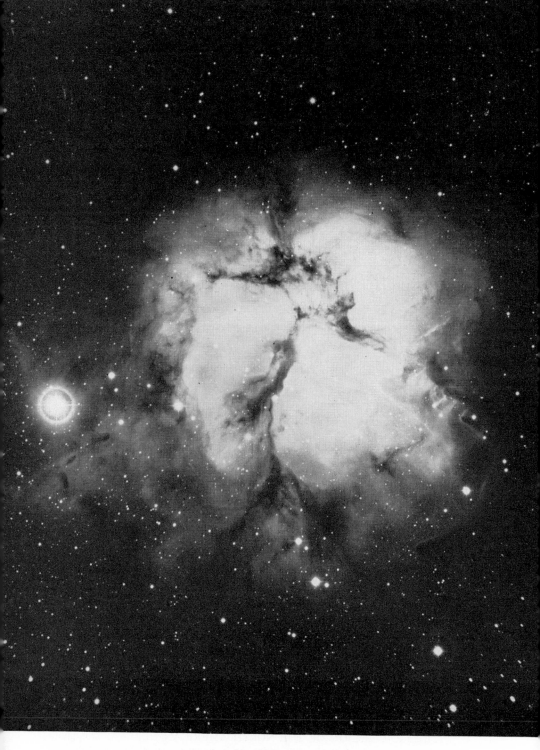

Figure 229. TRIFID NEBULA. The Trifid Nebula in Sagittarius is here photographed in red light with the 200-inch telescope. The membrane-like surfaces at the right are probably shock wave fronts in the nebular gas. (Mt. Wilson-Palomar Observatories Photo.)

Figure 230. REGION OF THE NORTH AMERICAN NEBULA. This photograph is a part of the first plate taken for the National Geographic Society-Palomar Observatory Sky Survey of that portion of the sky visible from southern California. Each region has been photographed in two colors by the 48-inch Schmidt telescope. This photograph shows an area in Cygnus near ξ Cygni (upper left). The Pelican Nebula is to the right of the North American Nebula. (National Geographic Society-Palomar Observatory Sky Survey.)

Figure 231. ROSETTE NEBULA. Another Sky Survey photograph shows the Rosette Nebula in Monoceros. (Mt. Wilson-Palomar Observatories Photo.)

inch, about $5/10^{22}$ the density of water. Such a typical density multiplied by a typical volume leads one to expect that a representative mass would be several hundred solar masses. The masses of some diffuse nebulae have been estimated as high as several thousand solar masses. These amounts are of the correct order of magnitude in view of the fact that the nebulae occupy volumes similar to those of the galactic clusters.

Many of the diffuse nebulae show irregular surfaces of discontinuity in brightness (Figs. 226, 228). These are probably shock-wave fronts or compression waves resulting from the collision of two clouds of inter-stellar matter or two parts of the same cloud. The radiation pressure from hot, newborn stars may also give rise to internal stresses, evident to the eye as bright fringes of gas at higher pressure, density, and temperature.

461 . . . .

The Structure of the Galaxy

Now that we have an acquaintance with the dimensions and dynamics of the galaxy and with the interstellar medium, it is possible to attempt a more synoptic view of the Milky Way. It is a system of some complexity, whose structural subtleties are only beginning to emerge.

At the heart of the system is the galactic nucleus, a vast cloud of population II stars about 15,000 light years thick and 30,000 light years in

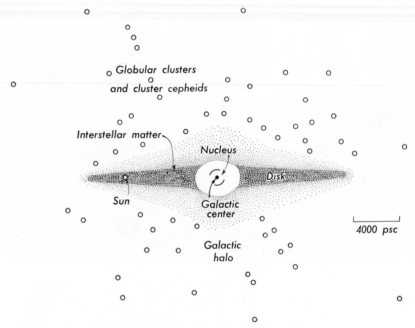

Figure 232. It is believed that a cross section of the Milky Way would look like the system schematized here. Its principal components are nucleus, disk, and halo or corona.

diameter. In the nucleus, the average density of stars is about twice that at the sun. Parts of the great star cloud in Sagittarius belong to the nucleus. The sun lies about 10,000 light years outside the nucleus in the strongly flattened portion of the stellar system known as the disk. The disk extends some 15,000 light years beyond the sun toward the anticenter, with individual stragglers found to nearly twice this distance.

Within the region of the disk are to be found the spiral arms. They are spaced about 6500 light years apart, are themselves about 2500 light years in diameter. The innermost arm is about 15,000 light years from the center of the galaxy; the second, 21,000 light years; and the third, 27,000 light years. The sun is on the inner edge of this Orion-Cygnus arm. Beyond it is a circular fourth arm at 35,000 light years and finally a faint, highly inclined, outermost arm at 40,000 light years from the galactic center. Probably the primary constituent of the arms are the gas clouds, which hatch stars as by-products. In the arms the interstellar gas has a density of about 25 atoms per cubic inch, whereas it is but a fifth or a tenth of this amount outside the arms.

The nucleus appears to be permeated by outward-streaming gas free of dust. In the sun's neighborhood, interstellar matter formed of 99 per cent gas and 1 per cent dust probably constitutes one-third to one-half of all matter. The interstellar clouds occupy about 5 per cent of the space within 150 parsecs of the galactic plane. Intimately associated with them are certain large, loose clusters of young stars called *associations* and the hot stars which produce the ionized hydrogen regions. Farther than 36,000 light years from the galactic center the density of the interstellar medium falls off sharply.

The spiral arms are the exclusive locus of population I stars in the galaxy. Since the arms' existence presupposes the presence of clouds of gas and dust, the interstellar medium must be recognized as the quintessential ingredient of population I; conversely, absence of interstellar matter marks population II. Actually, the arms of the galaxy share the region of the disk with stars of population II, which form a smooth featureless system increasing in brightness toward a brilliant nucleus at the galactic center. Surrounding both nucleus and disk is a symmetric spherical halo, or corona, of population II Cepheids and globular clusters. The over-all diameter of this enveloping corona is about 125,000 light years.

The galaxy's parts show distinctive dynamical differences. The arms move out from the galactic center with a speed that is a sizable fraction of the speed of rotation. The unknown cause of both the spiral arms and their expansion is conjectured to be large-scale magnetic forces. The trailing spiral arms have internal motions as well. Clouds collide with clouds, as some of the nebulous regions show, and with stellar associations and galactic clusters. The result is the disruption of the star groups. It is thought that galactic clusters may be the surviving, rich, central portions of former associations; it is even suggested that most associations become so dispersed after only one or two revolutions about the galactic center that they are the ultimate source of all population I stars of the general field.

In contrast to these motions, the system of globular clusters has a low speed of galactic rotation and shows no contraction or expansion. However, the individual clusters do revolve about the nucleus and each must have crossed the galactic plane several times since formation. The same may be said of the individual stars of the galactic corona.

There is an age difference, too, between the nucleus and corona on the one hand and the arms on the other. The bright population I stars in the arms have been born within a time not greater than their life spans. Though probably as much matter goes into the formation of luminous massive stars as into faint ones, the high-luminosity objects are scarce because of their relatively short lifetimes. Stars of type B2 are not over 40 million years old, A0 stars are less than 500 million years old, and F1 stars are under 4 billion years old. The presence of these stars only in the arms is, simultaneously, evidence for the impermanence of the present arms and the greater age of the galaxy's population II components. At the same time, spiral arms are such a common feature of galaxies in general that one is forced to conclude that arms continually re-form, even though their young stars wither rapidly and the arms themselves would be expected to wind up upon the nucleus and disintegrate.

With the differentiation of populations goes a difference of chemical compositions. Outside the stars and interstellar medium of the spiral arms, the abundance of elements heavier than hydrogen and helium is very much lower. Conversely, the 13 globular clusters known to belong to the nucleus-disk system, and therefore in greatest proximity to the arms, have in their spectra the greatest intensity of metal lines of any of the globular clusters.

Some of the correlations among the population distribution, dynamics, chemical composition, and star ages would be immediately apparent from outside the galaxy. For example, in the region of the arms, the population I stars of types B and O provide most of the luminosity per cubic parsec. In the corona and nucleus, however, the greatest contribution to the luminosity is from red giants of about luminosity 50. The arms of the galaxy will therefore appear blue and the nucleus red.

In the arms, where clouds of dust form numerous dark lanes, hundreds of stars condense almost simultaneously from the interstellar medium, forming stellar associations. The youthfulness of these star groups is attested to by the fact that no red giants are found in those clusters which have bright B stars. At the same time, neutral hydrogen is found in abundance in the Double Cluster in Perseus, the Pleiades, Coma Berenices, and Praesepe, which are astronomically young, but not in M 67 or NGC 188, which are very old. Plainly, interstellar matter is associated with young stars, and its absence is evidence of great age.

Such an index may be employed to decipher some of the outlines of the history of the galaxy. The ancient history of the Milky Way is to be learned from the oldest objects, the globular clusters. The globular clusters were probably formed from dense clouds of amorphous matter at large distances from the galactic center. Such regions of early star formation are now virtually free of dust. Not surprisingly, clusters 25,000 parsecs from the galactic center are larger than those 10,000 parsecs from the galactic center. The clusters having the weakest metallic spectrum lines, the most number of cluster variables, the widest range of peculiar velocities—in short, the most typically population II—are found at the greatest distance from the galactic plane.

Such evidence suggests that star formation first began far from the galactic plane. A protogalaxy of unformed matter would, like a protostar, contract and cool by radiating the energy generated in collisions. Such contraction would be arrested only by (1) the formation of stars, which would terminate the collisions and radiate the contractional energy piecemeal, or by (2) the existence of galactic rotation, which would allow contraction only in the direction perpendicular to the galactic plane. Therefore the process of star formation may well have survived to the present only in the vicinity of the galactic plane. A more slowly rotating galaxy or the less rapidly rotating portions of the Milky Way would have contracted to a greater degree before star formation was carried to completion. We may therefore conjecture that the globular clusters for the most part formed early from random condensations in the protogalaxy; the galactic nucleus formed long ago from the contracted, slowly rotating, central portion of the protogalaxy; the disk stars have waited on the formation of the disk by contraction perpendicular to the galactic plane; the arms are a contemporary formation from matter only recently arrived near the galactic plane. Such, at least, is a current working hypothesis.

B. OTHER GALAXIES

"And the great fleas themselves, in turn, have greater fleas to go on;
While these again have greater still, and greater still, and so on."

—DE MORGAN

It is plainly a hopeless effort to attempt any real subjective appreciation of a unit so incomprehensibly vast in extent and content as our galaxy. It is a most inadequate comparison, for example, to note that light we now receive from the galaxy's remoter corners was, in terms of distance come and distance remaining, practically on our threshold even in the days of Egypt's first Pharaohs; it is light of the generation of the ice age and the

Figure 233. SPIRAL GALAXY M51 IN CANES VENATICI. This beautiful spiral galaxy is seen almost squarely face on. The large bright mass at the bottom is a neighboring elliptical galaxy in the background. (Mt. Wilson-Palomar Observatories Photo.)

Figure 234. SPIRAL GALAXY M81 IN URSA MAJOR. This galaxy, also plainly a spiral, is more compact than M51. (Mt. Wilson-Palomar Observatories Photo.)

467 . . . .

mastodon and the saber-tooth. One can only dully sense the magnitude of the fact that the combined radiation from the entire galaxy is about 5 billion times the sun's, whose expenditure of energy in 1 second could light and heat the whole earth for more than 70 years. The mind's eye is totally incapable of picturing the galaxy's hundred billion suns, from each of which could be fashioned a third of a million earths. How little reserve is left to it, then, to cope with the fact that the space which our galaxy occupies is only a hundred-trillionth (10^{-14}) of the part of the universe thus far known, that through these awesome wastes of space are scattered billions of comparable systems to at least five billion light years in any direction. These systems are the *external galaxies,* known also as *extragalactic nebulae.*

Types of Galaxies

Galaxies are of three general types: spirals, ellipticals, and irregulars. The observed pinwheel symmetry of the Andromeda galaxy and the inferred similarity of the Milky Way show them to be spirals. The Andromeda galaxy's two attendants are elliptical galaxies, for they have no arms, show no structural detail, and with others of the class jointly vary in projected outline from perfect roundness to strong lenticularity. The Milky Way's two attendants, the Large and Small Magellanic Clouds, are probably irregulars, though their proper classification is not unanimously agreed upon. At any rate, irregulars are characterized by lack of symmetry, either spiral or elliptical.

The statistics of the several types of galaxies are somewhat uncertain because of the possible operation of selection effects which could work to favor notice of one type rather than another. Notwithstanding, current estimates assign 5 per cent of all galaxies to the irregular type, 23 per cent to the elliptical type, and the remaining 72 per cent to the spiral type. If any revision is needed, it will probably increase the proportion of ellipticals. About one galaxy in a hundred shows some marked visible peculiarity. Some 5 per cent are members of physical pairs or multiple systems. Only in 150 galaxies can individual stars be seen with present instruments.

The spirals are divided into two groups, the *normal* and the *barred* spirals. Among normal spirals the arms attach directly to a central nucleus, whereas the arms of barred spirals spring from the ends of a "bar" passing symmetrically through the nucleus. There appear to be twice as many normal as barred spirals. Among themselves, the normal and barred spirals differ chiefly in degree of compactness (Fig. 237).

Figure 239. NGC 147 IN ANDROMEDA. This galaxy is one of the Local Group. It is therefore near enough to have been resolved into individual stars, as this photograph by the 200-inch Hale telescope shows. (Mt. Wilson-Palomar Observatories Photo.)

Figure 240. THE GREAT ANDROMEDA NEBULA, M31. One of the most magnificent of all galaxies, M31's bright nucleus may be seen with the naked eye. The arms, however, may be seen only on photographs taken with large telescopes. The galaxy's two companions are dwarf elliptical galaxies. (Mt. Wilson-Palomar Observatories Photo.)

Elliptical galaxies may be ordered according to degree of elongation, having ratios of maximum to minimum diameters ranging from 1 to 4. This must represent a true variation in outline, for the relative numbers of the different shapes cannot all be accounted for as projections of a single form.

Our own galaxy is prototypical of an intermediate spiral. For an actual picture of such a galaxy from the outside, however, we must turn to the very similar Andromeda galaxy. An estimated 98 per cent of the mass of

Figure 241. STELLAR POPULATIONS I AND II. Galaxy NGC 205, companion to M31, contains pure population II stars. The photograph of it on the left was made in yellow light and shows some of its brightest individual stars, red giants. On the right is a resolved portion of the arms of M31, photographed in blue light and showing individual giant and supergiant stars of population I. The brightest population I stars are about 100 times more luminous than the brightest population II stars. Both photographs are peppered with numerous foreground stars belonging to our own galaxy. (Mt. Wilson-Palomar Observatories Photo.)

this galaxy consists of stars of population II; the most of these are in its nucleus, the rest forming a disk which extends far beyond the arms. A somewhat flattened corona of about 300 globular clusters envelopes both. The over-all dimensions of the Andromeda galaxy are about twice those of the Milky Way.

The spiral arms of the Andromeda galaxy were the first resolved extragalactic systems other than the relatively nearby Magellanic Clouds. They are predominantly, though not entirely, of population I. The most luminous population I stars in them are about 100 times brighter than the brightest stars of population II; for this reason the arms were resolved long before the nucleus and disk, which remained unresolved until very recently. For the same reason, the arms are prominent on blue-sensitive plates (and in the light of the red emission line of hydrogen), relatively inconspicuous in photographs in yellow light. Only in the arms does one find blue supergiant stars, dust, hydrogen emission lines from interstellar gas clouds, diffuse nebulae, and galactic clusters. There are four arms on the north side, five on the south, and two in the central region. They have an average width of 2500 light years and an average separation of 10,000 light years. The arms contribute less than one-fifth the total luminosity. Gas comprises only about 1 per cent of the entire galaxy. However, radio observations show that this galaxy and other spirals, such as M51 and M81, are embedded in a halo of thin neutral hydrogen which is much larger than the visible galaxy. The radio corona shows less central condensation than the corona of globular clusters.

Since it is arms which make the spirals, it might be said that it is lack of arms which make the ellipticals. Indeed, the luminosity distribution within ellipticals is similar to that of spiral nuclei. They are therefore of pure population II. They are classified among themselves according to their apparent elongation, the more lenticular being the more numerous.

The contents of irregular galaxies may be judged from that of the Magellanic Clouds. These objects appear much more open and less compact than ellipticals or the inner parts of spirals. They contain a relatively small proportion of population II stars. On the other hand, nearly half their total mass is gas and dust. In fact, the Magellanic Clouds have been shown to be connected by a bridge of such material, linking them in a manner visible only to radio telescopes.

A strange pair of galaxies, the Sculptor and Fornax systems, cannot be classed in any of the standard categories. They lack structure, yet possess symmetry, and appear open but give no evidence of characteristic population I objects such as supergiants, galactic clusters, or bright nebulae.

The causal basis of the present classification scheme is not known. It appears both significant and suggestive, however, that diffuse matter is absent from ellipticals, comprises a few per cent of spirals, and makes up as much as half of irregulars. This is at the same time a sequence of decreasing average age.

The Distances of the Galaxies

The existence of external galaxies has long been known, but their status as independent systems comparable to our own has been generally recognized only since the 1920's. Only then was the distance of any galaxy established even approximately. This was first accomplished by the discovery of a number of typical Cepheids in the Andromeda galaxy (M31). Since these stars' luminosities can be gotten from the period-luminosity relation, and since they are very faint, it is concluded that M31 is at a distance of 1,700,000 light years. The same method was applied almost simultaneously to several other galaxies and with comparable results. The Cepheids thus

Figure 242. VARIABLES IN M31. Two photographs of a resolved portion of the Andromeda Nebula show by markers the location of two variable stars. Their change of brightness is clearly evident. (Mt. Wilson-Palomar Observatories Photo.)

Figure 243. NOVA IN M101. The photograph on the right shows the galaxy M101 as it was on June 9, 1950. A similar photograph made on February 7, 1961, shows the presence of a nova, marked by the arrow on the left. (Mt. Wilson-Palomar Observatories Photo.)

provided the first conclusive demonstration of the galaxies' independence of the Milky Way.

The nearer galaxies, in turn, provided vital information about the Cepheids. We now know that Cepheids of populations I and II have distinct period-luminosity relations. This was not apparent, however, until both types could be observed more or less side by side; indeed, the very distinction between the two populations was originally unknown. Not until the 200-inch Hale telescope attempted to observe cluster Cepheids in M31 was it realized that population I Cepheids are more luminous than population II Cepheids of the same period by four or more times. As a consequence the Cepheids first observed in M31 were actually at least four times more luminous than thought; hence the distance must be twice or three times what it was first estimated.

The revision of the distance estimate of M31 simultaneously resolved several discrepancies. The luminosities of globular clusters and of novae at maximum, which had seemed to be less than those of similar objects in the Milky Way, now became comparable. At the same time, the Milky

Way was deposed from the unlikely eminence of the largest galaxy in its general neighborhood and M31 was installed in its stead; this embarrassment now plagues Andromedan astronomers. Observation of the Magellanic Clouds has since confirmed the disparate luminosities of the Cepheids

Figure 244. THE LARGE MAGELLANIC CLOUD. Nearest of any galaxy is the Large Magellanic Cloud in the constellation Dorado near the south celestial pole. It is also one of the largest irregular galaxies. (Courtesy Harvard College Observatory.)

of the two populations. It also establishes the Large Cloud at about 190,000 light years, the Small Cloud at about 160,000 light years.

Even the most luminous Cepheids can be observed in only a couple of dozen of the nearest galaxies. Therefore other methods have had to be devised to supplement and extend the measurement of galactic distances. It is natural to turn next to the observation of the very luminous, blue supergiants and to the normal novae at their maxima; these may be depended on to have luminosities of 50,000 to 100,000. An assumed luminosity and an observed apparent brightness imply the galaxy's distance. The observation of supergiants is clearly limited to not-too-distant irregulars and spirals; novae may be observed in ellipticals as well.

This method, too, has its pitfalls. What was assumed in the early investigations to have been a supergiant star has been shown in subsequent more careful scrutiny to be a supergiant and its associated region of ionized hydrogen. Again, an underestimate of luminosity has resulted in an underestimate of distance. This second error has compounded the first, so that the original determinations of the distances of remote galaxies have had to be increased five- to tenfold.

Though an occasional supernova will provide an index of the distance of a galaxy more remote than the 150 or so in which individual stars may be seen, most galaxies' distances must be estimated on the strength of statistical results compiled from the nearer ones. For example, it is found that within a factor of two, most galaxies have a luminosity of a few hundred million times the sun's. On the average, then, apparent faintness is a true measure of distance. However, results by this method are only statistically true, for the nearer galaxies show a range of intrinsic brightness of about 1000 to 1.

Of a similar nature is the method of estimating distance from apparent diameter. This is possible because galaxies of the same kind (spirals, for example) are uniformly of the same order of size. Thus, on the average, apparent smallness indicates true distance. This criterion is particularly reliable for those galaxies which are strong radio sources. Allowance must be made, however, for the fact that spirals differ in diameter by a factor of 5 to 1, all galaxies by a factor of 15 to 1.

The Vital Statistics of Galaxies

When the distances of galaxies are known, it then becomes possible to determine their respective vital statistics. The Milky Way, with its diameter of roughly 100,000 light years, is found to be a giant galaxy, for example; the even larger Andromeda galaxy, occupying an area as great as 70 full moons on the sky, is one of the largest galaxies known. At the other extreme, dwarf ellipticals may be only 7000 light years or so in diameter. Most irregular systems are not much larger. Generally speaking, spirals have diameters in the range 15 to 20 thousand light years and are one-third to one-half larger than ellipticals.

The range in luminosities is somewhat greater than the range in

Figure 245. NGC 4565 IN COMA BERENICES. An edgewise view of any spiral galaxy would probably be similar to what is shown in this photograph of NGC 4565 in Coma Berenices. Note the dark obscuring material similar to that near the central plane of our own galaxy. (Mt. Wilson-Palomar Observatories Photo.)

diameters. A giant galaxy like M31 has a luminosity of about 9 billion suns; an average spiral like M33 has a luminosity of about 1.5 billion suns. A representative elliptical galaxy has a luminosity not much different from 500 million. The Large Magellanic Cloud, which is quite outsize for an irregular galaxy, has a luminosity between 1 and 2 billion times the sun's. Most irregulars are only a few per cent as bright. The greatest and the least differ by a factor of about 1000.

Only gross estimates of the masses of galaxies are possible. One method of obtaining them is similar to the method used in our own galaxy. From observation of the radial velocity of like points on opposite sides of the nucleus of spirals, they are known to rotate about an axis through the nucleus and perpendicular to the central plane, the arms trailing; presumably elliptical galaxies rotate also, since they are flattened. A particular speed of rotation at a definite distance from the axis implies a specific period of rotation there; observed periods range from 5 million to more than 100

481 . . . .

million years. Kepler's harmonic law then gives an estimate of the mass of the galaxy. A second method utilizes observations of the gravitational effects of nearby galaxies on each other, somewhat as the masses of the planets may be compared when their mutual perturbations are known.

The giant M31 is thus estimated to have a mass of 300 billion suns, a dwarf spiral only about 5 billion. The mass of an average elliptical is about 70 billion. The mass of the Large Magellanic Cloud is probably between 2 and 10 billion solar masses, but most irregulars are only a small fraction of this. By comparing the masses and luminosities of similar objects, it is apparent that irregular galaxies give the most luminosity per unit mass and ellipticals give the least. This is no doubt related to the proportion of population I stars in the different types, for the population I stars consume hydrogen and liberate energy at the highest rate.

The age of a galaxy is to be judged by the age of its oldest objects. Our own galaxy, for example, is probably about as old as the oldest globular cluster—10 or perhaps 20 billion years. It has also been noted that galactic rotation would have achieved a complete dissolution of all the galactic clusters in not more than 50 rotations ("cosmic years") unless these clusters are being replenished at an improbable rate. This seems to indicate a maximum age of 10 billion years or so. For comparison, the color-brightness diagram of the one elliptical thus far observed in sufficient detail shows it to be similar to that of the globular clusters and, by inference, of the same general age. There is, in fact, no evidence for galaxies much older than this. The suggestion is that galaxies may not be much older than a few tens of billions of years old at most.

The Distribution of the Galaxies

To determine the larger structure of the universe is, in a considerable measure, to learn the distribution of the galaxies. The first step in this is a consideration of the galaxies' apparent distribution on the celestial sphere. Their apparent distribution is dominated by a symmetry with respect to the galactic plane. Galaxies appear in greatest numbers near the galactic poles, thin out continually in areas progressively nearer the galactic plane. In fact, the galactic plane marks the center of a belt of a number of degrees of galactic latitude in width in which no galaxies appear at all; this region is known as the *zone of avoidance*.

Contrary to what this term may suggest, the galaxies' avoidance of this zone is more apparent than real; it is the result of virtually complete obscuration of extragalactic objects by the interstellar medium, which is most extensive and most effective in and near the galactic plane. The correctness of this interpretation is confirmed by the presence of a few small "windows"—regions of less obscuration—through which some galaxies can be seen in low galactic latitudes.

As a by-product of this interpretation we are able to use counts of galaxies to any limiting faintness to determine the average amount of absorption by the interstellar medium. The difference in the frequencies of equally faint galaxies at two different galactic latitudes is an indication of how much light is cut off in the additional distance which it traverses through the interstellar medium at lower latitudes. This not only supple-

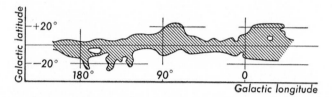

Figure 246. The shaded portion of the figure indicates the region of sky where no galaxies are observed. Galactic absorbing clouds produce this "zone of avoidance." Note the existence of small "windows" within the zone of avoidance. Portions of the Milky Way not observable in middle northern latitudes are not included.

ments galactic research on the interstellar medium but also enables us to say by what amount the light of galaxies in any part of the sky has been dimmed. This has to be known in computing galaxies' true distances from Cepheids, supergiants, or apparent brightness, for example.

Except for the Magellanic Clouds, M31 in Andromeda, and M33 in Triangulum, all galaxies are too faint to be seen with the unaided eye. It is therefore in purely relative terms that we speak of "bright" and "faint" galaxies; the faintest within reach of the largest telescopes are more than 10 million times fainter than the eye alone can see. Noticeable particularly among the brighter galaxies is a tendency to group or cluster. Let us see to what degree this is a significant feature of the universe of galaxies.

We may first note that the Milky Way is the second largest of two dozen galaxies forming a cluster known as the Local Group. All members of the group are within about 2 million light years of us. The most remote member is M33. The next nearest system outside the local group is a spiral 8 million light years away. The group contains two triple systems—the Milky Way and the two Magellanic Clouds for one, and M31 and its two satellites as the other. If the local group is at all representative of clusters of galaxies, it must be concluded that dwarf galaxies comprise the large majority of systems.

Figure 247. THE CORONA BOREALIS CLUSTER OF GALAXIES. This spectacular cluster of galaxies contains about 400 members within an area of sky equal to that covered by the full moon. Most of the galaxies visible here are elliptical galaxies; elliptical galaxies are more easily photographed than spiral galaxies of the same luminosity because of the ellipticals' greater compactness. (Mt. Wilson-Palomar Observatories Photo.)

Surveys of galaxies in general show that clustering is indeed the rule rather than the exception; though inhomogeneities in apparent distribution could be attributed to obscuration in low galactic latitudes, they must reflect real density variations in high latitudes. To a limit of brightness one two-hundred-fifty thousandth as bright as the faintest object the naked eye can see, there is an average of one cluster of galaxies per square degree. Clusters are thus about 100 times more common than was estimated from the first surveys, for the clustering of faint galaxies becomes apparent only on large-scale survey photographs made with wide-angle cameras. It now seems probable that the universe may be divided into cluster cells like suds are divided into bubbles. An average cell would have an estimated volume of 10 billion cubic light years.

Clusters of galaxies may not stand at the top of the natural organizational hierarchy. Recent evidence indicates that the local group is stationed at the outskirts of a cluster of clusters of galaxies—a supergalaxy. The supergalaxy is 40 to 50 million light years across, and several million light years thick. Its estimated membership runs to several tens of thousands of clusters of galaxies. It is centered at the Virgo cluster, some 15 million light years away. Radio observations of the supergalaxy corroborate the optical ones. The strong flattening of the system implies that it is rotating.

Similar supergalaxies have been found in Hydra and in Pavo-Indus. One supergalaxy in the southern hemisphere stretches 50° across the sky. Still more distant supergalaxies are coming to light.

Clusters can be used to supply valuable statistics concerning the range and distribution of sizes, luminosities, forms, velocities, etc.; for, because members of a particular cluster are all at substantially the same distance, apparent relationships indicate true relationships. Rich, compact clusters are almost spherical. The total population of rich clusters may run as high as 10,000 galaxies. In the Coma cluster there are about 500 galaxies in a region less than 3 million light years in diameter; in the Virgo cluster there are a thousand galaxies in only twice the volume of the local group.

An interesting feature of the densest clusters is the fact that they have few spirals and many galaxies which are described as armless spirals. These clusters also show clouds of dark intergalactic matter. The probable explanation seems to be that galaxies in dense clusters are especially prone to mutual collisions. In spite of what one might expect, even a direct encounter of two galaxies is not a world-shaking cataclysm since the volume of space actually occupied by their respective stars is but a tiny fraction of the total volume. Instead, the two sets of stars intermingle like the

Figure 248. COLLIDING GALAXIES. Galaxies NGC 4038 and 4039 are here seen in the process of collision. Note that they mutually distort each other. (Mt. Wilson-Palomar Observatories Photo.)

particles of two wisps of smoke. However, the diffuse matter in each is partially combed out and left betwixt the two.

A considerable number of collisions is required to sweep a galaxy entirely clean. In a dense cluster, however, most galaxies suffer enough collisions to rid themselves of interstellar matter. For example, a galaxy moving centrally through the Coma cluster could expect to experience from 5 to 30 collisions. In such a cluster, at least two collisions should be in progress at any time. Even outside clusters, collisions will occur, though on the average the distance between galaxies is 3 million light years. Among the 2 billion galaxies within 250 million light years of us, there should be an estimated ten collisions now in progress.

We are in fact witness to a number of collisions of galaxies. One of the best-known colliding pairs is designated Cygnus A, at a distance of about 270 million light years. In such a collision, the respective gas

Figure 249. CYGNUS *A* RADIO SOURCE. This pair of colliding galaxies is the strongest discrete extragalactic source of radio signals. The nuclei of the two galaxies are only 3000 light years apart. (Mt. Wilson-Palomar Observatories Photo.)

clouds encounter each other at relative speeds of hundreds to thousands of miles per second. They are thereby heated to temperatures of a million to a hundred million degrees absolute. As a result, almost half the light from Cygnus A is due to wide emission lines of interstellar hydrogen and forbidden lines of highly ionized O, Ne, S, and Fe. Were we within one of these galaxies, the glowing clouds of colliding gases would be so bright as to mask all celestial objects but the sun, moon, planets, and the few brightest stars.

The nuclei of the two galaxies of Cygnus A are only 3000 light years apart; such close encounters occur probably not oftener than once in a thousand. Such a collision is no mere transient display, moreover. It requires 100,000 years to enact.

Cygnus A would almost certainly have gone unnoticed, however, but for its very strong radio radiations. It was the first discrete radio source

487 . . . .

to be discovered by radio telescopes and remains the strongest of all the more than 200 strong extragalactic sources, the second most intense discrete source in all the sky. The radio output of Cygnus A is 10 times as great as its visible light. Such an enormous amount of energy could come only from the energy of collision. The mechanism by which this energy is converted to radio radiation is conjecturally the synchrotron mechanism such as takes place in the turbulent gases of the Crab Nebula and probably in the radio corona of our galaxy. Though only about two dozen galaxies have been identified as strong extragalactic radio sources, it seems reasonable that radio galaxies are the most common form of discrete source.

Cygnus A is 3000 times as strong as the faintest sources detectable with present radio telescopes. Such sources could therefore be seen to far greater distances, distances much greater than are penetrated by the largest existing optical telescopes. This is the ultimate importance of such colliding galaxies for studies of the structure of the universe. It is highly significant, then, that discrete extragalactic radio sources show no preferential distribution in direction. This is often stated by saying that on the very large scale, the universe appears *isotropic,* the same in all directions. Also arguing for uniformity on the large scale is the observation that clusters of galaxies seem to be the same at all distances and their brightest members are of about the same luminosity.

The Red Shift

Since galaxies are all faint, obtaining their spectra is a decidedly delicate observational task. Even with the 200-inch Hale telescope, the spectra obtained are only a fifth of an inch long and may require 30 hours' exposure time. The spectra are qualitatively similar to dwarf G stars; lines in them may be measured to an accuracy of about 0.5 per cent. Measures of about 600 galactic spectra have led to a most astonishing and unexpected result. *The spectra of all distant galaxies are shifted to the red and by an amount which increases with distance!* This is known as the *law of red shifts.*

The spectral shift is indistinguishable from a Doppler effect. In Cygnus A it has been observed both at optical wavelengths and in the 21-centimeter radio line of neutral hydrogen. The shift is faithfully proportional to wavelength over this entire 500,000 to 1 range. Its cause is therefore presumed to be high velocity of recession.

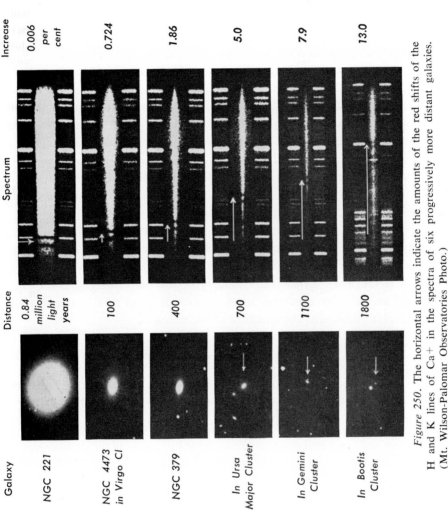

Wavelength Increase	Spectrum	Distance		Galaxy
0.006 per cent		0.84 million light years		NGC 221
0.724		100		NGC 4473 in Virgo Cl
1.86		400		NGC 379
5.0		700		In Ursa Major Cluster
7.9		1100		In Gemini Cluster
13.0		1800		In Bootis Cluster

Figure 250. The horizontal arrows indicate the amounts of the red shifts of the H and K lines of Ca+ in the spectra of six progressively more distant galaxies. (Mt. Wilson-Palomar Observatories Photo.)

Some concern is sometimes felt that such an interpretation may be suspect in the face of the magnitude of the shift and the implied recessional velocity. The greatest shift thus far measured is a 46 per cent increase in wavelength! Even with allowance for a correction due to relativity theory, this still requies the galaxy to be receding at 42 per cent of the velocity of light, or 78,000 miles per second. From another point of view, however, this is not so excessive, for an average galaxy would require a quarter of a million years to traverse its own diameter, even at this rate.

Two other features of the red shift are of considerably greater moment. First, the red shift increases with distance. To the limit of present observations, the shift appears to be directly proportional to distance. The shift amounts to a velocity increase at the rate of 12 to 15 miles per second every million light years. This means that if the galaxies are limited to speeds less than the velocity of light, as the theory of relativity requires, then they must at the same time be limited to distances less than about 14 billion light years. The red shifts thus seem to imply a very important limitation to the distribution of the galaxies.

The second important feature of the red shifts is their isotropy; i.e., there is no evidence that the law of red shifts depends upon direction. The galaxies appear to recede in the same fashion in every sector of the sky. This is the major dynamical symmetry of the universe. The law of red shifts and its two important implications will be of vital concern when we seek to determine the structure of the universe.

QUESTIONS

1. What is the apparent distribution of the stars on the sky? Explain the relation of the galactic coordinate system to the apparent distribution of the stars.

2. An uncritical glance at the sky shows the Milky Way circling it more or less uniformly in a great circle arc. What precedents in the development of astronomy should make one doubt that we are at the center of the Milky Way, as we appear to be?

3. From the names of the stars identified in Figure 213, list the constellations through which the winter Milky Way passes in the northern hemisphere. Make a similar list from Figure 214 for the summer Milky Way. (Consult the necessary sky maps at the end of the book.)

4. What features of the galaxy can be learned from the distribution of high-luminosity objects? How do the globular clusters and cluster-type Cepheids permit an estimate of the dimensions of the galaxy? Why will other types

of objects not do as well? What is the presumed size and shape of the galaxy? What is our position in it?

5. What support is there for the hypothesis of galactic rotation? How may galactic rotation be used (a) to determine approximate distances of remote stars, and (b) to determine the mass of the galaxy and the distance to the galactic center? What is the sun's velocity of galactic rotation? Its period?

6. What is the evidence for the interstellar gas? What is its distribution? Density? Composition? How may interstellar absorption lines help to determine the approximate distances of some stars?

7. The density of air is about 1.25×10^{-2} gram per cubic centimeter. How much denser is it than the interstellar gas about χ^2 Orionis?

8. What is the 21-centimeter line? Why is it so important? What does observation of it show about the structure of the galaxy?

9. If a drop of ink is placed in a glass of water, it soon spreads through the water. From this analogy, present an argument against the possibility that the dark areas in Figure 222 are regions free of stars.

10. What is the evidence for the existence of interstellar dust? How is the dust distributed? How do galactic clusters give evidence of the existence of interstellar dust?

11. How are the distances of dust clouds determined? Their absorptive powers? Draw a neat schematic Wolf diagram which might have been obtained in a section of sky where there is a thin but strongly absorbing dust cloud at moderate distance and a thick moderately absorbing cloud at great distance.

12. Why does interstellar dust redden passing starlight? How is the amount of this reddening expressed? How is the average size of the dust particles estimated? Their chemical compositions? What is the probable density of instellar dust?

13. How is it known that the diffuse nebulae do not generate the energy they radiate? What kinds of spectra do the diffuse nebulae show? What accounts for the differences?

14. Of what order of size are the diffuse nebulae? How are their distances determined? Their densities? Their chemical compositions?

15. What are the interpenetrating parts of the galaxy? How do they compare in distribution, content, chemical composition, and motion? Draw a neat schematic cross-section of the galaxy and label it with all principal dimensions. How may the internal structure be accounted for?

16. What types of galaxies are there? Describe each as to appearance and content. Cite prototypes of each. What are their respective diameters, masses, and luminosities?

17. Describe the methods of determining galaxies' distances. Show how errors in the primary methods may be compounded in the secondary methods.

18. How do galaxies appear to be distributed on the sky? What distribution do they probably have to an observer in the Andromeda galaxy? In an elliptical galaxy? To an intergalactic observer?

19. How common are clusters of galaxies? Superclusters? Why are dense clusters deficient in spiral galaxies? Describe a collision of two galaxies. Are any such collisions now observable? How?

20. What is the law of red shifts? What is the largest red shift thus far observed? How does the red shift suggest a limit for the age of the universe? What is the numerical value of this limit?

21. Why is isotropy an important property of the universe? In what two ways is it demonstrated observationally?

chapter 11
Cosmology, Cosmogony and Epistemology

• • •

A. THE STRUCTURE OF THE UNIVERSE

"That's just what I ask myself. I ask myself, What?"
"What do you think you'll answer?"

—A. A. MILNE

The Cosmological Problem

The large-scale universe is a universe of galaxies. It exhibits an isotropy in the apparent distribution of the galaxies and in the red shifts; galaxies probably appear in equal numbers in all directions, and their red shifts are the same in all directions. Such is the view of the observable universe as witnessed by an observer here and now. It constitutes what is called his *world picture*. The world picture is but one frame in an endless reel. It is supplied by the observational cosmologist, who acquaints us with the characters of the drama. From this single frame the theoretical cosmologist seeks to deduce the course of the action and the plot, if any.

This is not as idle or hopeless an ambition as it might seem at first sight; for, unlike the two-dimensional snapshot from a movie sequence, the world picture is four-dimensional. It spans the customary three dimensions of space and reaches back from the observer into time. Thus galaxies seen at a distance of a million light years are also seen as they were a million years ago. The world picture therefore shows the universe not as it is but as it was in each locality at a time in the past as long ago as its distance in light years from us. It is a sort of composite picture of space through times that range backward from the present.

This may be of advantage in that the past may be seen in the distance. Inorganic evolution may in principle be witnessed in a complete and detailed world picture, though in practice the world picture is as yet rather too sketchy for such purposes. On the other hand, the world picture requires translation into the *world map* before one can say how the universe is constituted. The world map is constructed mentally or mathematically so that each galaxy is located at its present position rather than at one which it held in the possibly distant past. For example, a galaxy which appears to be one million light years away actually occupied such a position a million years ago; a million years' recession has carried it to a present position which must be calculated from its recessional velocity.

The momentary structure of the universe is subsumed in the world map of that instant. The history of the universe is revealed in the unfolding of a succession of world maps. Knowledge of the world map therefore becomes a primary objective in the study of the cosmos. Clearly, two problems face the cosmologist: (1) What is the world map at any instant? (2) What governs the succession of world maps from each instant to the next?

We may illustrate a naïve method of attack upon these questions by supposing that all galaxies are of the same luminosity, that the luminosity is constant in time, and that the brightness of a galaxy is inversely proportional to the square of its distance. Galaxies' distribution in depth may then be inferred from their respective apparent brightnesses; specifically, a quartering of the brightness signifies a doubling of the distance. But doubling the radius of the volume under consideration increases the volume eightfold; hence, if the universe is homogeneous, the total number of galaxies brighter than any specified limit should increase eight times when that limit is quartered. Actual counts give a rate of increase less than eight times. This would seem to indicate a thinning out of galaxies at great distance. Such a conclusion, if vindicated by a more sophisticated analysis, would be disturbing. It would place us at the point of greatest density, the very hub of the universe. However, the entire history of astronomy argues against any such assumption of privileged position. The origin of the difficulty may in this case be attributed to neglect. Of the two most fundamental observed properties of the universe—that it is isotropic and that galaxies obey the law of red shifts—we have used only the former; let us take some account of the latter.

By the law of red shifts, one knows that photons from a distant galaxy will be reduced in frequency and by an amount which increases with distance. Since the photon's energy is proportional to its frequency, the radiations of distant galaxies will be less energetic than if they had not been red-shifted. They will on this account appear fainter in a photograph, and the effect will be exaggerated by the customary blue-sensitive photographic emulsions. Farther galaxies will be progressively dimmed by this *energy effect* and continually more of the fainter ones will fall beyond any set limit of faintness. When this effect is recognized and compensated for, the corrected counts of galaxies appear consistent with a distribution which is uniform in depth.

Though the original difficulty may now seem to be solved, the agent of solution has brought us to a fresh dilemma: Can we interpret the red shifts in galaxies' spectra as genuine Doppler effects indicating recession? It may seem strange now to question the Doppler principle, of which we have made so much use. The alternative is also strange. For, if the distant galaxies are actually receding from us at very high speed, their motion would produce not only a shift of wavelength but also an attenuation of the beam reaching us, since the beam would be stretched out by recession and fewer photons would arrive each second. The result would be an additional dimming over and above that produced by the energy effect. If the galaxies thus suffer dimming by the *attenuation effect* due to recession, it too must be compensated for in the analysis of the galaxy counts. Allowance for both energy and attenuation effects leads to the conclusion that the galaxies actually increase in numbers at great distance! Again we appear to be set at the mid-point of the universe, but now at the point of least density.

The seeming predicament into which we have been led is not as serious as our former one. Several cosmological theories which we shall consider are able to extricate us from the embarrassment of privilege. Leaving aside for the moment consideration of these theories, let us assume that at least we have constructed a world map. We may consider the second of the principal cosmological problems: What changes will occur in the world map in the course of time?

Changes on a world-wide scale would require very long times to become observable. They can therefore be anticipated only with the aid of some cosmological theory which states a possible form of the laws governing matter for the universe at large. The incompleteness of the present world picture and of the world map constructed from it renders it impossible now to frame world-wide laws unambiguously or uniquely. As a result, several theories vie for acceptance. A simple consideration may perhaps reconcile one to the legitimacy of this ambiguity. Thus, on the one hand, one may suppose that the recessional velocity of a remote galaxy will be the same in the future as it is at present; the universe would in this case be undergoing uniform expansion. On the other hand, one may equally well assume that as a galaxy recedes to greater distances, it will at all times have whatever velocity is at present observed to be characteristic of that distance. Since greater velocities are associated with greater distances, this would imply an accelerated expansion of the universe. Plainly, the universe obeys different laws in the two cases.

The cosmologist's problem is, therefore, to state a set of laws or principles whose operation is consistent with the present incomplete world picture. It is the goal of observational cosmology to discriminate that theory which alone describes the actual universe. The selection will be made on the basis of the fidelity of the complete theoretical world picture which each theory implies. As observations supply ever more detail for comparison, fewer theories will survive. Let us consider three cosmological theories of special interest. Each reproduces some of the features of the world picture more successfully than its rivals, fails in others. Whether any one of them will prove to be the foundation of an ultimate cosmological theory remains to be seen.

Cosmological Theories

THE COSMOLOGICAL PRINCIPLE

If one could somehow come into possession of a complete and detailed world picture, he could perhaps in principle frame the correct cosmological theory at the outset. The actual incomplete world picture, however, requires to be supplemented in some essential manner. Though different theories do this in different ways, all make use at some point of a premise which has come to be known as the *cosmological principle*. The cosmological principle is a statement of world-wide uniformity. For example, one form of it states that all observers to whom the universe is isotropic will witness identical world histories. This is a refined and sophisticated enunciation of the Copernican doctrine that we may not claim for ourselves a position of special privilege; aside from differences of detail, others will see substantially not only what we see at any moment but also the same historical sequence as the universe evolves. A modified form of the cosmological principle, perhaps immodestly called the *perfect cosmological principle,* goes further and states that all observers to whom the universe appears isotropic (equivalent observers) will have an unvarying world picture. It asserts that not only can we not claim any special vantage point in the universe but that neither can we suppose that we live in any favored era; individual objects in the universe will change with time, but the universe as a whole will not.

The cosmological principle, whatever particular form is made use of, stresses the identity of the world views of equivalent observers everywhere.

It supposes that a cosmologist situated in the Andromeda nebula or an elliptical of the Hydra cluster would, like a cosmologist on the earth, find about himself a universe of galaxies obeying the law of red shifts and distributed isotropically. It is the core of the cosmological principle that such representative observers are in principle freely interchangeable. Such interchangeability is a minimum guarantee of the impartiality and disinterestedness of an impersonal, inanimate nature.

The significance of the cosmological principle for a cosmological theory lies precisely in the principle's implication that an interchange of equivalent observers would effect no essential changes in their respective world maps. Though the actual exchange of observers located in widely separated galaxies is utterly out of the question, casting a cosmological theory into a form which would permit the interchange to be made mentally is both desirable and feasible. Such interchanges are commonly made by the mathematical device of *coordinate transformations*. A coordinate transformation is a recipe whereby the coordinates which an observer A uses to locate or map an object with respect to himself are used to *calculate* the coordinates which an observer B would assign to the same object; it is assumed that A knows also the coordinates of observer B.

Let us illustrate the application of a coordinate transformation with a homely example. Suppose that A is a station on the equator of the earth from which a mountain peak is seen to be due west 10′ of longitude. From A the station B is north 10′ of latitude. The observer at A will then have no difficulty in calculating that the observer at B maps the mountain peak 14.1 nautical miles southwest of B. He has been able to conclude what B's map will be even though he has never been to B.

Transparent as such an example seems, it conceals a snare. The particular solution we have attributed to A for the calculation of the position of the mountain peak from B could not have been made near the north or south poles. Thus suppose that A is 10′ south of the north pole and B is at the pole. The mountain peak would then be 10 nautical miles from B due south along a meridian of longitude west of A 10′ or 153 feet. Whereas the first solution derived from an application of Pythagoras' theorem for plane right triangles, the second solution requires the analogue of Pythagoras' theorem from spherical trigonometry. The new geometric ingredient which forces us to foresake the familiar Pythagorean theorem is called *curvature*. Any surface or volume on or in which the Pythagorean theorem does not apply without exception is called by the mathematician a *curved space;* crudely put, the curvature of the space is a measure of the extent to which the Pythagorean theorem fails. A space which is not curved, such as the plane of Euclidean geometry, is called *flat*.

The intrusion of curvature into our relatively simple example has its analogue in the more sophisticated cosmological mapping problem. The parallelism may be displayed by considering in slightly more detail the problem of terrestrial map making. Let us suppose that we set ourselves the problem of constructing *ab initio* a map of the earth's surface from an extensive catalogue of the longitudes and latitudes of numerous key points on the earth's surface—large cities, river confluences, seacoast headlands, bench marks, etc. Such a catalogue indicates to the map maker that city B is 10′ east of a certain mountain peak and 10′ north. This relationship may be accurately displayed by putting B and the mountain peak on a sheet of paper so that B is 10 units to the right and 10 units above the point representing the mountain peak. Adding the other catalogued points in similar fashion will in due course yield the features of a finished map.

A procedure of this sort yields a map which faithfully reproduces all the information of the original catalogue. For all this, as our example showed, the map cannot tell us how far it is from city B to the mountain peak. This requires in addition that we know at every point the number of degrees of longitude or latitude which span a foot or a mile. In short, we must know also what coordinate difference corresponds to a unit length. The prescription of what constitutes a unit length in different places or in different directions at the same place is called a *congruence relation*. A congruence relation is fundamental to any mensuration process whether it be surveying the earth or surveying the universe.

Practical men like surveyors use a congruence relation which we all take for granted—the Euclidean congruence relation. It states that a ruler represents the same length no matter where it may be nor how it is oriented. Surveyors using this congruence relation find the distances between various points of the earth's surface to be such that the various survey points can be fitted only on the surface of a spheroid. The curvature of the earth's surface is made apparent when the surface is explored by means of the Euclidean congruence relation.

Other practical men like map makers may use a congruence relation known as the Mercator congruence relation. It states that a ruler measures a length which increases (in a definite and well-known way) with increasing distance from the equator. Using the same raw data as the surveyors, map makers find the distances between various points on the earth's surface to be such that the various points of the survey can be fitted only on the surface of a flat sheet of paper. Such a Mercator map occupies a Euclidean plane and is therefore flat and without curvature. Evidently the curvature of the earth's surface disappears when it is explored with the Mercator congruence relation. (For skeptics and realtors, most Mercator maps include a comparative Euclidean scale).

By suitable choices of congruence relations, it is possible to find for the surface of the earth an endless variety of curvatures. There is thus a very intimate interpendence of curvature and congruence relation. Until a congruence relation has been chosen, it is not possible to say what the curvature of any surface or volume is. This conclusion contains two implications of consequence for cosmological theories: First, it is not possible to construct even one observer's world map until a congruence relation has been assumed; and second, the structure ascribed to the universe will depend critically upon the choice of congruence relation.

Let us illustrate these points with yet another comparison to the mapping of the earth's surface. We have already seen that the assumption of a congruence relation is implicit in the original construction of a terrestrial map. We note further that the area of the globe is finite when the Euclidean congruence relation is applied to it but infinite when the Mercator congruence relation is used; the sphere has a limited area, whereas the Euclidean plane occupied by a complete Mercator map is unbounded. Yet again, on the sphere the shortest path between two points is the great circle arc connecting them, whereas in the plane Mercator projection it is the straight line segment; these are different routes except along the equator or a meridian.

A final example will bring home the critical importance of congruence relations for cosmology. Imagine the surface of the earth to be speckled with spots of paint in such a way that they are distributed isotropically about some point on a globe. When these spots are charted on a Mercator map, they will lose their isotropy. Conversely, spots isotropic on a Mercator projection will not be so on a globe.

With these considerations in mind, we can now summarize the cosmologist's somewhat devious *modus operandi*. He first assumes a congruence relation which seems to him to have the warrant of some physical or astronomical observation to justify it. From the world picture he can then construct a world map. The cosmological principle then implies that the world maps of all other equivalent observers must be essentially the same. The theory which the cosmologist frames upon this basis must predict the course of world-wide events and supplement in a reasonable way the details which observation has not yet been able to supply in the world picture. He must be able to recover not only the world picture from which he started but also predict what the future can add to it. From the variety of world pictures predicted by different cosmological theories, we hope at some time to choose a lone survivor.

KINEMATIC RELATIVITY

We have seen that a necessary preliminary in the development of any cosmological theory is the choosing of a congruence relation. It must define what equal lengths are to be everywhere and always—lengths of space *and* lengths of time. This may be done by making two assumptions: First we suppose that light has the same velocity from any source, at any place, at any time, and in any direction; secondly we assume that galaxies' respective recessional velocities are constant. The first asumption is equivalent to saying that the distance between any two points of space may be expressed as the light-time between them. This is an eminently reasonable assumption, reinforced by our longstanding custom of stating the distance to various astronomical bodies in units of light years. The fact that the time, place, or direction of measurement does not matter shows this to be a Euclidean congruence relation. The second assumption provides a means of recognizing a uniformly running clock, namely, one which gives to each galaxy a constant velocity. The rotating earth would not do, for example, since we know it to be decelerating because of tidal friction. It would therefore make the galaxies appear to accelerate, even as it does the moon and planets. There is no refuting those who might prefer to say that the earth is rotating uniformly and that the planets of the solar system as well as the galaxies are accelerating; we could honor their choice of a different congruence relation for time intervals and wish them Godspeed in the successful formulation of laws which would account for the acceleration of all major astronomical phenomena except the rotation of the earth.

We next *choose* a space curvature or form of geometry. Though with the Euclidean congruence relation we had no choice of curvature on the earth's surface, empty space presents no constraints like those which bound us to the earth. We therefore elect to embed the galaxies of our present world model in flat space because of its greater simplicity; we therefore use not only the Euclidean congruence relation but also the theorems of Euclidean geometry. We have now set the stage for the construction of the world map of kinematic relativity. This very attractive theory was developed almost singlehandedly by the British cosmologist E. A. Milne between 1932 and 1950.

Picture a large number of randomly moving particles confined to a relatively small volume, like the molecules of gas in a container. Now imagine them to be simultaneously released. The initial disorderly helter-skelter of motions will before long give way to a systematic expansion. Those particles initially moving outward will continue to do so; those particles initially moving inward will cross the original small volume and thereafter will likewise be moving outward. All the while, the fastest will be forging ever farther ahead of the less rapidly moving particles, reaching distances proportional to their velocities. By the time the volume which the expanding particles occupy is very much larger than that in which they were initially confined, the particles' motions will be almost purely radial, the volume they occupy will be nearly spherical, and it will appear to any particle that the rest are expanding about him with velocities proportional to their distances. The law of red shifts is therefore inevitable!

Isotropy, however, is possible only to a particle at the center if the number of particles is finite. A particle on the boundary of the group, for example, would find all the rest on one side of him rather than in equal numbers in all directions. If we here invoke the cosmological principle, requiring isotropy for all particles, we are driven to conclude that the number of particles must be infinite. Only then could each one find others on all sides.

If for "particle" we now substitute "galaxy," the argument could be repeated word for word. If we suppose that the galaxies once occupied a small volume from which they have since been expanding uniformly, we would conclude that velocity segregation accounts for the law of red shifts and that the cosmological principle requires there be an infinite number of galaxies if the world picture of each is to be isotropic. But is there not a contradiction in speaking of an infinite number of galaxies within a finite volume of space?

To resolve this seeming paradox, we pursue further some of the consequences of the cosmological principle. First observe that the cosmological principle and the congruence relation together imply that no galaxy can have a velocity as great as the velocity of light; for if one galaxy appeared to another to have the velocity of light, it would likewise appear to all others including itself, to have the velocity of light—and this is plainly contradictory. Nor can it be doubted that the velocity of light is the same to all observers, even those in relative motion. Delicate experiments repeated with higher and higher accuracy ever since the latter decades of the nineteenth century leave little room for doubt.

Second, let us see how such a conclusion affects the mapping of one rapidly receding galaxy by another. For this purpose let us substitute momentarily a more mundane pair of observers, one standing by a railroad track and the other riding a passing train. Imagine that the strike of a pair of bolts of lightning leaves imprints upon the front and rear of the train as well as upon the ground beside the track. Imagine the stationary observer to see both flashes at the same time. When measurement shows that he stood midway between them, he concludes that they occurred simultaneously. Let us suppose that it was, in fact, the instant at which the moving observer passed him. The moving observer finds, by measuring the distances to the marks at the two ends of the train, that he too was midway between the flashes. He does not conclude that the flashes were simultaneous, however; before the light reached him, he had moved forward so that the signal from the front intercepted him before the one from the rear overtook him. Both observers credit the same velocity to light, and they agree that the flashes took place at equal distances from them, yet one believes the flashes to have occurred at the same time and the other is convinced that the forward flash occurred first. Neither has authority to claim preference for his own point of view, for if the earth, train, and track were removed without disturbing the experiment, we could not say even that one observer was at rest and the other in motion but only that they were in relative motion. The only tenable conclusion is that relatively moving observers will in general not agree upon the time of a distant event.

If there is a disagreement about the times of distant events, there will be also an honest difference of opinion about the dimensions of an object. Thus imagine a ruler to be viewed by two relatively moving observers. They agree that its length will be the distance between its two ends, the location of the ends of the ruler to be taken at the same time. However, what one observer thinks are simultaneous measurements, the other will find to be made at different times. This has the effect that the moving observer invariably finds the ruler shorter than does the stationary observer. Alternatively, any observer will see relatively moving objects contracted in the direction of their motion. This famous effect is called the *Lorentz contraction,* in honor of the Dutch physicist who gave it prominence. The Lorentz contraction is a well-established effect for high-speed particles of physics.

Galaxies are no exception to the Lorentz contraction. Those which appear to us to be moving rapidly outward along the line of sight will also appear to be very shallow in the radial dimension even though an observer in such a galaxy would find his galaxy quite as deep as we find ours. Indeed, he would think that it is we who are very thin in the line of sight! The radial compression from the Lorentz contraction allows galaxies to be packed without limit near the boundary of the finite sphere which bounds each observer's visible universe. Thus we see that it is not a contradiction to speak of an infinite number of galaxies in a finite volume of space.

With this difficulty thus disposed of, let us contemplate the world map proposed by kinematic relativity. Any one fundamental observer's map is like that of any other's. It shows an infinite number of galaxies distributed through a spherical volume. These galaxies are receding radially with velocities proportional to their distances. They are bounded by but do not occupy the boundary itself. Their velocities increase in direct proportion to distance, having values up to but not equal to the velocity of light. The boundary itself must therefore expand with the velocity of light. The density of galaxies rises without limit toward the boundary, and all but a finite number of them reside in the last inch of the radius of the universe. No new matter is created and no old matter is annihilated. The bonds of gravitational attraction and electromagnetic radiation interconnect all particles at all times. To each galaxy the rest appear distributed isotropically, so that it does not experience any net gravitational attraction by the remainder of the universe.

It should be clearly understood that *every* fundamental observer possesses just such a map. If an observer on any given galaxy, mapping the universe as above, were to transfer to another galaxy which is remote and rapidly receding from the first, he must needs acquire a speed of travel which will enable him to overtake his destination. In effecting the move, he will have so altered his own velocity that the fresh map he constructs from his new station is no different from the old, aside from the historical changes of the interim. The cosmological principle is thereby satisfied.

In such an expanding universe, every galaxy is being deserted by its neighbors. An unending process of material dilution is in progress. If, then, the universe is becoming larger and sparser, it must have been smaller and denser. How small it was any number of years ago can easily be determined from its present rate of expansion. In short, galaxies now observed could have got to where they are at their evident rates of recession only by having been on the way some 10^{10} years, give or take a factor of two. That is to say that the course of cosmic events is traceable back to about the year 10,000,000,000 B.C., at which date the universe was reduced to a point and history breaks off. This time and event are termed *creation*. Nothing can be said about the event itself, only what has followed it.

The universe of kinematic relativity is therefore an evolving universe, showing changes which mark every epoch of its history up to the present.

We see these different epochs as we look out toward the receding boundary 10 billion light years away. Our view of the boundary itself (or what is beyond) is cut off by an unresolvable curtain of infinitely many galaxies, each red-shifted almost out of perception. In a telescope powerful enough to show them, we could see them as they were in their early infancy. We can therefore in principle look back just short of creation. However, creation, like the boundary of the universe, will always elude us.

Such is the universe according to the theory of kinematic relativity.

GENERAL RELATIVITY

About 15 years before kinematic relativity was conceived, the theory of general relativity was put forward and its application to the cosmological problem commenced almost at once. The contrast which general relativity offers to classical gravitational theory is so striking and its methods so novel that it has become in the popular mind the acme of abstruse mathematical theory. Though it is true that the mathematical apparatus of the theory is forbidding to the uninitiated, the general principles of general relativity are not difficult to grasp. Let us consider them in a manner which parallels our previous discussion of kinematic relativity.

We must first agree upon a congruence relation for an exploration of space and time. As before, we agree that spatial lengths are to be measured in terms of the light times which correspond to them. However, we do not now stipulate that the speed of light is the same under all circumstances; it may depend upon the time, place, and velocity of the source in a way yet to be specified. But a method of measuring lengths is now available. There must be added to it a method of measuring time intervals.

In kinematic relativity, equal times were chosen by the condition that the motion of the galaxies should appear to be at constant speed along a straight line in Euclidean space. In general relativity, it is assumed that the motion of any body is along a line of minimum length in space-time; such a line is called a *geodesic*. In general relativity, therefore, the equality of time intervals depends upon a choice which will make the actual paths of all bodies—whether along straight lines in Euclidean space at constant speed or along curved paths in curved space—paths of minimum length in the four dimensions of space and time. It should be born in mind that the curvature is possessed by the four-dimensional space-time, not necessarily by three-dimensional space alone. For example, the motion of a ball dropped from rest near the surface of the earth will be along a vertical straight line; the graph of the ball's height against time, however, is a

stars are of population II only, and such galaxies must be elliptical. In those galaxies in which the condensation of stars was incomplete or to which dust and gas have since been added, the original stars form its population II component; subsequent stars and interstellar matter have concentrated in the arms and disk, and such a galaxy is a spiral.

If the universe is not in a steady state, we must conclude that the principal era of star formation is long past. Only a comparatively few population I stars are being formed in the arms of spirals. They probably form approximately simultaneously in a limited region as a stellar association or galactic cluster; the Double Cluster in Perseus, for example, must be of recent origin. However, existing stars tend to inhibit star formation on a large scale by heating the neighboring interstellar gas and thereby rendering condensation more difficult.

Let us now attempt to follow the early stages in the development of a particular star, the sun. We hope to gain some understanding of the manner in which its planetary system may have come about.

The Origin of the Solar System

THE AGE OF THE SYSTEM

There are two facts of prime importance in the cosmogony of the solar system: First, the system is an entity that is at the same time so complex and yet characterized by so many uniformities that it can only be supposed to have originated as a unit rather than by piecemeal acquisition; and second, several of its members have limited ages which may be estimated with fair accuracy. Together these facts give us warranty to speculate upon the particular processes and events which gave rise to the solar system.

A list of the dynamical uniformities is very compelling. For example, the orbits of the planets and nearly all the minor planets lie almost in a common plane; all revolve about the sun in the same sense; their orbits are of relatively small eccentricity; except for Uranus, the planets' equatorial planes are inclined but little to their orbital planes; the planets' satellites revolve approximately in the planets' respective equatorial planes; the direction of rotation of each of the planets (again, Uranus excepted) is in the same sense as its direction of revolution about the sun; and the sun's equatorial plane has only a small inclination to the planets' orbital planes.

There are chemical uniformities as well. Though the sun may be expected to have proportionately more of the light elements hydrogen and helium because its velocity of escape is 55 times as great as the earth's, the heavier elements may be expected to be of comparable relative abundance in the earth and sun. By and large, this is so. For example, iron, magnesium, aluminum, nickel, calcium, sodium, and potassium are the seven commonest terrestrial metals; of these, only nickel has a relative abundance in the sun, which may differ from that on the earth by as much as a factor of 10. Similar to the earth and sun in metallic content are the meteorites, the only other bodies of the solar system whose chemical compositions are known in any detail and with any certainty.

Earth, sun, and meteorites all have limited ages which can be estimated. Thus the earth's crust contains radioactive minerals whose proportions are continually changing as a result of the spontaneous disintegration of the unstable atoms of which they are composed. The earth is still young enough to have in its possession such perishable substances as uranium and radium. Indeed, the amounts of the various radioactive elements and their products are such as to indicate that the earth cannot be more than 4 or 5 billion years old. Analyses of the radioactive content of meteorites indicates for them a similar age. The theory of stellar evolution indicates for the sun a probable age of 5 or 6 billion years. Altogether, an age of 5 or 6 billion years for the solar system seems inescapable. What were the events which transpired that long ago?

THE FORMATION OF THE SOLAR NEBULA

Since the formation of the planetary system could not have preceded the birth of the sun, we may first attempt to recreate a probable sequence of events at the time of the sun's birth. As long ago as 1796, the philosopher Kant suggested that the sun condensed from a diffuse rotating cloud of primordial material, spawning planets in the process. The suggestion was put into a somewhat more precise mathematical form by the great French mathematician and astronomer Laplace. The original *nebular hypothesis,* as it came to be known, had to be abandoned when it was shown that the planets could not have been shed by a nebula which could condense to a star rotating as slowly as the sun.

The flaw in the original nebular hypothesis has only recently been repaired. It is not the postulation of a nebula but a misconception of its evolution. To appreciate more fully what this evolution is likely to be, imagine a newborn star like the sun to be surrounded by a nebulous rotating envelope. It must extend at least from the present orbit of Mercury to some such distance as the orbit of Pluto. Its rotation will define an equator which must either contain the orbit of every particle about the central sun or be crossed by every particle twice per revolution. As many particles must cross in one sense as the other, so that encounters between oppositely crossing particles will tend to cast both into an equatorial orbit. This will result in the nebula's becoming very much flattened. Such a development would require an estimated 10,000 to 100,000 years to effect.

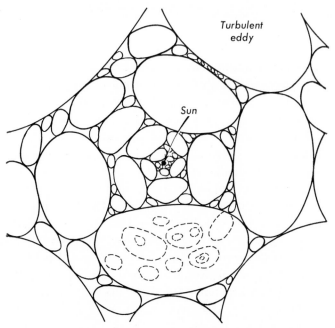

Figure 253. Turbulent eddies within the viscous primitive solar nebula may well have developed a pattern of cells and sub-cells such as this. The formation of such eddies was a necessary prelude to the condensation of planets.

The mass of the solar nebula may be surmised to have been about one-tenth the mass of the sun. This is indicated by the fact that the matter of which the earth and planets are composed represents the heavy fraction of the original material, amounting to probably no more than 1 per cent of the original nebula and 0.1 per cent of the present sun.

If the material of the nebula, like that of the sun, were 99 per cent hydrogen and helium gas, it would be somewhat viscous or sticky. One very important effect of this would be to cause turbulent eddies to develop in the rotating disk. Without such eddies, the heavy material of the nebula would condense into a multitude of flakes or droplets like the particles of Saturn's rings. The eddies, however, represent large-scale inhomogeneities which may persist for a hundred years or so, giving scope to other formative agencies.

THE FORMATION OF THE PROTOPLANETS

Such an agency is gravitation. It will cause the material of the eddies to coalesce if it can. Tending to counter it is the sun's tidal force. The internal cohesive forces of gravitation will prevail if and only if the density of the eddy is great enough to put it outside the Roche limit of the sun. The existence of the planets is evidence that this was the case. At the same time, the size of the eddies which could coalesce is limited by the sun's tidal force, for the larger the eddy, the greater the tidal force upon it. The largest eddies which could coalesce therefore did so, becoming *protoplanets*.

Their actual sizes were determined by the local density of matter in the flattened nebular disk; had it been half or a third of what it was, the largest protoplanets would have been of cometary dimensions, whereas if the density had been two or three times larger, the protoplanets would have provided the sun with a stellar companion.

It would have taken only a few years for particles the size of pebbles to grow from the original dust of the nebula. The large particles would sweep up the small, a process accelerated by the gravitational contraction of the protoplanet. About 10 or a 100 million years would have been required to form a body of the size of proto-Jupiter. It is clear that the masses of the protoplanets were determined by the density distribution in the nebular disk. The inner planets were limited in size by the stronger tidal force of the sun at small distances. The giant planets capitalized upon the greater eddy size possible at greater distances from the sun. Near the sun, relatively high density is offset by limited eddy volume; at great distance, great eddy size is countered by greatly reduced nebular density. At mid-distance they give the largest body, proto-Jupiter.

The picture we have sketched of the process of formation of the protoplanets gives a very natural account of the origin of a number of the features of the solar system. Thus the common direction of revolution of the planets is a direct consequence of the rotation of the original solar nebula. Their low orbital inclinations result from the flattening of the nebula. The low eccentricity of their orbits is due to the fact that eccentric orbits tend to become rounded if the body moves in a viscous or resisting medium. And Bode's law is an indirect consequence of Roche's theorem and the particular density distribution of the original solar nebula.

It is further possible to suggest how the planets' rotations come all (except Uranus) to be in the sense of their revolutions. The large, loose protoplanets must have been tidally distorted to a considerable degree, having formed as they did at a density only slightly more than the Roche limit requires. They would then be tidally braked, like the moon about the earth, until their rotations kept one bulge always toward the sun. This rotation would be counterclockwise and with a period equal to the period of revolution about the sun. Once established, the sense of rotation would remain the same even though the period had since grown much shorter in consequence of the protoplanets' further contraction.

THE ULTIMATE FORM OF THE SYSTEM

The protoplanets must have been many times the size of the planets we know at the present time. It is estimated that Jupiter has not more than a twentieth the mass of proto-Jupiter, the earth only a thousandth the mass of proto-earth, and the other planets in like proportion. What has become of the rest? In short, it has evaporated. Most of what was lost consisted of the two lightest elements, hydrogen and helium. Even today, the earth cannot prevent the escape of these gases from its atmosphere. A more extended protoplanet would have even less authority over the light constituents of its atmosphere. As a result, there is a general deficiency of all atmospheric gases in the present planets as well as a selective deficiency of the lighter gases due to evaporation. The earth's present atmosphere, for example, is probably not the residue of its primordial gases but a secondary one acquired by volcanic release of interior gases and vapors, modified by the action of green plants, photodissociation, radioactive decay of unstable isotopes, etc.

Those portions of the flattened solar nebula which failed to become a permanent part of a planet were expelled from the solar system. The faster-moving inner parts of the viscous gas accelerated the outer parts to the velocity of escape; the inner parts were by the same token reduced to orbits which swept them into the sun. Abetting this process was the radiation pressure of the sun, which in the course of a hundred million years or so must have swept the debris of the original nebula out of the solar system, much as it still scours away the remnants of comets.

One of the protoplanets formed a double system, the earth and moon. Most of the rest formed satellite systems, much as the sun formed the system of planets. In the process, however, some of the outer satellites must have slipped from the planet's control as the planet lost most of its original mass. These emancipated satellites would have followed orbits which would frequently place the satellite in the planet's vicinity. Some were in this way recaptured, some in retrograde orbits. Very possibly the Trojan group of minor planets are former satellites of proto-Jupiter.

It is reasonable to suppose that proto-Jupiter forestalled by its tidal force the coalescence of a body of planetary proportions in the present minor planet zone, where there formed instead a brood of 10 to 100 smaller bodies which grew by accretion. Some of these have since suffered collisions, some probably as recently as a billion years ago. The fragments of these encounters are known to us as small irregular asteroids and as meteorites.

At the very fringes of the original solar nebula the matter condensed into solids which collected into many small bodies which we now see as comets. Only those remain which have been perturbed by Pluto and, thereafter, by the other planets into the comet cloud, which extends from the limits of the planetary system to the halfway point to the next star.

Such, at least, is an outline of one theory of the origin of the solar system. It should be remembered, however, that it shares the field with a number of other theories.

The Existence of Life

THE ORIGIN OF LIFE ON THE EARTH

Since life is found on one of the planets of the solar system, it becomes in a sense an astronomical phenomenon, and its origin a proper cosmogonical question. In attempting to fathom the origin of life on the earth, we may at the same time be able to form an opinion as to how rare or how commonplace life is in the universe at large.

Let us first note that living things are composed of carbon, oxygen, nitrogen, and hydrogen, with only 1 per cent of other substances, chiefly mineral salts. These are organized into amino acids from which, in turn, are formed proteins, the characteristic molecules of living substance. The special properties of carbon permit an almost endless array of different kinds of protein molecules to be formed, and it is on this variety that the great diversity of living forms depends; no two species of plant or animal possess all the same proteins.

It was for a long time believed that organic matter such as proteins could be produced only by living matter. The entire field of organic chemistry shows that this is not so. Moreover, recent experiments have shown that amino acids may be created by processes that could very well occur commonly in nature. Thus, a mixture of water vapor, methane, ammonia, and hydrogen—probable principal constituents of the earth's early atmosphere—subjected to electrical discharge (lightning) was found to form amino acids.

Such substances are highly perishable; they are vulnerable to reactions with oxygen or with other organic substances. On the primeval earth, however, there were no organisms to attack them and no free oxygen in the atmosphere. These first organic substances should therefore have been stable over long periods of time. They could not survive on the present earth for long, so that the spontaneous generation of life today is probably impossible.

Simple protein molecules might therefore be expected to grow in numbers. In solution in the oceans, they were continually mixed and circulated, given repeated opportunity to react with other molecules and to form more complex molecules. Step by step, molecules of progressive complexity would be formed. When once one had been formed which could replicate itself, life on the earth would have begun.

Even the simplest living substance such as a virus is an extremely complicated chemical structure. The likelihood of its spontaneous formation is consequently almost infinitesimal. However, it need have occurred only once, for it is self-perpetuating. We must therefore consider how likely is at least one occurrence of an extremely unlikely event.

For the sake of illustration, consider an event whose probability in given circumstances is only 1 in 1000. This means that the chance that it will not occur in the given circumstances is 999 in 1000. If the circumstances are repeated once again, however, the probability that the event will not have occurred either time is 0.999×0.999. Further, the chance that the event will not occur in any of n repetitions of the circumstances is the nth power of 0.999. If n is a very large number, the nth power of 0.999 can be very small. For example, if n is 10,000, the probability that the event will *not* have occurred at least once has dropped to $1/20,000$; that is to say, the probability of the occurrence of the event has reached 0.99995, almost a certainty.

Since the formation of a self-reproducing molecule is necessary only once, then no matter how small the probability of its occurrence, its appearance seems almost certain in a sufficiently long time. A period of 3 billion years or so seems sufficient for bringing off even such an unlikely event as the spontaneous creation of a living molecule.

A hazard to be surmounted in any such chemical reaction, however, is the fact that the reaction is reversible and in fact may more often than not be expected to be undone. In order that synthesis may prevail against dissociation, living things expend energy. They derive such energy from food, and they spend it upon growth and reproduction.

The first living matter must therefore have fed upon the oceanic broth of organic molecules. With no oxygen to draw upon, it must have utilized a process of fermentation. It and its descendants would in time have exhausted the larder had it not been for the opportune invention by some organism of the process of photosynthesis. This process enabled living matter to create its own food from water and carbon dioxide with the help of sunlight.

Photosynthesis did more than emancipate living things from dependence upon reserves of food from the past. One of its by-products is oxygen. The photosynthetic process therefore began an inexorable transformation of the atmosphere by contributing free oxygen to it. It is estimated that the present atmospheric oxygen is renewed every 300 years by photosynthesis. The presence of oxygen now made it feasible for living things to replace the very inefficient fermentation process by the highly efficient respiration process and to realize a far greater return upon the consumption of the available food. Self-sustaining, efficient organisms were now free to embark upon the amazing evolutionary venture which has culminated in nominally intelligent life. Such life could now leave the protection of the sea, for the oxygen also formed an ozone layer in the atmosphere which provided protection against the harmful ultraviolet light of the sun. Such, in outline, is a sketch of the origin of life on the earth which does not do violence to reason or scientific principle.

LIFE ON OTHER WORLDS

Life on the earth is a certainty; life elsewhere in the universe is wholly conjectural. What can be surmised concerning its existence?

It seems quite certain that other forms of life, no matter how different their morphology, must depend upon the chemical versatility of the carbon atom to the same degree as does life on the earth. The formation of complex organic molecules containing carbon is thus a *sine qua non,* and this in turn requires that the environment satisfy the restriction that it remain within a rather severely limited temperature range.

Any required temperature range may be achieved by a planet's remaining within certain distance limits from the central star of the planetary system. The extent of these limits is found to be proportional to the square root of the luminosity of the star. The more luminous the star, the better the chance that one of its planets will fall within the habitable zone; stars of low luminosity, on the other hand, stand a very slim chance of having a planet within the required range of distances. Moreover, planetary orbits of any but small eccentricity will carry a planet beyond the habitable zone. With this added restriction, it seems very improbable that dwarf stars of types K or M possess life-supporting planets.

Our present understanding of how life arose on the earth also makes it appear necessary that a sufficiently long period of time be available for the operation of the evolutionary process. This is a time of the order of 2 or 3 billion years. This means that stars whose luminosities do not remain constant for at least this length of time cannot be accompanied by planets that support advanced forms of life. Consequently, stars of spectral types O, B, A, and probably early F may be eliminated from further consideration.

The prospects have been narrowed to main-sequence stars of spectral types late F, G, and early K. They may be further restricted by ruling out binary stars as suitable primaries. Planets in such a system could hardly be expected to stay within the habitable zone for several billion years in the face of the inevitable gravitational perturbations which a double primary would give rise to. Further, the chances are small that both components would be of suitable spectral type, and if one were a white dwarf, it is almost certain that this star has passed through a nova-active stage which would have been fatal to life.

We may be sure that the biochemistry on other planets is governed by the same laws of atomic physics as our own, because the spectra of distant stars show these laws to be in operation everywhere in the universe. Within 5 parsecs, therefore, only the sun and two other stars are known to meet all the conditions which seem to circumscribe the possibilities for the existence of life; significantly, the sun has the greatest luminosity of the three, and thus the best chance of supporting life. This suggests that at most 5 per cent of the stars can be attended by planets upon which life exists. Because of the many contingencies upon which life depends, the fraction may actually be much smaller. For example, the probability that a protostar will have a small enough velocity of rotation to lead to the formation of a single star rather than a binary system is probably less than 1 in 1000. The density of the surrounding nebula must be within close tolerances in order that planets emerge. A first living organism must arise spontaneously. It must invent fermentation, photosynthesis, and respiration, or their equivalents. It is almost impossible to assess the probability of a concatenation of such events or to foresee their alternatives. It therefore remains a very unsettled matter whether life is common about the universe; even informed opinion spans the wide spectrum from certainty to doubt.

The Origin of the Elements

Hydrogen and helium constitute about 99 per cent of all the matter in the universe, according to present estimates. It might seem, therefore, that all the other elements could be dismissed as almost trifling impurities. It is precisely upon these impurities that the formation of planetary systems and the existence of life depend, however. This is motive enough for asking how it comes about that there are any elements whatsoever beside hydrogen and helium.

We have already seen that helium is a product of thermonuclear synthesis from hydrogen. It is natural to inquire first whether the synthesis might not be carried on step by step from helium by additional thermonuclear reactions with hydrogen. The immediate answer is that it cannot, for the nucleus to be expected from a fusion of H_1^1 and He_4^2 would be Li_5^3 which, unfortunately, does not exist.

The only avenue open seems to be a reaction of He_4^2 with itself. This would produce the beryllium isotope Be_8^4, which immediately disintegrates into two helium nuclei under conditions such as those at the center of the sun and most stars. However, as we have already noted, the cores of stars at the top of the giant branch in the Hertzsprung-Russell diagram have temperatures and densities such that the beryllium isotope forms as fast as it decays. This ensures a small but important transient population of beryllium nuclei which react further with helium to form the stable carbon isotope C_{12}^6. This is the triple-alpha process.

The triple-alpha process surmounts the most formidable hurdle of the entire synthesis problem. Thereafter it is a matter of exploring the possible reactions for ones which are suitable to the situations within exhausted, shrinking, moribund stars. In such stars, hydrogen is entirely used up in all but the relatively cool envelops; it is helium which is "burned." For example, He_4^2 unites with C_{12}^6 to form O_{16}^8; this in turn combines with He_4^2 to form Ne_{20}^{10}, which itself may further yield some Mg_{24}^{12}. Stars are known which show spectra with abnormally weak hydrogen lines and abnormally strong lines of elements produced by helium burning.

Since helium burning yields only about a tenth as much energy as hydrogen burning, the life of a star in this phase is comparatively short —perhaps 10 or 100 million years. Thereafter, gravitational contraction will resume and the core of the star will rise still further in temperature and density. When a temperature of 1 billion degrees has been reached, there will be present γ-rays of such intensity that they can actually dissociate some of the neon into O_{16}^8 and He_4^2 to provide a temporary supply of the otherwise scarce helium. The helium can now combine with undissociated neon to produce magnesium (Mg_{24}^{12}), silicon (Si_{28}^{14}), sulfur (S_{32}^{16}), argon (Ar_{36}^{18}), and calcium (Ca_{40}^{20}). This would be done quickly in from 100 to 10,000 years.

Again contraction would come into play to raise the temperature of the core of the star to 3,000,000,000° K. The only energy-yielding reactions possible are those which synthesize from the elements magnesium to calcium the elements of the *iron group,* namely, titanium, chromium, manganese, iron (the most abundant), cobalt, nickel, copper, and zinc. These are the most stable of all nuclei; no further energy can be squeezed from them. Such reactions are thought to be taking place in stars of the horizontal branch of the Hertzsprung-Russell diagram. They probably occur in a matter of seconds, culminating the star's active career. They also represent the final step in the build-up of the elements within a star, which began as pure hydrogen or even hydrogen and helium. Such stars are first-generation stars, whose more massive members may have long since seeded intergalactic space with the heavy elements they have produced; they may simply have spiced the interstellar medium by continuous mass ejection or have peppered it by nova or supernova explosion. Stars formed since will be seasoned with elements of the iron group.

Second-generation stars will fashion many new elements, since they can transmute members of the iron group without first creating them. At a certain stage of the star's career, it will sustain neutron-producing reactions. Transmutations will then occur as a result of neutron captures and subsequent spontaneous disintegration with the emission of an electron. This increases the atomic number by one unit. Place by place, a nucleus may be advanced in the table of the elements. There is convincing evidence that this does indeed occur. The evidence is in the form of data on the comparative abundance of the elements. If the neutron-capture mechanism did operate, we should expect that elements which capture neutrons most readily would be least abundant, for they are the most transmuted; those which are least likely to capture neutrons will accumulate. A comparison of the abundance of the elements heavier than the iron group shows a striking correlation in the predicted sense between abundance and likelihood of neutron capture.

Other special circumstances can produce heavy elements by somewhat different means. Supernova explosions undoubtedly generate heavy elements within in a matter of hours or minutes. There is evidence of this in the light curve of a supernova which declines just as would be expected if it were maintained by the artificially produced trans-uranian element californium (Cf_{254}^{98}). By one means or another, the whole set of different chemical elements is produced in the interiors of some of the stars. Those stars rich in the heavy elements during their prime, the stars of population I, are second- and third-generation stars; the sun, for example, is probably of the third generation.

That the elements are produced in the interiors of stars seems undeniable. That they may also have been produced in a similar fashion during a highly compressed state early in the history of an expanding universe also seems possible.

The Fate of the Universe

The eventual fate of the universe is somewhat easier to foresee than details of the aging of the stars or the future of life on the earth (or even next year's weather). It must surely be governed by a law of thermodynamics known as the *law of entropy*. In effect, the law of entropy declares certain physical processes to be irreversible by natural means. For instance, a pail of hot water set on a cake of ice will melt the ice by giving up its heat to the ice. The process has been irreversible, since we cannot place a pail of cold water in a puddle of melted ice and expect it, by natural means, to become a pail of hot water upon a cake of ice. The heat energy originally in the pail of water has been transferred to the ice. The amount of energy they have in common has never varied, but nonetheless it cannot in any wise be retrieved in its original state by a spontaneous action of the water and the ice. The quantity known as "entropy" is a measure of the amount of energy thus degraded and made unrecoverable for re-use. Every irreversible process therefore increases the entropy of the universe.

Stellar energy generation and radiation are distinctly irreversible processes. In the course of time the stars will expend all their available energies in irreversible processes; there will be no means left to them to radiate. The entropy in any given region of the universe will approach its maximum possible value, the stars will burn out and will gradually become cold and dark. Fortunately this dreary prospect is again immensely far in the future for our galaxy, though it seems a remorselessly certain distant fate.

The operation of the second law of thermodynamics will have rather different effects in the different kinds of universes. In the steady-state uni-

agencies which were essential to the process. Specify the physical conditions which were essential to the formation of a planetary system.

12. What general conditions seem to be necessary for the existence of life? How may life have originated on the earth? What special developments made possible the evolution of higher forms?

13. What conditions circumscribe the possibility of other habitable planets in the universe?

14. Suppose that all the matter in the universe began as hydrogen. Trace the thermonuclear process in stars by which some of this matter could by now have become heavier elements. In what kinds of stars are these reactions to be expected? Might they have occurred in any other way or place?

15. What is the law of entropy? What does it imply for the matter within a limited region of space? How does it affect the world pictures of the representative cosmological theories?

16. What is Mach's principle? What does it imply concerning large- and small-scale phenomena? How do the pure numbers of nature tend to bear this out? What explanation did Eddington purport to give for the distribution of the values of the pure numbers? Why is an explanation called for? What precedent is there for axiomatic analysis of nature?

appendix 1
The Constellations

• • •

"Why did no one teach me the constellations when I was a child?"
—THOMAS CARLYLE

The unequal brightness and random distribution of the stars upon the sky force on one's attention certain suggestive natural groupings of stars called *constellations*. As a rule, the stars of any constellation bear no significant physical relation to each other; it is only by happenstance that they appear projected upon the same general neighborhood of the celestial sphere.

With few exceptions, the stars of part or all of a constellation show an arrangement upon the sky which approximates some familiar geometric forms such as straight lines, rectangles, and crosses. Thus, the most conspicuous stars of Cygnus form a Latin cross, the brightest stars of Ursa Major delineate "the Big Dipper," the stars of Cassiopeia outline a letter "W," and so on. Ancient peoples imaginatively traced in these various groups the forms of some of the beasts and heroes of their respective mythologies. There is therefore generally associated with each of the major constellations one or more fanciful accounts of its origin. Since western civilization is rather directly descended from the Greek and Roman cultures, it is from the Greek and Roman mythologies that the names of the oldest constellations have come. The Greco-Roman nomenclature has even been extended beyond the parts of the sky visible from Greece or Italy so that constellations of the far southern sky likewise bear the names of Greek or Roman heroes or of objects which in some way relate to their exploits. It should be recognized, however, that there are alternative East Indian, Persian, Arabic, Egyptian, Polynesian, Chinese, Incan, Mayan, Eskimo, and other equivalent mythologies which presume to account for the most impressive star groups.

In modern times the term constellation has come to denote not merely the stars of some conspicuous group but rather the whole area of the sky over which it is spread. Therefore constellations now signify regions upon the celestial sphere, just as the Mediterranean Sea or the Island of Borneo specify definite areas upon the terrestrial sphere. Because the original 48 ancient constellations do not occupy the whole of the celestial sphere, they have been supplemented by 40 more since the beginning of the seventeenth century. Since 1928, definite (though arbitrary) boundaries have been agreed upon for each. Any celestial object may therefore be specified as within the bounds of some particular constellation; this is frequently a convenient method of locating it approximately.

Individual stars have also received proper names. Though the list of them runs to several hundred, only the two or three dozen brightest stars are generally called by name. All but these few stars are identified by their designation in one or another of various star catalogues. The designations given to most naked-eye stars are those taken from Bayer's catalogue of 1603. Bayer's system gives Greek letter designations to the stars of each constellation, usually in order of brightness or of position; to the Greek letter is added the genitive of the constellation name. Thus Vega, the brightest star in the constellation Lyra, is known also as α Lyrae. However, since Vega is set down as star number 172167 in the Henry Draper Catalogue or as star number $+38°3238$ in the Bonn Durchmusterung, it may also be correctly (though less familiarly) designated as HD 172167 or as BD $+38°3238$.

As an aid to identifiction, star maps and star catalogues always give some approximate measure of the star's relative brightness. On star maps this is usually done by representing a star by a dot whose area is larger or smaller according as the star is brighter or fainter. In catalogues, a specification of stellar magnitude (see Appendix 2) suffices; greater magnitude indicates greater faintness.

The forms and locations of the constellations may be displayed upon maps of the sky just as the forms and locations of continents may be shown on a map of the earth. Maps of the sky, like maps of the earth, will be distorted by any transfer from the original spherical surface (the sky) to a flat surface (the map). As with geographical maps, sky maps employ a variety of kinds of projection and are to be read in the corresponding way. Two differences should be noted, however: (1) The sky is the interior surface of a sphere, whereas the land and water areas of the earth cover the outer suface of a sphere. On this account, east is at the left and west at the right of a sky map on which north is at the top. (2) The part of the sky which is visible at any given hour of the night will change with the seasons. Therefore constellations are usually arranged and grouped according to the season in which they are most prominent at a convenient evening hour. A star map should therefore be read by holding it in a position appropriate to the current season. It should be noted, too, that the positions of the planets are usually not included upon a star map, since the planets' positions among the stars continually change. A set of maps of the entire sky will be found following the index.

Tables

• • •

GREEK ALPHABET

α	Alpha	ι	Iota	ρ	Rho
β	Beta	κ	Kappa	σ	Sigma
γ	Gamma	λ	Lambda	τ	Tau
δ	Delta	μ	Mu	υ	Upsilon
ϵ	Epsilon	ν	Nu	φ	Phi
ζ	Zeta	ξ	Xi	χ	Chi
η	Eta	o	Omicron	ψ	Psi
θ	Theta	π	Pi	ω	Omega

SIGNS OF THE ZODIAC

♈	Aries	♎	Libra
♉	Taurus	♏	Scorpius
♊	Gemini	♐	Sagittarius
♋	Cancer	♑	Capricornus
♌	Leo	♒	Aquarius
♍	Virgo	♓	Pisces

appendix 2
The Magnitude System

• • •

"The reader must not allow himself to be humbugged by mathematics."
—E. A. Milne

The system most used by astronomers for the designations of the relative strength of the light of different stars is the *magnitude system*. Magnitudes measure numerically the response appreciated by some receiver; this receiver is usually the eye, sometimes a photographic plate. The original magnitude system was necessarily based upon the strength of visual stimulus. The naked-eye stars were divided into six magnitude classes, each differing by one step or *magnitude*. The faintest stars to be seen by a person with good vision were defined to be of the sixth magnitude; the average of the 20 brightest stars defined the first magnitude.

This more or less rule-of-thumb definition has been considerably refined in modern times. In particular, it has been found that what the human eye appreciates as equal *intervals* of brightness are in fact equal *ratios* of brightness. Thus if r is the ratio of the amounts of light received from two stars whose magnitudes differ by 1, then $r \times r = r^2$ is the ratio of the amounts of light (or brightnesses) received from two stars whose magnitudes differ by 2, and $r \times r \times r = r^3$ is the ratio of the brightnesses of two stars whose magnitudes differ by 3, etc. Early measurements showed that stars differing by 5 magnitudes—the difference between first and sixth magnitude stars—have brightnesses which differ by a factor of approximately 100. This approximate relation is the basis for the definition that *the magnitude scale shall be so defined that a difference of 5 magnitudes is the equivalent of a brightness ratio of exactly 100.*

From this definition we can infer at once that

$$r \times r \times r \times r \times r = r^5 = 100$$

whence

$$r = \sqrt[5]{100} = 2.512 \cdots.$$

We can therefore say that stars differing by 1 magnitude have a ratio of brightnesses of 2.512; in other words, a star of magnitude 1 is 2.512 times as bright as a star of magnitude 2, a star of magnitude 6 is 2.512 times as bright as a star of magnitude 7 or 2.512 times as faint as a star of magnitude 5, etc. Note that larger positive magnitudes correspond to fainter stars.

From the definition of the relation between the magnitude and brightness systems, the explicit relation between the brightnesses b_A and b_B and the magnitudes m_A and m_B of two stars A and B can be put down in symbols as

$$\frac{b_A}{b_B} = (2.512)^{m_B - m_A} = 10^{0.4(m_B - m_A)}.$$

Now the units of brightness have been so defined (p. 301) that a star of brightness $b = 1$ would be found to have a magnitude of $m = -0.13$. Therefore, if we choose for star B one whose brightness is 1 and substitute into the above formula the values $b_B = 1$ and $m_B = -0.13$, we shall have

$$= 0.8872 \times 10^{0.4m} = \frac{0.8872}{10^{0.4m}}$$

as the relation between brightness and magnitude. (Here we have dropped the subscript A, which is no longer necessary, and have substituted for $10^{-0.4 \times 0.13}$ its value of 0.8872.) From this formula we may calculate the brightness b corresponding to any magnitude m. From its inverse,

$$m = -0.13 - 2.5 \log b,$$

we can also calculate the magnitude m corresponding to any brightness b. The table on page 536 shows the relation between them.

The magnitude and brightness systems have their respective advantages. One of the primary advantages of magnitudes is that they are much better suited to visual estimate than are brightnesses. Carefully trained observers can make magnitude estimates reliable to within one-tenth of a magnitude. Moreover, the magnitude scale encompasses the range of stellar brightnesses much more comfortably than the brightness scale; while the brightest star is only about 23 magnitudes brighter than the faintest that can be photographed, on the brightness scale they differ by about 15×10^8 times! On the other hand, the brightness scale gives physically meaningful units, whereas the magnitude system does not; brightness is proportional to the actual energy received each second.

In making magnitude or brightness observations, it has been found necessary to give explicit recognition to the dissimilar sensitivities of different kinds of receptors. For example, for red or blue stars a color-blind observer would make different estimates from those of an observer with normal vision. For the same reason, estimates made from a calibrated photograph or by means of a photocell cannot be expected to agree entirely with visual estimates or with each other. Therefore it is necessary to specify that any given magnitude is a visual magnitude, photographic magnitude, or whatever it may be. This is usually done with the aid of an appropriate subscript, as m_v (visual magnitude), or m_{pg} (photographic magnitude).

We distinguish also between true and apparent brightness systems. On the one hand are apparent brightness and apparent magnitude—the measures of the strengths of stars' light as they appear in our sky. On the other hand are true brightness (luminosity) and absolute magnitude—the measures of the strengths of stars' light as they would appear at a standard distance. *Absolute magnitude* is defined as the magnitude a star would have at a distance of 10 parsecs.

MAGNITUDE DIFFERENCE	BRIGHTNESS RATIO	BRIGHTNESS RATIO	MAGNITUDE DIFFERENCE
0.00	1.00	1.0	0.0
0.01	1.009	1.1	0.10
0.02	1.019	1.2	0.20
0.03	1.028	1.3	0.28
0.04	1.038	1.4	0.37
0.05	1.047	1.5	0.44
0.06	1.057	1.6	0.51
0.07	1.067	1.7	0.58
0.08	1.076	1.8	0.64
0.09	1.086	1.9	0.70
0.10	1.096	2.0	0.75
0.20	1.202	3.0	1.19
0.3	1.318	4.0	1.51
0.4	1.445	5.0	1.75
0.5	1.585	6.0	1.95
0.6	1.738	7.0	2.11
0.7	1.905	8.0	2.26
0.8	2.089	9.0	2.39
0.9	2.291	10.0	2.50
1.0	2.512	100.0	5.0
2.0	6.310	1000.	7.5
2.5	10.000	10,000.	10.0
5.0	100.00	100,000.	12.5

The relation of the absolute magnitude, apparent magnitude, and distance of a star may be easily found by the following argument: If the star has an apparent brightness b at a distance of d parsecs, it will have a brightness $b' = b \times (d/10)^2$ at a distance of 10 parsecs (because of the inverse square law of decrease of the strength of radiation with distance from its source). Now, by definition, the absolute magnitude M is

$$M = -0.13 - 2.5 \log b'$$

so that if we substitute $b \times (d^2/100)$ for b', we get

$$M = -0.13 - 2.5 \log \left(b \times \frac{d^2}{100} \right)$$

$$= (-0.13 - 2.5 \log b) - 5 \log d + 5$$

according to the rules for logarithms. We now note that the quantity in parentheses in the last line is merely the apparent magnitude m. Hence we finally arrive at the formula

$$M = m + 5 - 5 \log d$$

or

$$M = m + 5 + 5 \log p$$

where $p = 1/d$ is the parallax corresponding to a distance of d parsecs. The following table shows the apparent brightnesses, apparent magnitudes, parallaxes, distances, luminosities, and absolute magnitudes of a number of well-known stars. Note that absolute magnitudes, like visual magnitudes, must be specified as visual, photographic, etc.

STAR	APPARENT BRIGHT-NESS	APPAR-ENT MAGNI-TUDE	PARAL-LAX	DISTANCE (PARSECS)	LUMINOSITY	ABSO-LUTE MAGNI-TUDE
Sirius A	3.598	−1.52	0″371	2.70	26.2	+ 1.3
B	0.000366	+8.46			0.0027	+11.3
Capella	0.731	0.21	0.063	15.81	184.	− 0.8
Arcturus	0.711	0.24	0.092	10.9	84.	+ 0.1
Rigel	0.649	0.34	0.0043	230.	35,000.	− 6.5
Barnard's star	0.000146	9.46	0.543	1.84	0.00049	+13.1
61 Cygni A	0.00643	5.35	0.296	3.38	0.073	+ 7.7
van Maanen's star	0.0000105	12.3	0.249	4.02	0.00017	+14.3
Spica	0.291	1.21	0.017	59.	1,000.	− 2.6
Sun	42.5 × 10⁹	−26.7	206265.	0.000005	1.0	4.87

QUESTIONS

1. Find the brightness ratio corresponding to the magnitude differences (a) 1.1, (b) 2.38, (c) 4.63, (d) 14.06.
2. Find the brightness corresponding to the magnitudes (a) 1.0, (b) −1.6, (c) 6.0, (d) 11.2, (e) 20.85.
3. Find the magnitude difference corresponding to a brightness ratio of (a) 2, (b) 5, (c) 250, (d) 11,400.
4. Find the magnitude corresponding to the brightnesses (a) 2.3, (b) 0.075, (c) 0.000825.
5. If the sun has an absolute magnitude of +4.87, what is the luminosity of stars whose absolute magnitudes are (a) −0.13, (b) 10, (c) 13.15, (d) −4.02?

Figure 254. THE 40-INCH REFRACTOR. This photograph gives an observer's impression of the largest refractor in the world, the 40-inch refractor of the Yerkes Observatory. The small telescopes are finders whose larger fields of view facilitate more rapid setting of the large telescope on faint objects. The wheels operate right ascension and declination clamps and slow motion adjustments. As shown here, the telescope is fitted with a plate holder for direct photography. This may be replaced with a stellar spectrograph or with an eyepiece mount for visual observations. (Courtesy P. J. Krogdahl.)

appendix 3
Telescopes and
Observatories

• • •

"I do not say: science is useful because it allows us to construct machines; I do say: machines are useful, for by working for us they permit us more time to study science."

—Henri Poincaré

A. TELESCOPES

The most important single tool of the astronomer is the telescope; without it astronomy could have advanced but little beyond what Tycho Brahe knew in the sixteenth century. In short, astronomical progress since Tycho Brahe's day has, in major outline, been strictly dependent upon improvements in the design, construction, and performance of telescopes and their numerous accessories. To the optical telescopes which have been in use for the past three and a half centuries there have been added the radio telescopes in recent decades. Let us consider first the one and then the other.

Optical Telescopes

TELESCOPE DESIGN

The great majority of existing telescopes are of two types, refractors (lens type) and reflectors (mirror type); the remainder are in a sense hybrids of special design for special purposes (see p. 546). The more familiar refractor is simply a large spyglass. Its principal optical element, called its objective, is a convex lens (Fig. 255) whose function it is to form behind it an image of objects before it. The image of an ideal lens lies precisely in a plane called the *focal plane* of the lens. The distance from focal plane to the center of the lens is the focal length of the lens. The gross specifications of an objective (and thereby of a telescope) are its diameter and its focal length. It is these two quantities which primarily determine the capabilities of the telescope, as we shall see.

The image formed by the objective in the focal plane may be studied by visual inspection, by photographic impression, or by spectrographic, photoelectric, or other means. It looks exactly like a picture suspended in mid-air; as with a picture, its details may be examined with a magnifier or eyepiece. The

539 . . . .

objective and an eyepiece are, in fact, the entire optics of a visual refractor. The rest of the telescope is merely an empty tube or rigid tubular frame in which the objective and eyepiece may be mounted in permanent alignment at the proper separation. It is evident that in principle a refracting telescope is really a very simple instrument.

A reflecting telescope is likewise a very simple instrument. After a manner of speaking, a reflector is merely a refractor "inside out." In place of a convex

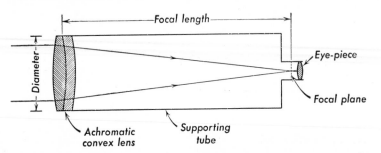

Figure 255. The essential parts of a refracting telescope are here shown in cross section.

lens through which the light passes, at the "top" of the telescope is a concave mirror from which the light is reflected at the "bottom" of the telescope (Fig. 256). Such a concave mirror forms an image in its focal plane, which lies one focal length in front of the mirror. A photographic plate placed here would record an image of whatever the mirror sees, just as the plate would record the image formed by a lens if placed in the lens' focal plane. In the position before

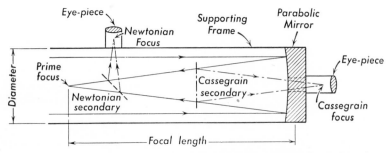

Figure 256. The essential parts of a reflecting telescope are shown here in cross section. Note the optional focal planes.

the mirror the plate occupies the *prime focus* of the reflecting telescope. It would, of course, partially obscure the mirror's view, but this cannot be avoided; the resultant loss of light is accepted and kept to a minimum, generally less than 10 per cent.

While photographic observations may be made at the prime focus of a reflector, visual observations are impractical there except with very large

Figure 257. THE HALE TELESCOPE. The largest optical telescope in the world is the Hale 200-inch telescope of the Palomar Observatory. The 200-inch mirror is at the bottom of the frame tube and is covered by an iris for protection when not in use. The large pivoted yoke constitutes the polar axis of the mounting. Note the observer's cage at the prime focus in the center at the top of the tube. (Mt. Wilson-Palomar Observatories Photo.)

reflectors such as the 200-inch reflector at Mt. Palomar. Most commonly, the beam reflected from the concave mirror is turned at right angles by an oblique plane mirror suspended [1] at a convenient distance before the objective mirror. The secondary, being perfectly flat, merely diverts the beam of light and in no way affects the image except to cause it to be formed outside the telescope tube where one's head and body will not block incoming light. An eyepiece, photographic plate, or other recorder or analyzer may then be applied to the image as with a refractor. Such a mirror system constitutes a *Newtonian reflector.* Again, part of the field of the objective is occulted, this time by the secondary mirror.

By a third possible arrangement, a secondary reflects the convergent beam from the objective back through a hole in the center of the objective,

[1] The supporting vanes for the secondary mirror are responsible for the diffraction patterns which appear as "points" on the images of the brighter stars.

which has been bored for the purpose. With this arrangement the focal plane is behind the objective and the observer will look in the direction of the object he wishes to see, rather than at right angles to it or opposite it. This third scheme is called a *Cassegrain telescope*.

TELESCOPES' LIGHT-GATHERING POWER

Precisely what is it that telescopes of one of these principal types (or their variants) are supposed to do? Their usefulness lies in (1) their light-gathering power and (2) their resolving power. A large telescope objective gathers more light than a small one or than the eye, just as a lake catches more rain than a rain barrel. Light-gathering power is in proportion to the clear area of the objective. Since the cross-sectional areas of lenses and mirrors are in proportion to the squares of their diameters, the light-gathering powers of telescopes will be in the ratio of the squares of the diameters of their objectives; thus the relative light-gathering powers of telescopes of diameters 1 inch, 5 inches, and 20 inches will be in the proportion $1^2 : 5^2 : 20^2 = 1 : 25 : 400$.

That light-gathering power is a prime desideratum in a telescope is plain; for if a telescope concentrates 1000 times as much light in the image of a star as does the unaided eye, the limit of visibility becomes stars 1000 times fainter than ordinary. In theory, therefore, for every factor of $1.585 = \sqrt{2.512}$ . . . by which the diameter of a telescope objective is increased, it should be possible to reach another stellar magnitude fainter. Specifically, the limiting visual magnitude of a 2-inch telescope is magnitude 10.3, that of a 3.17-inch telescope 11.3, that of a 5.2-inch telescope 12.3, etc. By this argument, the faintest stars visible in the 200-inch telescope at Palomar should be of a visual magnitude of about 20.

The full advantage of increased light-gathering power is effective in reaching fainter stars because stars' images are in all cases sensibly points, having virtually no area. By contrast, the images of objects such as nebulae (or objects of the landscape) occupy a definite area in the focal plane. The areal brightness of the image of such an object will be determined by both (1) the total amount of light in which the image is formed and (2) the area over which the image is spread. The former is again fixed by the light-gathering power of a telescope and is proportional to d^2, the square of the diameter of the objective; the latter depends upon the scale of the image and is determined by the focal length, f, of the objective. Specifically, any object which subtends $1°$ at the objective will span $f/57.3$ units of length in the image or on a direct photograph; the units will be the same as those given for the focal length f. For example, a direct photograph by a telescope of focal length 50 inches would have a scale of $50/57.3 = 0.872$ . . . inches per degree, or 1.46 degrees per inch. In short, linear plate scale is proportional to focal length f. Therefore areal plate scale will be proportional to f^2.

By taking account of factors (1) and (2) jointly, we conclude that the areal brightness of the image of any object will be proportional to $d^2/f^2 = (d/f)^2$, since the total light is proportional to d^2 and its areal extent is proportional to f^2. The ratio of d/f is thus an index of the speed of a telescope for photographic purposes, just as it is an index of the speed of an ordinary camera; for the greater the areal brightness of an image, the less is the exposure time required to register it upon a photographic emulsion. Since it is very seldom that f is not greater than d, it is generally more convenient to specify the inverse ratio f/d for any lens or mirror. This is called the focal ratio, or $f/$ratio, of the objective. Smaller values of the focal ratio correspond to *greater* photographic speed than do large values. A focal ratio of 5 (expressed as $f/5$) is common for reflectors, whereas $f/15$ is common for refractors. On this account reflectors are generally preferable to refractors for the observation and photography of faint, extended nebulosity, etc.

RESOLVING POWER

In addition to a telescope's value as a light gatherer, there is its indispensable function as a resolver. That is to say, a telescope permits one to distinguish clearly between points whose angular separation is less than the least angle the eye can appreciate. To illustrate, let us consider the print of a book page. It can be comfortably read at a distance of 20 inches. As the reader backs away, however, the letters subtend progressively smaller angles until the angular separation of the upper and lower parts of the letters is less than the resolving power of the eye. At this point the print can no longer be read unless resort is had to a device of greater resolving power, such as a pair of binoculars. At a still greater distance a telescope would be required, and so on.

Evidently resolving power can be expressed as the smallest angular separation which can be appreciated by an optical system. The theoretical limit of resolution of any telescope is

$$L = \frac{4.56}{d} \text{ seconds of arc}$$

if the diameter of the objective, d, is given in inches. Thus a 10-inch telescope should just barely separate the components of a visual binary only $0''.456$ apart, while the 100-inch Mt. Wilson telescope should separate binaries only $0''.0456$ apart, etc. A telescope's resolving power is therefore in direct proportion to the aperture of its objective.

Resolving power is not to be confused with magnification. The magnifying power of a visual telescope is the factor by which it makes any object appear larger than it does to the naked eye; alternatively, it is the factor by which the telescope appears to reduce the object's distance. A magnification of 100 times would cause the moon (true distance: 240,000 miles) to appear as it would at a distance of $240,000/100 = 2400$ miles.

Magnifying power, M, may be readily determined from the formula

$$M = \frac{f}{F},$$

where f is the focal length of the objective and F is the focal length of the eyepiece. Thus, if an eyepiece of focal length ½-inch is used with an objective of focal length 50 inches, the resulting magnification will be $50/\frac{1}{2} = 100$ times. By substituting eyepieces of a variety of focal lengths, a variety of magnifying powers can be achieved with a single objective.

This latter possibility helps emphasize the distinction between magnifying power and resolving power. For, even though the image formed by a telescope objective be magnified arbitrarily greatly, no amount of magnification will permit one to distinguish image points whose separation is less than the objective's resolving power. Excessive magnification simply shows more detail of the points' diffraction disks (see p. 302)—those spurious small "spots" which any lens or mirror forms for the images of a point object. If these ultimate "tiles" of the "optical mosaic" overlap appreciably, details of the same order of size become intrinsically blurred and cannot be unblurred by greater magnification. This fact sets an upper limit to the useful magnifying power of any telescope. Great magnification may be used only with telescopes of correspondingly great resolving power (larger aperture), and as a rule-of-thumb, one may take a maximum magnification of 50 times for each inch of aperture. This implies that a total magnification of about 150 is the useful limit of a 3-inch telescope, while 10,000 is the greatest magnifying power that could be used satisfactorily with the 200-inch at Palomar.

It is frequently impossible to realize the full potentialities of a telescope, however. There are usually additional limitations upon astronomical telescopes because of (1) the presence of aberrations in the objective and (2) certain effects of the earth's atmosphere. Aberrations are imperfections of the lens or mirror. They may be either shortcomings of design or manufacture or they may be limitations inherent in lenses and mirrors. For the former the remedy is greater ingenuity and skill; for the latter there is no remedy.

ABERRATIONS

For example, all refractors suffer from *chromatic aberration*. Chromatic aberration is the inability of a lens to form images of different colors in one and the same focal plane. Since blue light is more refracted than red during its passage through the lens, beams of blue light will be more strongly convergent, and the image formed in blue light falls short of the images formed by the same lens in red light. The result is a fringe of rainbow colors outlining every object in the image in any particular focal plane.

While chromatic aberration cannot be entirely eliminated from a lens, it can be minimized by suitably designing a compound lens. This is possible since the components of a compound lens may be made of different kinds of glass; because of their unequal dispersive powers, the several components may be made to compensate one another in any particular color. As a result, two colors may be brought to focus in the same focal plane by a lens of two components, three colors may be brought to focus in the same focal plane by a lens of three components, etc.

Reflectors are free from chromatic aberration since the light in them does not pass *through* glass but is reflected from a silvered or aluminized surface. Reflectors have their own aberrations, however. Their mirrors, which are parabolic in cross-section, possess an aberration known as *coma*. Coma ap-

Figure 258. COMA AND DIFFRACTION RAYS. This photograph shows nebulosity near the star 15 Monocerotis. The brightest stars in the field show "points" or "rays" produced by diffraction by the vanes supporting the secondary mirror (visible in Figures 263 and 264). Note also the presence of the aberration coma in the distorted stellar images near the edges of the field; contrast these with the small round images of the stars near the center of the plate. (Courtesy McDonald Observatory.)

pears as a sort of flare in the image of off-axis points, i.e., points out from the center of the focal plane. Even a perfectly figured parabolic mirror would produce coma, and the amount of it increases with distance from the center of the field; it is this which oftentimes causes stars near the edge of the field to simulate small comets in photographs taken with reflectors.

Telescopes of both kinds are heir to numerous other aberrations such as astigmatism, distortion, spherical aberration, and curvature of field. Though these are not unavoidable defects, it requires a great nicety of design and optician's skill to eliminate them for all practical purposes. Such an optimum combination is usually less practical than a compromise by which the optics are made to meet the requirements of some particular kind of work. Thus, astrometric work requires large plate scale and round images; these demands are practicable for telescopes of long focal length but small field of view. On the other hand, statistical astronomy finds more advantage in smaller plate scale, great speed, and large field of view. Consistent with these requirements are telescopes of small f/ratio.

The choice of telescope for a particular kind of astronomical work no longer need be confined just to refractor or reflector, however. In recent years continually more use has been made of a sort of hybrid known as a *Schmidt telescope*. At the lower end of the telescope tube is a concave mirror of *circular* cross-section (known as a spherical mirror). Such a mirror by itself is unsuitable because of large spherical aberrations which render images from it indistinct or blurred. Consequently, incoming light is first "corrected" by a correcting plate of glass at the upper end of the tube. Light which passes through the correcting plate is made to diverge or converge just such an amount as is needed to allow the spherical mirror to form an undistorted image from it. Since the correcting plate is a very weak lens, it introduces

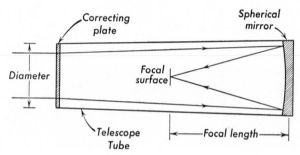

Figure 259. The essential parts of a Schmidt telescope are here shown in cross section. The diameter of the correcting plate is usually less than that of the spherical mirror. It is customary to state both in giving the size of the telescope. Note that there is no provision for visual use of a Schmidt telescope.

very little chromatic aberration, and since the light is focused by a spherical (rather than parabolic) mirror, coma may be eliminated.

The image in the Schmidt telescope is formed between the correcting plate and the mirror. It is most advantageous to photograph this image at the prime focus. For one thing, the image lies in a focal *surface* which is curved rather than plane; a film or plate can be bent to this surface, whereas an eyepiece cannot. Then, too, it is one of the chief advantages of Schmidt telescopes that they can be made to have relatively small f/ratio (f/3 or less) and for these the light loss due to a secondary would be appreciably more at the Newtonian or Cassegrain positions than at the prime focus.

What are the relative advantages and disadvantages of the several types of telescopes? (1) Well-designed refractors give images of fine quality over most of their fields, which are usually moderate in size and vary with the specifications of the instrument. However, refracting telescopes possess chromatic aberrations which can be minimized only by use of a compound objective. Each component of the objective must be made of optical glass of high quality and be figured and aligned with great precision. Large refractors present special engineering problems, since they require the support of great weights of glass at the far end of the telescope. (2) Ordinary reflectors are chromatic and can more easily be made to have small f/ratios and therefore great photographic

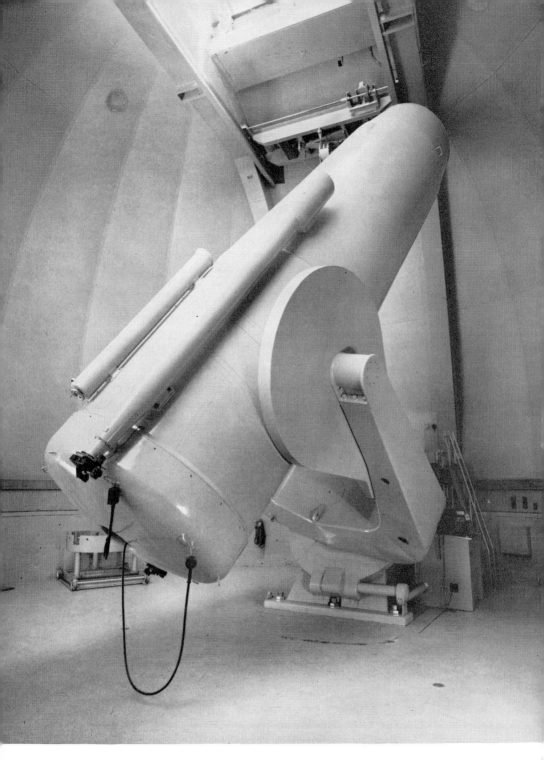

Figure 260. THE 48-INCH SCHMIDT TELESCOPE. The largest Schmidt telescope in the world is this instrument at the Palomar Observatory. It is with this that
the Sky Survey was made. (Mt. Wilson-Palomar Observatories Photo.)

speed. Moreover, they can more easily be made of large size, since they do not require flawless optical glass (no light passes through it), there is only one surface to figure and polish with great precision, and they can be supported more easily because the mirror is at the lower end of the telescope. However, they suffer from coma, which may severly limit the size of the field of view. What is more, their mirrors require resilvering every seveal years. (3) Schmidt telescopes have very little chromatic aberration, no coma, great speed, the largest fields of good definition (usually 5° to 25° square). At the same time, because of the position of the correcting plate, they must be nearly twice as long as a regular reflector of the same size, they are not adapted to visual observations, a curved plate must be used, periodic resurfacing is necessary, and their size is somewhat limited by the fact that correcting plates are thin and a large one is too easily distorted by the strains of its own weight. The choice of a telescope will plainly be dictated by the uses to which it is to be put.

ATMOSPHERIC LIMITATIONS

But even a fine telescope cannot surmount certain restrictions imposed upon it by our atmosphere. These are the conditions of *transparency* and *seeing*. Transparency is a measure of the degree to which the atmosphere allows the passage of light through it. If there is very little dust, smoke, water droplets, ice crystals, etc., the transparency is high, and we say that the atmosphere is very clear. High transparency is needed for accurate measures of stars' colors or apparent brightnesses.

"Seeing" is a measure of the atmosphere's stillness and tranquility, not only near the ground but at all heights. If the stars twinkle very little, the seeing is good, whereas much twinkling indicates poor seeing. Any work requiring the utmost resolving power can be carried on only when the seeing is good, for only then can even the best telescope form small, round, steady images of stars.

In respect to the ways in which our atmosphere modifies observing conditions, we may liken ourselves to fish in a river: The transparency of the river will vary as the water is clear or muddy, while the "seeing" from the river bottom will depend upon whether the surface of the river is still or ruffled by a wind or roiled by a current.

Radio Telescopes

Having the principles of optical telescopes in mind, we may compare them with the newer radio telescopes. Radio telescopes are only of the reflecting type. The large parabolic mirror is of metal rather than glass and is used to collect radio waves instead of light. The radio signals are concentrated at the prime focus of the mirror or "dish," as it is called. There they are picked up not by a photographic plate but by a small antenna which sends them to a very sensitive radio set to be amplified. They could be and sometimes are then converted to sound, but more often their intensity is recorded automatically by a moving pen and roll of tracing paper.

Figure 261. RADIO TELESCOPE OF THE NATIONAL RADIO ASTRON-
OMY OBSERVATORY. This telescope at Green Bank, West Virginia, has an 85-foot
parabolic "dish." (Courtesy Associated Universities, Inc.)

In two important respects radio telescopes are similar to optical telescopes: (1) Their signal-gathering power is proportional to the square of the diameter of the objective, and (2) their resolving power is proportional to the diameter itself. Radio telescopes contrast with optical telescopes, however, in that their signal-gathering power is relatively far greater than their resolving power. They pick up radio signals from such unwanted sources as distant electric motors, electric storms, etc. On the other hand, they fail completely to discern detail less than a few minutes of arc. This is because the length of radio waves is far greater than the length of light waves. Since the smallest angle discernible is directly proportional to the wavelength and inversely proportional to the diameter of the telescope, a radio telescope is at a disadvantage of 20,000 to 20,000,000 times in comparison to an optical telescope. Thus a radio telescope with the resolving power of the eye at wavelengths of 3 feet would need to have a diameter of more than 6 miles; the thousandfold greater resolving power of the 200-inch telescope would require a radio telescope of 6000 mile aperture.

The wavelength difference has one compensation, however. This is the fact that the figure of the mirror need not be so exact by absolute standards. The surface of a fine mirror conforms to a parabolic cross-section to within an eighth of a wavelength. For a radio telescope this could mean anything from about an eighth of an inch to more than a foot. Plainly, this is a much more sufferable tolerance for an instrument such as the large radio telescope at Jodrell Bank in England, whose diameter is 250 feet.

Other differences set radio telescopes apart from optical ones. For one, they observe only one wavelength at a time, just as an ordinary radio set. For another, they may be used on cloudy nights or in the daytime. Thirdly, they scan radio sources rather than produce images of them; this is largely a consequence of their low resolving power.

The limitations of resolving power are partially overcome by the use of interferometers, even as with optical telescopes. Antennas or arrays of antennas of very great linear dimensions have been set up so as to resolve in one dimension radio sources of only a few seconds of arc diameter. Often, interferometers at right angles provide resolution in two coordinates. Sometimes radio telescopes themselves may be paired to provide interferometric resolution.

B. OBSERVATORIES

"Nothing could be more noble than to contemplate the manifold wisdom of the Creator, but not with the gaze of vulgar admiration but with a desire to know the causes, and to feed upon this beauty by a more careful examination of their mechanism."

—JEREMIAH HORROCKS

Because of the size, delicacy, and importability of most telescopes large enough to be astronomically useful, they are housed in observatories. The telescope and mounting are placed upon a large pier that is usually made of steel and concrete or brick; such a pier is usually sunk into the ground and is intended to provide a base of the utmost steadiness. Over the telescope

Figure 262. YERKES OBSERVATORY. The large dome at the left houses the 40-inch telescope, largest refractor in the world. The two lesser domes on the right house smaller instruments. (Courtesy Yerkes Observatory.)

is a movable dome set upon tracks. By motor or hand-gear the dome can be turned into any position. A section of the dome itself can be rolled aside to provide a slitlike aperture through which the observer can watch the skies. By revolving the dome, this slit can be faced toward any section of the sky. The more rugged radio telescopes do not require the protection of a dome.

The telescope itself is held in a mounting. The only moving parts of the mounting are the two axes. The *declination axis* is attached to the telescope at right angles to the telescope tube or frame. The declination axis is in turn joined at right angles to the *polar axis*. The rest of the mounting is merely a frame to support the polar axis securely at its two ends.

The polar axis is so called because it is set parallel to the earth's axis of rotation; i.e., the ends of the polar axis are directed toward the celestial poles. Simply by turning the telescope about the polar axis, therefore, it may be made to trace an arc of a parallel of declination or, what is the same thing, a portion of the diurnal circle of any star having that declination.

The declination axis is so called because, by being at right angles to the polar axis, a motion of the telescope about this axis swings the telescope at right angles to the parallels of declination, i.e., along an hour circle, through a range of declinations. By this motion the telescope may be set for any desired declination. By motion about the polar axis, the telescope can be

551 . . . .

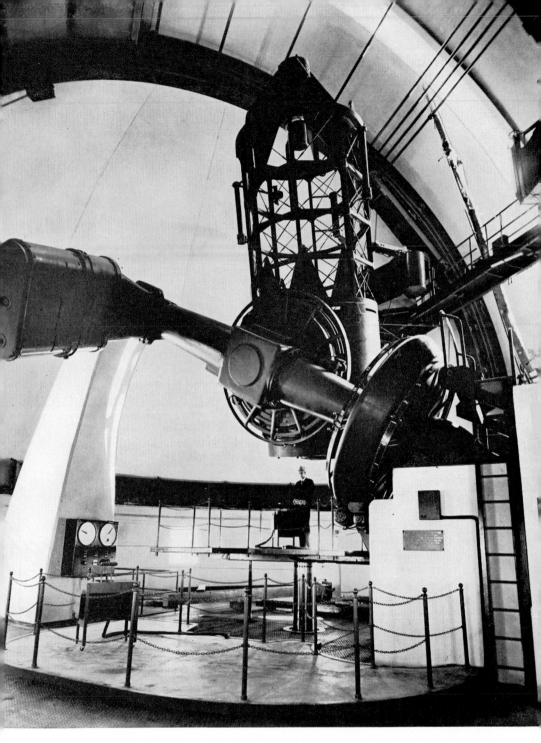

Figure 263. THE 82-INCH McDONALD REFLECTOR. The observer on the movable platform holds push-button controls by which the telescope, platform, or dome may be moved. The secondary mirror and its supporting vanes may be seen at the top of the tubular frame. (Courtesy The Warner and Swasey Company.)

.... 552

given any desired hour angle. Such a mounting is therefore called an *equatorial mounting* since its settings are substantially just the coordinates of the equatorial coordinate system. This type of mounting is universally used for astronomical telescopes.

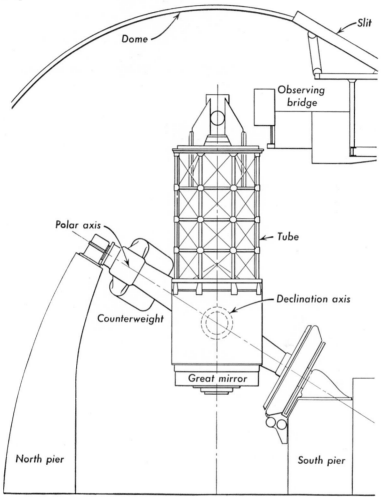

Figure 264. The various parts of the mounting of the telescope in Fig. 263 are diagrammed here for clarity. (Adapted from drawing, courtesy The Warner and Swasey Company.)

For convenience of telescope operation, all large telescopes are supplied with a clockwork drive which may be engaged to turn the polar axis from east to west. In this way, an equatorially mounted telescope can be made to follow any star automatically in its diurnal motion.

In most observatories of any size, the telescope housing is adjoined by

Figure 265. PALOMAR OBSERVATORY. The 200-inch Hale telescope may be seen through the slit of the dome. The two men on the catwalk give an indication of the scale. (Mt. Wilson-Palomar Observatories Photo.)

offices, dark rooms, sometimes mechanical or optical shops, class rooms, and even living quarters. Such facilities are usually more than just conveniences, for observatories are often isolated or distant from some parent institution.

Amply staffed research institutions engage in research programs which, in some instances, span decades or even centuries. Generally the observing for such programs is both cooperative and routine. A schedule is drawn up assigning each observer the responsibility for using the telescope on a particular part of certain specified nights, provided weather permits. In this way it is usually possible to achieve the maximum use of a large telescope.

Since large telescopes are very expensive, even as modern scientific instruments go, and since an adequate staff of trained astronomers is expensive to maintain, modern astronomical research is costly and is undertaken only by institutions of means. Because of the considerable expense of a large observatory, such institutions cannot generally afford to divert more than a little time to the numerous interested and curious visitors which observatories everywhere attract. Most observatories therefore establish visitors' hours when the public is welcome.

The widespread and genuine interest in telescopes and what they show of the heavens has led to the development of amateur astronomy to a truly amazing degree. A very few amateurs are able to afford small refractors manufactured by reliable optical firms. The majority make their own reflectors, of apertures from 4 to 15 inches. From inexpensive kits they grind and polish parabolic mirrors which they mount and house cheaply by using commonly available materials and considerable ingenuity. Such amateurs band themselves into local, regional, and national societies and are found the world around. They offer each other mutual assistance and stimulation, provide a large measure of the support of several popular journals, and enjoy a fascinating and constructive hobby. Moreover, some of them are able to render welcome assistance to the professional astronomer by their observations of variable stars and meteors and their discovery of comets. There is even record of amateurs' having built a special optical system for one large observatory whose specifications for a piece of auxiliary apparatus were so unusual that optical companies declined to undertake its construction; this relation between professional and amateur is probably unique to astronomy. No other branch of science can boast of such a large and active following of intelligent and enthusiastic amateurs.

QUESTIONS

1. Compare the light-gathering powers of the eye (diameter $= \frac{1}{5}$ inch), a 1-inch spyglass, and the 100-inch reflector at Mount Wilson. Find the approximate limiting magnitude visible in each if the unaided eye can reach sixth magnitude stars.

2. How large would the image of the moon appear in a direct photograph with a telescope of focal length 5 feet? 20 feet? 60 feet? (Angular diameter of the moon is $31'5''.2$.)

3. Compare the photographic speeds of telescope A, having an aperture of 12 inches and focal length 18 feet, with telescope B, having an aperture of 4 inches and a focal length of 10 inches.

4. What is the theoretical resolving power of the eye? The 40-inch Yerkes refractor?

5. What is the magnification achieved by a telescope whose focal length is 30 feet if the eyepiece used has a focal length of $\frac{1}{2}$ inch? What would the focal length of an eyepiece need to be to obtain the same magnification with an objective whose focal length is 20 feet?

6. What angle should the polar axis of an equatorial mounting make with the horizontal?

Glossary

"God put it into my head and I can't put it into yours."
—ZERAH COLBURN

Absolute magnitude: the apparent magnitude an object would have at a distance of 10 parsecs.

Absolute orbit: the orbit of any body when referred to an absolute reference frame, such as one attached to the center of gravity of an entire system.

Absolute temperature: temperature on a scale whose zero is at $-273°$ C and which uses 100 degrees between the temperatures of freezing and boiling water.

Absorption spectrum: a spectrum of dark lines upon a continuous background.

Acceleration: rate of change of velocity.

Active sun: the sun at times of enhanced intensity of radio radiation, noise storms, bursts, or outbursts.

Angular diameter: the angle subtended by the linear diameter of an object.

Angular distance: the difference in direction of two points, measured in degrees.

Annular eclipse: an eclipse in which the entire perimeter of the eclipsed body remains visible.

Annulus cone: that portion of a shadow cone from which an annular eclipse would be visible.

Antapex of solar motion: point on the celestial sphere from which the sun appears to be receding.

Apastron: point in the orbit of a binary star at which it is farthest from its companion.

Aphelion: point in the orbit of a body revolving about the sun at which it is farthest from the sun.

Apparent noon: instant of time at which the apparent sun reaches the celestial meridian.

Apparent solar day: interval of time between successive apparent noons.

Aperture: diameter of a telescope objective.

Apex of solar motion: point on the celestial sphere toward which the sun appears to be moving.

Apogee: in the orbit of a body revolving about the earth, the point at which it is farthest from the earth.

Ascending node: point on the celestial sphere at which an orbit crosses the ecliptic from south to north.

Asteroid: a minor planet.

Astronomical horizon: imaginary circle everywhere 90° from the zenith.

Astronomical latitude: angle between the vertical of a locality and the plane of the earth's equator.

Atom: the smallest unit of any chemical element.

Atomic number: the number of electric charges on an atomic nucleus.

Atomic weight: the mass of an atom, using $\frac{1}{12}$ the mass of a carbon atom as a unit.

Attenuation effect: reduction in brightness of a receding source because of the arrival of fewer photons each second than from a similar stationary source.

Autumnal equinox: the point on the celestial sphere at which the sun crosses the celestial equator southward; also the time of the sun's crossing the celestial equator southward.

Barred spiral: a galaxy whose arms attach to the ends of a transverse bar rather than directly to the nucleus.

Binary star: a pair of mutually revolving stars.

Bode's law: an expression of the approximate regularity in the spacing of the planets.

Bolide: a spectacularly bright meteor.

Brightness: intensity of radiation on a scale in which the sun at 1 parsec would have unit intensity.

Burst: sudden increase in the intensity of an isolated wavelength of solar radio radiation, lasting only a few seconds.

Butterfly diagram: graph used to display the migration of the sunspot zone during a cycle.

Canal: on Mars, an approximately linear marking of unknown significance.

Capture: in celestial mechanics, the modification by a primary of an orbit of a previously independent body so as to bring it under gravitational control or subject to major influence.

Carbon cycle: a set of thermonuclear reactions by which helium is synthesized from hydrogen with the aid of carbon.

Cassegrain telescope: a type of reflecting telescope in which the eyepiece is placed behind the objective mirror.

Cassini division: the vacancy which separates the two bright portions of Saturn's rings.

Celestial equator: the imaginary circle on the celestial sphere midway between the celestial poles.

Celestial latitude: angular distance from the ecliptic.

Celestial longitude: angular distance from the vernal equinox, measured eastward and parallel to the ecliptic.

Celestial meridian: the imaginary circle on the celestial sphere passing through the celestial poles and the zenith.

Celestial pole: one of the two points on the celestial sphere in which it is intersected by the extension of the earth's axis of rotation.

Celestial sphere: the apparent sphere of the sky.

Center of activity: a solar facula and its associated spot group, flares, prominences, and coronal disturbances.

Center of gravity: the weighted mean position of all the mass elements of a system.

Centrifugal force: the force necessary to divert a body from straight line motion to circular motion.

Cepheid variable: a class of pulsating intrinsic variable stars.

Chromatic aberration: a defect of lenses due to their inherent inability to focus all colors in the same focal plane.

Chromosphere: the bright scarlet lower layer of the sun's atmosphere.

Circumpolar cap: the region of any observer's sky which never sets or never rises.

Circumpolar star: a star which appears never to go below the horizon.

Cleft: a crevice on the surface of the moon.

Color equivalent: a numerical measure of the color of light.

Color excess: the difference between the observed color index and the normal color index.

Color index: a color equivalent defined to be 2.5 times the logarithm of the ratio of the visual brightness to the photographic brightness.

Color temperature: temperature of a body determined from the intensity of one or several wavelengths of its radiations.

Coma: the diffuse head of a comet; also an aberration of reflecting telescopes which gives off-center star images a cometary appearance.

Comet family: a set of comets whose aphelia lie near the orbit of a given planet.

Comet group: a set of comets with near-identical orbits.

Congruence relation: a rule for determining the equality of space or time intervals at different times, places, or in different directions.

Conic section: a curve of intersection between plane and right circular cone; a circle, ellipse, parabola, or hyperbola.

Conjunction: configuration in which two celestial bodies have the same celestial longitude or the same right ascension.

Constellation: a configuration of stars or the area of sky which they occupy.

Continuous spectrum: an unbroken ordered sequence of spectrum lines.

Convective zone: a layer of rising and falling currents just beneath the photosphere of the sun.

Coordinate: a number used to specify location.

Copernican theory: the doctrine that the sun is the center of the universe and that the planets revolve around it.

Corona: the faint extended outer portion of the sun's atmosphere.

Cosmogony: the study of the ultimate origins of physical systems.

Cosmology: the study of the content and arrangement of the physical universe.

Cosmological principle: a statement of world-wide uniformity.

Critical temperature: temperature above which a gas cannot be liquefied regardless of pressure.

Curvature: in cosmology and geometry, a measure of the extent to which the theorems of Euclidean geometry require to be modified in a given region of space.

Declination: angular distance from the celestial equator.

Degenerate matter: matter in the "crushed state."

Descending node: point on the celestial sphere at which an orbit crosses the ecliptic from north to south.

Diffuse nebula: cloud of relatively dense interstellar matter, often in the vicinity of an illuminating star.

Diffusion: the scattering of light by many small particles.

Dilution effect: a spectral anomaly from a source subject to irradiation by dilute radiation.

Direct motion: orbital or rotational motion from west to east on the celestial sphere or counterclockwise as seen from above the north pole.

Dispersion: separation of light into its constituent colors.

Diurnal circle: path on the sky traced out by daily motion of the celestial sphere.

Doppler broadening: increase in the width of a spectrum line, due to Doppler effect caused by thermal motion of the radiating atoms.

Doppler effect: apparent change in the wavelength of light from a source moving in the line of sight.

Dwarf star: a star of small or moderate luminosity and diameter.

Dynamical parallax: parallax of a binary system, computed with the aid of the mass-luminosity relation and the harmonic law.

Earthlight: light reflected from earth to moon and back, visible on the dark portion of the moon.

Eccentricity: in an ellipse, the ratio of focal distance to mean distance.

Eccentricity effect: shift in the relative position of primary and secondary minimum in the light curve of an eclipsing binary, due to orbital eccentricity of the secondary.

Eclipse: the cutting off of one body's light by another which passes in front of it.

Eclipse path: the strip over the earth's surface along which an eclipse of the sun may be witnessed as total.

Eclipse year: the interval of time required by the sun to move around the ecliptic from one node of the moon and return to the same node.

Eclipsing binary: a binary star whose components mutually eclipse as seen from the earth.

Ecliptic: the sun's apparent annual path amongst the stars.

Ecliptic coordinates: celestial latitude and longitude.

Ecliptic limit: the maximum distance from a node of the moon's orbit at which the sun can be eclipsed by the moon or at which the moon can be eclipsed by the earth.

Electron: the fundamental negative electric charge within an atom.

Ellipse: a closed plane curve whose every point is the same total distance from two fixed foci within.

Elliptical galaxy: an assemblage of stars comparable in size to the Milky Way system but lacking arms and showing elliptical outline.

Ellipticity effect: modification of the light curve of an eclipsing binary, due to the mutual tidal distortion of the two components.

Elongation: the amount by which a body's right ascension or celestial longitude differs from that of the sun.

Effective temperature: the temperature which a perfect radiator of the same surface brightness would have.

Einstein-de Sitter model: a universe constructed according to the laws of general relativity and with curvature and cosmological constant both zero.

Emission nebula: a diffuse nebula which is excited to radiate by a hot nearby star.

Opposition: configuration in which a planet is most nearly opposite the sun in the sky.

Orbital elements: the set of quantities by which a planet's orbit may be located and described.

Outburst: sudden and brief large increase of intensity in selected wavelength of solar radio radiation.

Parallactic ellipse: the curve executed upon the celestial sphere by any star in consequence of the earth's motion about the sun.

Parallax: the apparent difference of direction of an object when seen from the two ends of a base line.

Parallel of declination: a circle on the celestial sphere everywhere the same number of degrees from the celestial equator.

Parallel of latitude: an imaginary circle on the surface of the earth everywhere the same number of degrees from the equator.

Parabola: the conic section of eccentricity 1.0.

Parsec: the distance at which a star's parallax would be 1 second of arc.

Partial eclipse: an eclipse in which the eclipsed body is covered over part but not all of the limb.

Penumbra (of shadow cone) : the region of semi-shadow.

Penumbra (of sunspot) : the less dark outer region of a sunspot.

Perfect cosmological principle: the proposition that it is impossible to know either one's absolute location or epoch in the universe.

Perfect radiator: an incandescent body which radiates with the maximum possible efficiency in every wavelength.

Periastron: point in a double star orbit at which the secondary is nearest the primary.

Perigee: point of an orbit at which a body is nearest the earth.

Perihelion: the point of an orbit at which a body is nearest the sun.

Perturbation: a deviation produced by some external agency.

Phase: a measure of the extent to which a cyclic process has been completed, as a lunar phase.

Photon: a corpuscle of light.

Photosphere: the sun's radiating surface.

Planetoid: a minor planet.

Plasma: a highly ionized gas.

Precession of the equinoxes: slow westward motion along the ecliptic of the position of the vernal equinox.

Pressure broadening: widening of spectrum lines traceable to the high pressure of the gases of the source.

Primary component: the larger member of a binary system.

Prime focus: the natural focus on the axis of a parabolic mirror.

Prime meridian: the standard reference meridian through Greenwich.

Prominence: a large projecting cloud of chromospheric material.

Proper motion: a star's apparent annual motion across the sky.

Proton: fundamental nuclear particle, identical with a hydrogen nucleus.

Polar axis: that axis of a telescope mounting which is directed toward the celestial poles.

Polarity: an index of the direction of a magnetic force.

Population (atomic): the number of atoms in a particular excited state.

Population (stellar): a class to which stars may be assigned according to age, motion, and chemical composition.

Positron: a subatomic particle similar to the electron but of positive electric charge.

Ptolemaic system: the geometric scheme devised in the second century to account for the celestial bodies' apparent motions.

Quadrature: configuration at which a body is 90° from the sun.

Quiet sun: condition of the sun when no extraordinarily intense optical or radio radiations are being emitted.

Radial velocity: velocity in the line of sight.

Radiant: apparent increase in wavelength of the spectrum lines of a star or galaxy.

Reflection: the bending of a beam of light at the surface of an extended body.

Reflection nebula: a diffuse nebula which shines by reflected light.

Reflector: a telescope whose principal optical element is a mirror.

Reflex motion: apparent contrary motion due to the sun's motion toward the solar apex.

Refraction: the bending of a beam of light as it passes from one medium to another of different density or composition.

Refractor: a telescope whose principal optical element is a lens.

Relative orbit: the orbit of a secondary, assuming the primary to be a fixed point of reference.

Relative parallax: the parallax of a nearby object, using for a reference direction a body not infinitely remote.

Resolving power: the ability of an optical system to discriminate small angles.

Resonance: the exaggeration of a small effect by periodic repetition.

Resonance lines: those lines of an atom's spectrum which are produced by transitions to or from the ground state.

Retrograde motion: motion counter to the prevailing norm; westward motion on the celestial sphere; clockwise motion as seen from above the north pole.

Revolution: motion about a point outside a body.

Right ascension: angular distance east from the vernal equinox, expressed in units of time.

Roche limit: the least distance at which purely gravitational cohesion can prevent the tidal disruption of a secondary by a primary.

Rotation: motion about a line through a body.

Saros: the 18-year cycle of eclipse recurrences.

Satellite: a lesser body attendant upon a major one.

Scarp: a lunar cliff.

Schmidt telescope: a telescope having a spherical mirror and correcting lens as its principal optical elements.

Secondary component: the smaller of a pair of revolving bodies.

Secondary mirror: in a reflecting telescope, an auxiliary mirror introduced so as to locate the focus elsewhere than at the prime focus.

Secular parallax: apparent annual reflex motion.

Seeing: the state of atmospheric tranquility.

Shadow transit: passage of a satellite's shadow across the disk of a planet.

Short-period comets: comets with periods less than about a century.

Sidereal period: period with respect to the stars.

Sidereal time: time by the stars.

Sidereal year: the earth's sidereal period of revolution.

Sign of the zodiac: a 30° section of the zodiac bearing the name of one of the zodiacal constellations.

Solar constant: a measure of the intensity of solar radiation at the earth's distance from the sun.

Solstice: one of the two points on the ecliptic at which the sun is farthest from the celestial equator; also the moment of the sun's arrival at this point.

Spectroheliograph: a device to photograph the sun in light of a single wavelength.

Spectroscope: an instrument for viewing the spectra of light sources.

Spectroscopic binary: a binary system identified as such by the cyclic variation of radial velocity of its components.

Spectroscopic parallax: parallax calculated on the basis of a luminosity determined from spectroscopic criteria.

Spectrum: the ordered set of all spectrum lines from a given source.

Spectrum line: monochromatic image of the spectroscope slit.

Spheroid: a solid of revolution having elliptical cross-section through its axis.

Spiral galaxy: a galaxy with spiral symmetry.

Spontaneous disintegration: the breaking-up of an atomic nucleus into two or more parts independent of any external effects.

Sporadic meteor: a meteor which bears no apparent relation to members of any shower.

Spring tide: a tide at full or new moon.

Standard time: local mean solar time at a standard meridian.

Standard meridian: meridians of longitude which are multiples of 15°.

Stellar association: a loose galactic cluster.

Stellar magnitude: a system of indicating the brightnesses of stars on a negative logarithmic scale.

Subdwarf: a star slightly below the main sequence in the Hertzsprung-Russell diagram.

Summer solstice: the sun's northernmost point on the ecliptic; also the moment of the sun's arrival at this point.

Superior conjunction: that configuration at which a planet is most nearly in line with the sun in the sky and at the same time on the far side of the sun.

Supergiant: the class of most luminous stars.

Supernova: a cataclysmic stellar explosion.

Surface gravity: the magnitude of the pull of gravity at the surface of a body.

Surge: a rapid, short-lived solar prominence associated with a solar flare.

Synchrotron radiation: radiation produced by the magnetic acceleration of high-speed electrons, as in a synchrotron.

Synodic period: period in relation to some relative rather than absolute standard of reference, as the sun instead of the fixed stars.

Temperature gradient: increase or decrease of temperature with depth.

Thermonuclear reaction: nuclear reaction brought about because of high temperature.

Tides: ebb and flow of the level of the ocean because of the attraction of the sun and moon.

Total eclipse: an eclipse in which the eclipsed body is wholly obscured.

Transit: apparent passage of a planet across the face of the sun.

Transition: an atom's change from one energy state to another.

Transparency: state of clarity of the atomsphere.

Transverse velocity: velocity at right angles to the line of sight.

Triangulation: determination of the distance of a body by observing it from two widely separated points.

Triple-alpha process: thermonuclear reaction which produces carbon nuclei from three helium nuclei.

Trojan group: a group of minor planets which remain approximately equidistant from Jupiter and the sun.

Tropical year: the length of time from one vernal equinox to the next.

Turbulence: disorderly, agitated motion.

Turbulent broadening: widening of spectrum lines because of turbulent motion within the source.

Twilight: the period of partial light following sunset and preceding sunrise.

Twinkling: a dancing of stellar images, due to unsteadiness of the earth's atmosphere.

Two-body problem: the problem of predicting the motion of two mutually gravitating bodies.

Tychonic system: the hypothetical celestial mechanism proposed by Tycho to explain the apparent motions of celestial bodies.

Ultraviolet radiation: radiation of the wavelength region just shorter than the eye can appreciate.

Umbra (of a shadow cone): the region of total shadow.

Umbra (of a sunspot): the dark, central portion of a sunspot.

Unstable nucleus: an atomic nucleus subject to spontaneous disintegration.

Upper transit: arrival of an object at the portion of the celestial meridian which contains the zenith.

Variable star: a star which varies in luminosity, radius, or spectral type.

Velocity: rate of change of position.

Velocity of escape: minimum speed needed to leave permanently the vicinity of an attracting body.

Vernal equinox: point of intersection of the celestial equator and the ecliptic at which the sun crosses northward; also the time of the sun's crossing.

Viscosity: internal friction in a gas or liquid.

Visual binary: a physically connected pair of stars which are separately visible in a telescope.

Wavelength: distance between corresponding points on successive waves of a train.

White dwarf: a star of high surface temperature, low luminosity, small radius, and normal mass.

Winter solstice: the sun's southernmost point on the ecliptic; also the time of the sun's arrival there.

World map: a representation of the entire universe in which each particle is located at the position it occupied at one particular time.

World picture: a representation of the visible universe as it appears to a particular observer at a particular instant.

Zeeman effect: the splitting of spectrum lines by magnetic forces at the source.

Zenith: the point on the celestial sphere directly overhead.

Zodiac: a belt of sky centered on the ecliptic and containing the 12 constellations of the zodiac.

Zodiacal light: a faint glow preceding and following the sun and symmetric about the ecliptic.

Zone of avoidance: a region along the galactic equator in which few or no galaxies are found.

The Sky Maps

...

Maps of portions of the celestial sphere, like maps of portions of the terrestrial sphere, cannot be made upon a flat surface such as a sheet of paper without introducing some manner of distortion into the mutual relations of the various points mapped. Any specific mode of distortion is termed *a projection,* and the projection chosen for the following maps is that known as the *transverse Mercator projection.* Its special advantage, as a Mercator map, is its property that small areas of sky appear on the map as small areas of the same shape; this is not generally true of map projections of other kinds. By such a property we can achieve a near-perfect fidelity in the mapped outlines of small constellations and a minimum distortion in the shapes of the largest ones, thereby assuring a greater ease of recognition of the constellations in the sky. The designation "transverse" reflects our choice of the central vertical line to be the "equator" of the projection rather than the central horizontal line (as in Mercator maps of the earth). This choice is more in accord with one's natural tendency to scan the sky parallel to one's celestial meridian rather than parallel to the celestial equator; the length of the map therefore runs north and south rather than the map-wise more conventional east and west.

The central vertical line of each map is an hour circle—0^h in Map 1, 4^h in Map 2, 8^h in Map 3, etc. It will coincide with the observer's meridian at the hours and dates given in the table opposite the map. Each map shows the portion of sky within $60°$ of this hour circle, from pole to pole and $40°$ beyond. Hence any one map displays five-eighths of the entire sky, nearly seven-eighths of the part of the sky that can be seen by any single observer at one of the indicated times. The scale of the map increases, slowly at first, to right or left of the meridian (central vertical line) from its value along the meridian, to twice that value at the extreme edges of the map. The effects of such distortion may be seen by comparing the scale of given constellations on a map on which they appear near the center of the map with the scale of the same constellations on other maps on which they appear near the right or left margins.

At the hours specified in the table with each map, the northern and southern horizons are horizontal lines drawn at heights determined by the scale of latitudes in the margins. Thus, an observer in latitude $30°$ N would draw a horizontal line connecting the $+30°$ markers at the top and another connecting the $+30°$ markers at the bottom; these would be his northern and southern horizons, respectively. A similar construction is to be made for any other latitude. The zenith will be on the meridian midway between the northern and southern horizons.

The Sky Maps

In using a map, hold the map upright when facing south, inverted when facing north, right margin down when facing west, and left margin down when facing east. (Ideally the map should be held overhead, arched cylindrically with axis directed east and west.) One can then begin by identifying certain of the brightest stars (listed in the Key for each map) or a few of the well-known and unmistakable constellations such as the Big Dipper (UMa) or Orion (Ori). It is then possible to proceed, with the aid of the map, to the identification of adjacent constellations, working step by step over the entire visible hemisphere. Constellations are designated on the maps by three-letter abbreviations for which a key is given below. The specific outline which one can read into configuration of stars is to a large extent a matter of taste; the outlines in black are therefore given solely as an aid to identification and may be modified to suit the user's whim. As a further aid, less arbitrary, the stars have been given sizes in order of magnitudes (see Appendix 2). The brightest stars, having the largest diameters, are of the first magnitude; the faintest stars, having the smallest diameters, are of the fourth magnitude; the two intermediate-size stars are of the second and third magnitudes, respectively.

The map shows also the position of the ecliptic, the celestial equator, and the equinoctial and solstitial colures. The moon and planets will be found within a few degrees of the ecliptic. The sun, of course, is precisely on the ecliptic and will arrive at the designated points at the various dates indicated.

The Sky Maps

Key to Constellation Abbreviations

ABBRE-VIATION	CONSTELLATION	GENITIVE	FIGURE REPRESENTED
And	Andromeda	Andromedae	Princess of Ethiopia
Ant	Antlia	Antliae	Air pump
Aps	Apus	Apodis	Bird of Paradise
Aqr	Aquarius	Aquarii	Water bearer
Aql	Aquila	Aquilae	Eagle
Ara	Ara	Arae	Altar
Ari	Aries	Arietis	Ram
Aur	Auriga	Aurigae	Charioteer
Boo	Bootes	Bootis	Herdsman
Cam	Camelopardus	Camelopardalis	Giraffe
Cnc	Cancer	Cancri	Crab
CVn	Canes Venatici	Canum Venaticorum	Hunting Dogs
CMa	Canis Major	Canis Majoris	Big Dog
CMi	Canis Minor	Canis Minoris	Little Dog
Cap	Capricornus	Capricorni	Sea Goat
Car	Carina	Carinae	Ship's Keel
Cas	Cassiopeia	Cassiopeiae	Queen of Ethiopia
Cen	Centaurus	Centauri	Centaur
Cep	Cepheus	Cephei	King of Ethiopia
Cet	Cetus	Ceti	Whale
Cha	Chameleon	Chameleonis	Chameleon
Cir	Circinus	Circini	Compass
Col	Columba	Columbae	Dove
Com	Coma Berenices	Comae Berenices	Berenice's hair
CrA	Corona Austrina	Coronae Austrinae	Southern crown
CrB	Corona Borealis	Coronae Borealis	Northern crown
Crv	Corvus	Corvi	Crow
Crt	Crater	Crateris	Cup
Cru	Crux	Crucis	Cross (southern)
Cyg	Cygnus	Cygni	Swan
Del	Delphinus	Delphini	Dolphin
Dor	Dorado	Doradus	Swordfish
Dra	Draco	Draconis	Dragon
Equ	Equuleus	Equulei	Little horse
Eri	Eridanus	Eridani	Po River
For	Fornax	Fornacis	Furnace
Gem	Gemini	Geminorum	Twins
Gru	Grus	Gruis	Crane
Her	Hercules	Herculis	Hercules
Hor	Horologium	Horologii	Clock
Hya	Hydra	Hydrae	Sea serpent
Hyi	Hydrus	Hydri	Water serpent
Ind	Indus	Indi	American Indian
Lac	Lacerta	Lacertae	Lizard
Leo	Leo	Leonis	Lion
LMi	Leo Minor	Leonis Minoris	Little lion
Lep	Lepus	Leporis	Hare

Key to Constellation Abbreviations (Continued)

ABBRE-VIATION	CONSTELLATION	GENITIVE	FIGURE REPRESENTED
Lib	Libra	Librae	Balance scales
Lup	Lupus	Lupi	Wolf
Lyn	Lynx	Lyncis	Lynx
Lyr	Lyra	Lyrae	Harp
Mon	Monoceros	Monocerotis	Unicorn
Mus	Musca	Muscae	Fly
Nor	Norma	Normae	Carpenter's square
Oct	Octans	Octantis	Hadley's octant
Oph	Ophiuchus	Ophiuchi	Aesculapius grappling the serpent
Ori	Orion	Orionis	Hunter
Pav	Pavo	Pavonis	Peacock
Peg	Pegasus	Pegasi	Winged horse
Per	Perseus	Persei	Savior of Andromeda
Phe	Phoenix	Phoenicis	Periodically resurrecting bird
Pic	Pictor	Pictoris	Painter
Psc	Pisces	Piscium	Fishes
PsA	Piscis Austrinus	Piscis Austrini	Southern fish
Pup	Puppis	Puppis	Stern of the Argonauts' ship
Pyx	Pyxis	Pyxidis	Mariner's compass
Ret	Reticulum	Reticuli	Net
Sge	Sagitta	Sagittae	Arrow
Sgr	Sagittarius	Sagittarii	Archer
Sco	Scorpius	Scorpii	Scorpion
Scl	Sculptor	Sculptoris	Sculptor
Sct	Scutum	Scuti	Shield
Ser	Serpens	Serpentis	Serpent
Sex	Sextans	Sextantis	Sextant
Tau	Taurus	Tauri	Bull
Tel	Telescopium	Telescopii	Telescope
Tri	Triangulum	Trianguli	Triangle
TrA	Triangulum Australe	Trianguli Australis	Southern triangle
Tuc	Tucana	Tucanae	Toucan
UMa	Ursa Major	Ursae Majoris	Big bear
UMi	Ursa Minor	Ursae Minoris	Little bear
Vel	Vela	Velorum	Sail
Vir	Virgo	Virginis	Maiden
Vol	Volans	Volantis	Flying fish
Vul	Vulpecula	Vulpeculae	Little fox

MAP 1

This map shows the sky
as it appears at

6	P.M. (LMST) on	December 22	
8		November 21	
10		October 22	
12		September 21	
2	A.M.	August 22	
4		July 22	
6		June 22	

Bright Stars

Fomalhaut (α Piscis Austrini)
Achernar (α Eridani)

Double Star

ζ Aquarii: magnitudes 4.4, 4.6, separation 3″.

Variable Stars

δ Cephei: original Cepheid variable, period 5.4 days, magnitudes 3.6–4.3.
ρ Cassiopeiae: irregular, magnitudes 4.1–5.1 in periods from 110–1100
days.

Clusters and Nebulae

Small Magellanic Cloud (SMC): irregular galaxy in Tucana.
47 Tucanae: globular cluster.
M 33: Open spiral galaxy in Triangulum.
M 31: Great Andromeda galaxy (see Fig. 240).

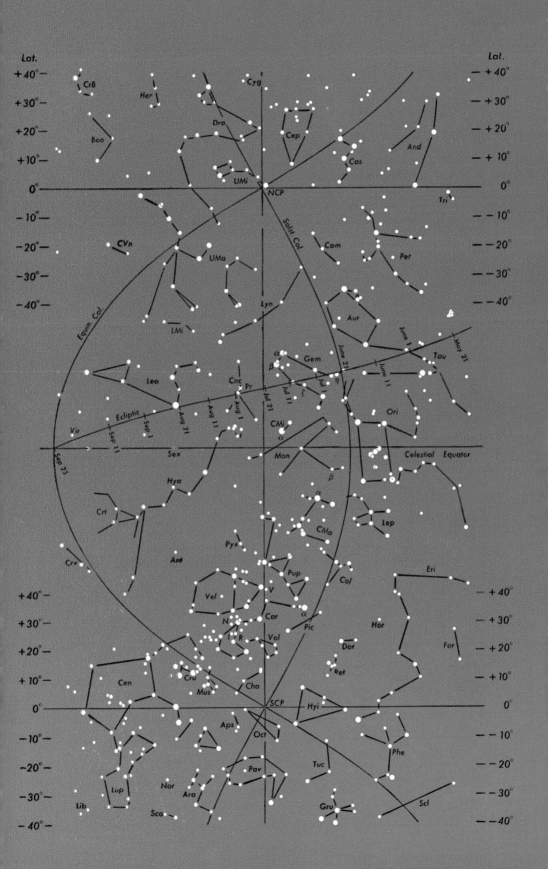

MAP 4

This map shows the sky
as it appears at

6 P.M. (LMST) on	June 22
8	May 22
10	April 22
12	March 23
2 A.M.	February 21
4	January 22
6	December 22

Bright Stars

Regulus (α Leonis)
Spica (α Virginis)
α Crucis
β Crucis
α, β Ursae Majoris: the "pointers," second magnitude.

Double or Multiple Stars

γ Leonis: magnitudes 2.6, 3.8, separation 4″.
γ Virginis: magnitudes 3.7, 3.7, separation 6″.
α Canum Venaticorum (Cor Caroli): magnitudes 2.9, 5.4, separation 20″.
ζ Ursae Majoris (Mizar): magnitudes 2.4, 4.0, separation 15″; Alcor, magnitude 4.0 is 12′ from Mizar.

Variable Stars

η Carinae: possible nova (1843), magnitudes −0.8–7.9.
R Hydrae: long-period variable, magnitudes 3.5–10.9, period 387 days.

Clusters

ω Centauri: brightest globular cluster in the sky.
M 3: globular cluster in Canes Venatici.

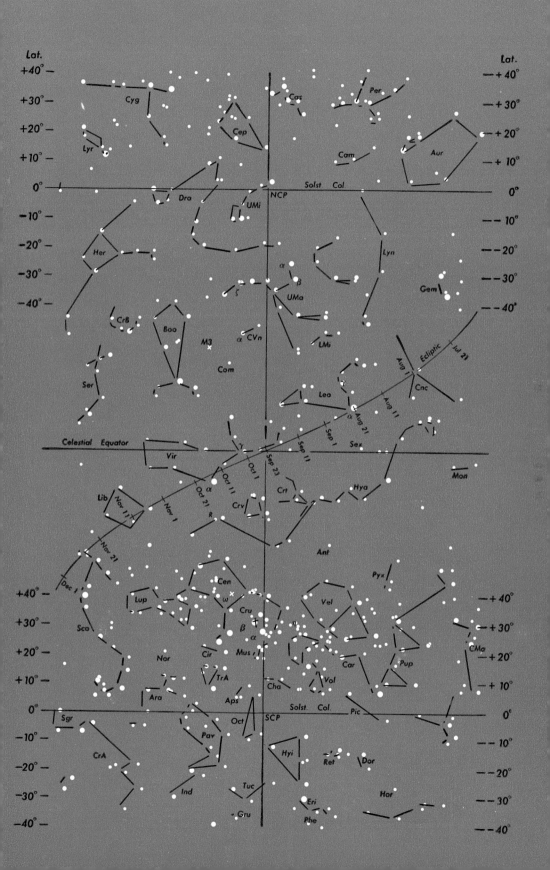

MAP 5

This map shows the sky
as it appears at

6	P.M.	(LMST) on	August 22
8			July 22
10			June 22
12			May 22
2	A.M.		April 22
4			March 23
6			February 21

Bright Stars

Arcturus (α Bootis)
α Centauri
β Centauri
Antares (α Scorpii)

Double Star

ν Draconis: magnitudes 5.0, 5.0, separation 62″.

Variable Stars

T Coronae Borealis: recurrent nova (see p. 412).
Nova Ophiuci 1604: Kepler's star, possible supernova (see p. 422).

Clusters

M 80: globular cluster in Scorpius.
M 13: fine globular cluster in Hercules (see Fig. 177).